THE AFRICAN HUSBANDMAN

THE AFRICAN HUSBANDMAN

WILLIAM ALLAN

OLIVER & BOYD
EDINBURGH
LONDON
1965

OLIVER AND BOYD LTD

Tweeddale Court
14 High Steet
Edinburgh 1

39A Welbeck Street
London W.1

First published 1965

PRINTED IN GREAT BRITAIN
BY HAZELL WATSON AND VINEY LTD
AYLESBURY
BUCKS
ENGLAND

FOREWORD

In the 1940s, Northern Rhodesia (now Zambia) was fortunate in having in its Department of Agriculture a number of brilliant research men. Besides those working on the problems of farming, crops, and forestry, three of them worked on the margins of agricultural problems, where these involved social relations among the African peoples of the territory. Mr Colin G. Trapnell, the Government Ecologist, had already established an international reputation with two reports on the soils, vegetation, and agricultural systems of north-western and of north-eastern Rhodesia, the first written in collaboration with Mr J. Clothier. Work on these surveys had begun in the 1930s. In the retrenchment of staff which the Government had to carry out in the great Depression, the soil chemist in the survey team was sacrificed. Mr Trapnell worked out a mode of classifying the soils on ecological characteristics, which enabled the Department of Agriculture to make fairly rapid classification of the suitability of different areas for different types of agriculture, and in addition he made analyses of the use of land in African agricultural systems and of the amount of land different systems required. Here Mr Allan, the Deputy Director of Agriculture, developed a method of calculating the carrying capacities, in terms of population, of various indigenous and changing agricultural practices on different types of soils. Allan further formulated a mode of working out the critical population density for different systems, a point beyond which the land would begin to deteriorate. This was a theoretical analysis of high practical importance. In making these analyses, Allan was led into investigating what people were dependent on particular sets of land as well as into investigating the social organisation of production, distribution, and consumption of crops. He had to enquire into family and other forms of social structure, and into the effect on these of labour migration and new forms of cash-cropping.

At that time I was Director of the Rhodes-Livingstone Institute of Social Studies in British Central Africa. I met Allan and Trapnell when they came to give evidence before a tribunal

assessing the compensation to be paid by the Government of
Northern Rhodesia for land which was required to re-settle
Africans from over-crowded areas in the Eastern Province. We
saw that there was a large field in which agriculturalist and anthropologist should co-operate in field research and analysis; and
in 1945 I joined them in a study of land-holding and land-usage
among the Plateau Tonga of Mazabuka District. This was an
area in which land had been set aside for European farms, and in
which seemingly some Africans had expanded their acreages,
reputedly at the expense of their fellows, to develop maize-farming
for markets. The railway-line splitting Northern Rhodesia ran
through the region, and the Government had set up buying
stations throughout the African reserves, so that marketing of
maize was easily possible. The fourth member of our team was
the late Mr D. U. Peters, then on his maiden research, but later,
before his unhappily youthful death, to do fine work among the
Lala, Lamba, Lima, and Barotse peoples.

I believe that our team's investigation was one of the all too few
examples of happy and fruitful collaboration between practitioners
of different disciplines. Allan was largely responsible for this,
since he provided the bridge between soil plus agriculture and
agriculture plus social relationships. We used to work from
relatively early in the cold winter mornings till we had a very late
lunch, after which we went for a long walk while we discussed
the day's findings. One day we had been out for some couple of
miles along a dirt road, and then returned to camp by it. Trapnell
stopped, picked some soil off the road, sniffed at it and said: "I
thought there was once a pig kraal here." Allan commented to
me: "I've been walking between you symbolically, because he sees
only the soil and trees, and you see only villages and people.
Someone had to see both sides."

Allan's ability to see both sides of these complex problems was
manifest throughout our collaboration. We carried this through,
without difference of opinion, to make a series of recommendations
to Government on how the output of the mass of subsistence producers in the area could be helped to raise their output and their
incomes. The scattering of the staff involved (Allan to become
Director of Agriculture in Mauritius, Trapnell to found a school
for ecologists in East Africa) perhaps prevented these recommendations from being implemented, but the report was pub-

lished.[1] I was also able to rescue out of the Department of
Agriculture's files reports written by Allan and his colleagues on
agricultural problems among the Lamba-Lima and the Lala.[2]

In this latter paper, Allan also set out the general theory by
which the carrying capacity of different agricultural systems could
be calculated. It would be impertinent for me to comment on
the agronomic importance of his work: but I can say that his
theory and its applications were a revelation to my social anthropological colleagues, as they had been to me. On his leaves
in Britain, he was invited by alert Departments of Social Anthropology to teach staff and research students his methods, and
several anthropologists were able to apply them successfully.
Very soon after I came to the University of Manchester in 1949,
Allan ran seminars there, and he so impressed my colleagues in
other disciplines as well, that the University offered him a Senior
Simon Fellowship to write a general book on tribal systems of
agriculture and their developments, as soon as he could get leave
from the Colonial Office. This he could not do for some time,
as he served as Director of Agriculture for six years in Mauritius
and then four years in Cyprus. Eventually, he retired from the
Colonial Service, and took up his Fellowship for two years. The
Rockefeller Foundation, to which we sent his earlier publications,
generously provided a grant to enable Allan to study again those
areas of Northern Rhodesia where he had worked for many years,
and to visit research workers in other regions of Africa. The
Foundation also provided funds for him to go to the rice-growing
deltas of Asia, but this proved too big a commitment. We are
most grateful to the Foundation for its generosity. The result
is this book, an authoritative study of the ecological background,
the agricultural systems, and the relevant economic and social
relations, of the hunters and pastoralists and husbandmen of
Africa.

Africa has been changing rapidly in recent years, particularly in
the years since Allan completed his manuscript and became a
leading organiser in the Food and Agricultural Organisation's
project for the rehabilitation of Antalya in Turkish Asia. But my

[1] Allan, Gluckman, Peters and Trapnell, *Land Holding and Land Usage
among the Plateau Tonga of Mazabuka District*, Rhodes-Livingstone Paper
No. 14 [1948].

[2] *Studies in African Land Usage in Northern Rhodesia*, Rhodes-Livingstone
Paper 16 [1949]

own recent observations of Kenya, Ethiopia, and Nigeria, like all
reports, emphasise that the basic problems of African development
still reside in its peasant agriculture: the problems of soil and
climate, of agricultural tools and innovation, of the social relations
which organise production, distribution, and consumption of the
fruits of the land within the family and in groups and networks of
kinsfolk. In my judgment, this book is an authoritative introduction to the complexity of these problems, and yet sets out, as a
masterpiece of scientific method, formulae by which that complexity can be simplified and handled in theoretical terms. It
provides, too, cogent answers to many practical problems. I know
that it is an essential study for those concerned with the theoretical
study of African society as well as for men and women dealing
with the practical problems of peasant life. I dare affirm that it is
equally essential to agricultural scientists.

MAX GLUCKMAN

Dept. of Social Anthropology
University of Manchester
June 1964

CONTENTS

PART III

HUNTERS AND HERDSMEN

ILLUSTRATIONS

PART I

THE BASIS OF AFRICAN LAND-USE

CHAPTER I

SOILS AND AGRICULTURAL SYSTEMS

1. THE ECOLOGICAL BASIS OF LAND-USE

The basis of African land-use is still commonly described as "shifting cultivation," a term which is singularly inappropriate when applied on a continental scale to a great range of systems differing as much from one another, in their more extreme variants, as the *Secano* cultivation of the Spanish Saragossa steppe differs from high farming on the carse lands of eastern Scotland. It is more appropriate to apply the term to soils and environments rather than to systems, for, as Lord Hailey has put it, "shifting cultivation is less a device of barbarism than a concession to the character of the soil." This means, simply, that the traditional land-use systems of Africa are adapted to the limitations of their environments, as any viable system of agriculture must be. The danger of disregarding or underestimating these limitations, even with all the resources of Western science, technology, and capital, is well illustrated by the failure of "the grisly Groundnut Scheme," as Negley Farson calls it, and other ambitious post-war projects—failures that cost the British taxpayer many millions of pounds.

To the subsistence cultivator, crop failure does not mean mere financial loss. It means—or did mean, before suzerain governments distributed famine relief—starvation and the destruction or dispersal of the community. We may assume, therefore, that as communities of men changed their way of life from hunting and food-gathering, or herding and shepherding, to an increasing dependence on hoe cultivation, they acquired a working knowledge of the soils they used and a means of recognising and distinguishing them. Without this knowledge hoe cultivation on the weaker soils that cover much of Africa would have been too precarious a means of livelihood. No community could have survived for long.

All the cultivating peoples did acquire—and, where the systems have not altogether broken down, still preserve—a large body of unwritten knowledge. The foundations of this knowledge were, no doubt, laid at a very early stage in human development. Food-gatherers and hunters must have observed the association between plant communities and the places where edible fruits, seeds, and roots were to be found, and they certainly acquired a profound knowledge of the feeding habits and movements of game animals. Survival depended on a highly specialised knowledge of environment, such as the Bindibu still possess. Dr D. F. Thomson of the University of Melbourne says of these Australian Aborigines that they are "expert ecologists and display a knowledge of the economic resources of their country far beyond that possessed by most white men. They have names for each type of country and botanical association and can name every tree and plant. They can also describe the food harvest or the fibre and resin that these will yield each season."

The Bushmen hunters and food-gatherers have comparable knowledge and skills. Elizabeth Marshal Thomas (164) says of them that "each group knows its own territory very well; although it may be several hundred square miles in area the people who live there know every bush and stone, every convolution of the ground, and have usually named every place in it where a certain kind of veld food may grow, even if that place is only a few square yards in diameter." Such precise knowledge is a condition of survival, for, she adds, "the great plains of the Kalahari may seem undiversified but really they are divided into countless little patches, some barren, some fertile, depending probably on the soil." This patchwork, this mosaic of barrenness and comparative fertility, is a characteristic of much of the land of Africa, which, as we shall see, is as important for the cultivators as for the hunters and food-gatherers.

The pastoralists know their grasslands. They are, one might say, authorities on grasses. They know the feed value of the different grazing-and-browse species, which they usually distinguish by specific names; and they recognise ecological associations, or pasture types, and can assess their value and stock-carrying capacity at different times of year. Masai herdsmen in Kenya and Tanganyika pointed out to me various species and associations that they regarded as good for supplying mineral deficiencies, for conditioning animals, for improving the potency of bulls, and for making milk and beef.

The "shifting" cultivator also has an understanding of his environment suited to his needs. He can rate the fertility of a piece of land and its suitability for one or other of his crops by the vegetation which covers it and by the physical characteristics of the soil; and he can assess the "staying-power" of a soil, the number of seasons for which it can be cropped with satisfactory results, and the number of seasons for which it must be rested before such results can be obtained again. His indicator of initial fertility is the *climax* vegetation and his index of returning fertility is the succession of vegetational phases that follows cultivation. In many cases his knowledge is precise and remarkably complete. He has a vocabulary of hundreds of names of trees, grasses, and other plants, and he indentifies particular vegetation associations by specific terms. This fund of ecological knowledge is the basis of "shifting" cultivation.

2. Shifting Cultivation

The most important factor determining the nature of a system— the extent to which it is a "shifting" system—is the ratio between the length of time the soil will sustain cultivation with satisfactory results and the period required for the restoration of fertility. Some forms of traditional agriculture make use of animal manure and other means of enhancing and prolonging fertility: but, in general, the character of the soil determines the nature of the system. In this respect, structural and textural characteristics are as important as inherent fertility; declining fertility on over-cultivated soils is very often accompanied by the structural breakdown that precedes erosion. These qualities vary enormously in African soils; indeed this largely accounts for the great range and variability of the systems of land-use and for the distribution and densities of population.

In Africa, as elsewhere, there are "permanent" soils which will sustain permanent crops or repeated cultivation of annuals almost indefinitely, or which will regain their fertility after a rest period not longer than the period of cultivation if this is not unduly prolonged. On such soils, where climatic conditions are favourable, one finds systems of permanent cultivation and stable habitations— or, at least, an agriculture that is "shifting" in a degree not much greater than the "shift" from arable to ley on a well-managed English farm. At the other extreme, there are weak, leached soils

of the ancient plateaux which, under a Sudanian climatic regime of
short rains and a long dry season, may require twenty-five years
or even more to regain a brief fertility after two or three years of
cultivation. Between these extremes there is an almost complete
range of gradations, so that it is very difficult to say where
shifting cultivation begins and ends; and the difficulty of definition
is increased by the fact that many systems cover a wide range of
soils used in different ways. Permanent and shifting use of land
may be found within the same system. It has therefore been
proposed to substitute "land rotation cultivation" for "shifting
cultivation" as a general term, and to restrict the use of the latter
to the more extreme variants in which the whole community of
cultivators moves.

On the basis of this definition one might distinguish two forms
of shifting cultivation, obligatory and voluntary. A periodic move
of the exploiting group from one area of land to another is a matter
of agricultural necessity for unaided African cultivators on what
Trapnell (175, 171, 176) has called "partial cultivation land."
This is land of a type largely unsuitable for cultivation but which
may be cultivated for longer or shorter periods in restricted belts
or patches of better soil. Very considerable areas of the poorest
plateau woodland soils, escarpment hill types, variants of the
Kalahari sands and "bush group" country in Northern Rhodesia
fall within this category.

Voluntary shifting cultivation is found where land is so
abundant, in relation to the population and its requirements, that
the period of natural soil regeneration has no practical significance
and a man need not think in terms of returning to land he has
cultivated within the foreseeable future or, perhaps, within his
lifetime. In these circumstances—which obtain, for example,
over part of the Congo basin and much of the Kalahari Sands
region in central and south-central Africa—communities are free
to move over considerable distances unhampered by the strict
requirements of the cycle of cultivation and land regeneration,
but within limits imposed by the distribution of land among the
sections of the tribe.

Another cause of shift of cultivated lands and habitations
which is also in a sense "voluntary," since it is not imposed by
agricultural necessity, is the grouping of communities together to
produce local overcrowding, although the total land area available

may be ample for the requirements of the population and the system. This is not uncommon in some areas of generally low fertility, such as the *citemene* regions of north-eastern Rhodesia. A village or other group within such a concentration will use up the accessible land in its neighbourhood before the area first cultivated has had time to regenerate and a move must then be made to regenerated land beyond the periphery of the concentration. A series of pictures or aerial photographs made at suitable intervals would show a gradual movement of the larger community across the countryside in a manner suggestive of the progress of an amoeba on a microscope slide. Human gregariousness within the system of cultural rules may be a sufficient explanation of this custom in regions where periodic moves can be avoided only by a wide dispersal of population, but in some cases at least—as in the Chad district of what was formerly French Equatorial Africa—it probably originated in a need to concentrate for defence. More recently, concentration of population has been encouraged or enforced by administrative action, generally to control disease or to facilitate the provision of schools and other social services—and sometimes mainly to serve the convenience of touring administrators and other agents of improvement, who may find it difficult to understand why, sooner or later, the people drift from their new centres of enlightenment and development.

These shifting cultivation movements must not be confused with the rebuilding of villages, which is a frequent occurrence in nearly all village-dwelling societies, or with the movement of part of a village because of schism within the group. Villages move for ritual reasons, because deaths or repeated misfortunes have occurred, or simply because it is time to re-build. The huts become delapidated after some years, the site foul and eroded, the kitchen gardens reach the point of exhaustion, and it is better to move to a new site than to attempt to rehabilitate the old dwellings. These rebuilding moves are generally short, sometimes a mile or more but often no more than a few hundred yards, in contrast with the "shift" over many miles. Another factor which may sometimes influence the decision to rebuild is a desire to use the old site for cultivation. Priestley and Greening have suggested (132), as a result of observations on the frequency of village movements, that the Ngoni who cultivate the poorer sandy soils in the Fort Jameson district "deliberately move their villages in order to benefit from the better crops they know will follow." This may, however, be a comparatively recent development symptomatic of extreme land shortage.

Migratory movements of peoples obviously differ in kind from movements associated with shifting cultivation or the fission or rebuilding of villages. Such movements were common in the past and were usually activated by uncongenial political conditions or land shortage within the tribal area.

3. The Human Carrying Capacity of Land

We must now consider what we mean when we speak of land shortage, or of ample or abundant land. These terms are by no means self-explanatory, for they can be understood and defined only in relation to environments and systems of land-use.

The subject of the human-carrying capacity of land has received surprisingly little attention, although it is clearly of great importance to an understanding of African agrarian problems. Widely different views on the same land problem are often expressed by agriculturists and administrators, and sometimes even by agriculturists of presumably equal competence. This confusion arises largely from the lack of any generally understood criteria for assessing whether land is not fully used or is overcrowded. Yet, if the land itself and the agriculture of its people are adequately studied, a reasonably accurate calculation of the carrying capacity of any land area, and further estimation of the effect of change on this capacity should present no insuperable difficulties. The main difficulties commonly arise from lack of the basic data required or from failure to understand the system and the extent to which it has been modified by extraneous forces or under the compulsion of population pressure.

The essential data required to formulate an estimate of the carrying capacity of a traditional system of land-use are:

(1) a soil or land map based on a suitable form of land classification;

(2) an estimate, for each of the land classes employed, of the proportion of land which is practicable for cultivation under the prevailing system of agriculture:

(3) a survey of the customary land-usage of the people concerned, with particular reference to the duration of cultivation and subsequent rest on the soils of each land class; and

(4) an average for the acreage under cultivation per head of population at any one time.

In the case of systems in which livestock are kept further data are required, including a determination of the grazing requirements of the livestock and the extent to which this is supplied by crop residues and by the resting and uncultivable land.

4. SOIL AND LAND CLASSIFICATION AND MAPPING

The problems and controversies of soil survey and classification are matters for the specialist in that branch of science. The field-worker in agriculture is concerned with the practical use of the information the specialist can provide, but it often happens that the pedologist's soil map is not what he wants. Soil characteristics of importance in a genetical or morphological classification are by no means always the same as those of major importance to local agriculture, and the latter may be shown, if they are shown at all, merely as phases or variants of the main soil types. The soil scientist's approach is necessarily objective; he aims at a classification based on the evolution of soils—a genetical classification arranged in order of complexity from the simplest forms developed under uniform conditions to very complex soils where all the soil-forming agencies have played their part. Therefore, he maintains, very rightly, that such a basis must be used if the classification is to be of general and comparative value.

Soils are mapped on the basis of "profile" description. The profile is the series of "horizons" that can be seen in a vertical section through the soil from the surface layer down to the parent rock or other underlying material, and the description is a field record of everything of relevance that can be observed in the profile. Study of soil profiles and the way in which they have been developed under the influence of soil-forming factors such as climate, both past and present, organisms, parent materials, topography, and time, provides the pedologist with his basis for classification. These field records are supplemented by chemical and physical analyses of the soil in the laboratory, but such analyses alone, without additional data from suitably designed field experiments, may be of little value to the farmer or field worker and may even leave him in a greater state of doubt or confusion than before.

As soon as we begin to think about land in terms of the uses to which it can or should be put—as a medium of production rather than a collection of soils that can be described and classified as we describe and classify plants and animals—our approach must change to some extent. We are bound to think in terms of particular crops, agricultural systems, and economic circumstances, and our ideas are also likely to be influenced by the capabilities and resources of the people who use the land and by existing relationships between land and population. We must also take into consideration environmental factors such as climate, topography, drainage, and susceptibility to erosion.

Many countries are trying to evaluate their land resources, but the units they have adopted for classifying and mapping land differ with local conditions, a circumstance that has given rise to the much-quoted saying that there are almost as many systems of land classification as there are classifiers. In the peculiar conditions of Holland, for example, the height of groundwater in the soil is a factor of very great importance and differences of as little as ten centimetres may affect the value of land very significantly. In New Zealand, where pasture land is of major economic importance, the permanence or otherwise of the clovers and the measures required to establish or maintain them are factors which must be given much weight in any land classification system. The system of "land capability" classification developed in the United States, and often used rather indiscriminately elsewhere, places much emphasis on susceptibility to erosion as a factor limiting the uses to which land may be put. In classifying the sugar-cane lands of Mauritius the main emphasis has been placed on rainfall and temperature, which vary greatly with altitude and affect the nature of the soil and its capacity to produce sugar, and on the local phenomena of rocky, stony, and boulder-strewn soils; consequently, the main land classes here correspond even more closely than usual to climatic zones.

Land classification may be based partly on economic, social, or other factors which are not permanent, and so the classification itself may be liable to change. Soil survey, on the other hand, is a collection of basic, physical facts which are permanent and unchangeable. This is not to say that soils cannot be altered. They can be, and often are, degraded in productive value, and they can be improved by skilled management and the application of capital. It may be true to say, as Louis Bromfield has said, that "we know

how to *make* good soils—better and more productive soils than all
but three or four types of soil created by Nature herself." But the
extent to which this technical knowledge can be applied is strictly
limited by many factors. Soils can, of course, be upgraded by the
right treatment, sometimes at very heavy or prohibitive expense:
but the fundamental type remains the same. The physical
characteristics of the soil profile are, in a very large degree, unalter-
able. The restrictions imposed by these physical characteristics
and by climate and topography, natural soil poverty and the cost of
the measures required to create fertility, or lack of the resources
with which to do so, set very definite limits to what we can do with
land. It must also be admitted that for great regions of the world,
including the inter-tropical zone, our knowledge is still woefully
meagre.

5. Soil Work in Africa

Inter-tropical Africa is no exception, and the past record of the
areas under British administration is particularly poor. For a long
period between the Wars and during and after the last War there
was practically no work at all in East and Central Africa directed
towards a general understanding, classification, and mapping of
soils. In the late 1920s a pioneer study of the soils of East Africa—
Kenya, Uganda, Tanganyika, and Zanzibar, a vast area more than
seven times as large as Great Britain—was started by Geoffrey
Milne and his colleagues, and in 1936 they produced (114) a
provisional and very general soil map. But after this promising
beginning the collaboration came to an end. Milne died at a
tragically early age, and no further advance was made in fifteen
years, until the setting up of the East African Agricultural and
Forestry Research Organisation. The one soil specialist in Northern Rhodesia was retrenched during the depression of the early
1930s almost before he had time to look round, and for nearly
twenty years this enormous territory was left without a single
specialist soil worker and with no more than the merest handful of
agricultural staff. In West Africa the story is not very different.
The Rice Commission of 1948 "could get no record of soil classification over most of West Africa" and President Truman's "Three
Wise Men"—a trio of American experts who visited Africa in
1949—expressed polite astonishment at meeting only three
officers whose time was devoted to soil problems. France and

Belgium have much more commendable records of consistent soil work in their parts of Africa.

In the last ten years there has been a very material change in this picture. Nearly every territory now has at least some staff and equipment for soil work and has begun to survey, classify, and assess its soil resources. Regional co-ordination is much more effective and an admirable effort is being made to bring all the data together in a general African classification and to compile a soil map of the regions south of the Sahara. This general co-ordination is the work of an international body, the African Pedological Service of the Commission for Technical Co-operation South of the Sahara, which has its headquarters at Yangambi, the research centre of INEAC,[1] in the Belgian Congo. Dr D'Hoore, who is in charge of the work, would be the first to emphasise that this initial classification and soil map is necessarily provisional and tentative in character. Each territory has its own classification and the task of bringing them together in a general system is complicated and, inevitably, in any pioneer work, controversial. The main competing systems are the French and Belgian. They started work at two opposite poles of environment, the former in semi-desert and the latter in the equatorial forest zone. They accept one another's views on their respective specialities, but there is less agreement in the regions of overlap and it is likely to be a good many years before sufficient data are accumulated to enable a generally agreed and accepted nomenclature and classification to be hammered out. Over most of Africa soil science is still in its infancy; indeed, the same might be said of the whole field of applied science in relation to agriculture.

It is not enough for the purposes of the field agriculturist, merely to describe and name a soil type or to assess its productivity in such general terms as nil, low, medium, and high. This may well be regarded as an essential beginning, but a great deal of experiment and experience is required to relate the findings of soil science to the actual cropping potential of soils in the field. For example, we cannot assess with any certainty the response of a soil to a certain fertiliser treatment simply by reference to analytical figures for available plant nutrients; and it sometimes happens that a soil is in fact fertile, given suitable climatic conditions, when according to the description and chemical analysis one would

[1] L'Institut National pour l'Etude Agronomique Du Congo Belge.

expect it to be very poor. Few if any of the countries of inter-
tropical Africa have as yet sufficient data from field experiments
over a wide enough range of soils to provide anything like an
efficient yardstick.

6. Use of Ecology in Land Classification and Mapping

The ecological method of distinguishing vegetation-soil types,
which was the basis of Colin Trapnell's remarkable pioneer survey
of Northern Rhodesia (175, 171) has the advantage that the land
units distinguished in this way can be related fairly readily to
African traditional knowledge and practice. The basic conception
behind this survey was that in an underdeveloped country the
study of vegetation in relation to soils, climate, and other environmental factors, and the classification of plant associations in
accordance with these factors, should provide the most practical
single guide to agricultural and forestry potentialities. This concept does not, of course, deny the value of or the need for soil
survey and field experiment; indeed, the lack of such data and of
adequate scientific services was felt as a severe handicap to the
ecological work.

Ecological survey, as a method of assessing land potential, has
its limits and limitations. It is not readily applicable and may be of
little value in regions where biotic and climatic factors, most
commonly the former, obscure the relationship between vegetation and soil. By burning, cutting, cultivating, and grazing, man
and his animals can change vegetation radically. This has happened in many parts of the world. In Cyprus and other ancient
lands of the Mediterranean, millennia of use and misuse have put
their stamp upon the land; vegetation has been reduced to almost
uniform levels of *maquis, garigue, batha,* poor annual grassland, or,
in the last stages of degradation, bare rock and barren, eroded slopes.
In such regions the character of the vegetation is more indicative
of past misuse than of agricultural potential and there is little one
can learn from it that is not equally obvious from a fairly cursory
examination of the soils themselves (96). A soil can also be changed
in some of its characteristics by cultivation and erosion, but sufficient criteria usually remain to allow of its classification with
similar undisturbed soils.

Over much of Africa, however, the association between vegetation and land potential remains relatively clear and uncomplicated.

Trapnell's work demonstrated this for Northern Rhodesia and from it there emerged a striking picture of the pattern of relationships between vegetation, soils, and the African systems of land-use. In the last few years a good deal of information on Northern Rhodesian soils has been accumulated from soil survey and chemical analyses. This new knowledge has, very largely, confirmed and reinforced the field observations of the ecological survey, but it has also led to the recognition of separate soil groups and to the explanation of some apparent anomalies (25). The practical value of ecological work has been recognised also in other parts of Africa. Vegetation surveys are being made in the Congo, Uganda, and elsewhere, in conjunction with soil survey and study of traditional agricultural systems, but the link is not always as close as it should be since the surveys are sometimes carried out as separate exercises by teams of specialists rather than as combined operations. In the Sudan, Smith (150) has shown that there is a close relationship between the distribution of tree species, rainfall, and soil texture, jointly evaluated; while in Kenya, following Trapnell's later work there, agricultural policy in the African areas is based partly on ecological criteria. In discussing the relevance of these criteria to land development and farm planning in the African areas of Kenya, Brown (31) makes the following observation: " . . . natural vegetation is the best indicator available of the potential of any area of land, resulting as it does from the sum of the effects of rainfall, soil type and temperature. From a knowledge and understanding of the grasses and trees—especially grasses—it is possible to arrive at a fair estimate of the agricultural potential of almost any area. It is the natural vegetation which is the key to the whole matter."

In woodland and forest regions, tree species and their associations are generally the most convenient indicators of land potential. Thus, in Ghana, the forest zone has been divided on the basis of associations of dominant tree species into belts corresponding closely with soil and rainfall, including the *Celtis-Triplochiton* association which indicates the extent of the region eminently suited to the establishment and growth of the cocoa plant, a matter of vital importance to the country's economy (162, 4). In the traditional lore of the forest cultivators the same criteria are used to select land for food crop cultivation. The cultivators of the great equatorial forests of Africa undoubtedly distinguish a wide range of indicator trees, but unfortunately little of this knowledge has yet been collected and assessed. According to the French scientist Pierre Gourou (69), the people of the Brazilian forest have a similar fund of knowledge. They recognise indicator trees they call *padroes*, one of the most important being *Gallesia gorasema*, and rely on these trees in selecting sites for cultivation. The Boulou of the Cameroons, he adds, choose for their gardens soils carrying *Thaumatococcus danielli* and *Cassia alata*.

The association between vegetation, land, and land-use in tropical regions is so striking that Jacks and Whyte, in their *Rape of the Earth*, put forward the proposition that: "Mastery over tropical soils must be secured with the help of the ecologist rather than of the engineer or chemist."

7. APPLICATION OF ECOLOGICAL SURVEY TO THE STUDY OF TRADITIONAL AGRICULTURAL SYSTEMS IN NORTHERN RHODESIA

The need for some means of estimating, however approximately, the land requirements of the traditional systems of land-usage in Northern Rhodesia became apparent in 1940 when the question of the adequacy or otherwise of certain Native Reserves arose as a matter of immediate practical importance. Estimates of the land requirements of a particular system had already been made, in connexion with the *citemene* control scheme in the Abercorn district which we will discuss later, but this is a specialised form of land-use in which fertility is created by the burning of branchwood cut from a large area of woodland. For this reason the suitability of an area could be expressed in terms of its woodland cover and the complications of soil fertility and cultivability were not involved. In the case of the much more widely distributed "soil selection" systems, however, no approach to the problem could be made without some means of distinguishing and mapping soil or land units recognised by the cultivators and relating these to traditional agricultural practices. For this purpose ecological criteria have the great advantage that the units they define are recognisable to the African, and they enable us to see the habitat through the eyes of the inhabitants and to understand its potentialities and limitations for a people with no material resources but the hoe, the axe, and the labour of a small group of workers. In any case, no other method was available at that time.

Trapnell's work was therefore used as a basis. The first step in estimating land requirements for a particular system and area was to make reconnaissance surveys of the land and the system of land-use, and to define for the area appropriate vegetation-soil units. The area was then surveyed and mapped by recording the occurrence of these units along straight-line traverses. Generally the traverse system consisted of a demarcated base line from which parallel lines covering the whole of the area were laid off, the distance between the lines varying from half a mile to two or even three miles according to the degree of detail required, the staff and time available, the nature of the country, and the distribution of water supplies. In the later work, when there was some improvement in the staff position, a grid system was used with east-west traverse lines not more than one mile apart and north-south lines generally at intervals of two miles.

The base line of each survey was demarcated and the starting points of traverses beaconed by an Agricultural officer, while trained African staff using prismatic compasses marked the traverse lines by means of a simple blaze through woodland, felled bushes in areas of scrub growth, and lines of posts across grassland. Numbered beacons were put up at the beginning and end of each traverse and at intervals of two miles along the line, to serve as points of reference and, in the case of the grid system, as a check on accuracy. Recording of vegetation-soil types along the traverse lines was done by European staff, using cyclometer wheels fitted with additional strikers to measure distances, and the line records were supplemented by offset traverses and lateral observations and sketches to fill in details between the parallels. Finally, the field data were plotted on a scale of 1 : 50,000 and used to construct working maps, generally on a scale of 1 : 125,000, showing the distribution of the vegetation-soil types. The total area of each type was then computed from these maps by planimeter measurements.

This type of survey gains in accuracy with repetition, but the field work becomes wearisome in the extreme when it is carried out, as it was, at relatively high speed by the same few individuals for months on end. Occasional encounters with elephant, buffalo, and lion provided some relief from the monotony of walking through seemingly endless, dry, and empty woodland. Now and again the unarmed advance parties were treed for an hour or two, on one occasion by an inquisitive rhinoceros, on another by an irritated buffalo, and quite frequently by herds of elephant browsing along the traverse line. One such herd gave me an anxious half-hour by following up the advance party ahead of me and stripping the bark from the trees, including the blazed trees of the guide line. They did this so neatly and with such confusing effect that the incident looked like a well-planned elephantine joke. But the real obstacles were thorn and bamboo thicket, grass ten feet high, swamps and reed-beds, and the worst annoyances biting insects, snakes, veld sores, and the intolerable itch caused by "seed" ticks and the urticarious hairs of buffalo bean. It was rough work in rough country. Each survey was a separate exercise designed for a practical purpose, generally in connexion with redistribution of population and relief of local congestion. Speed was essential and trained staff so few that only the simpler data (vegetation associations, and soil colour and texture within hoe-depth of the surface) could be consistently recorded; other information such as soil depth, profile descriptions and the occurrence of uncultivable variants was obtained only for a very limited range of samples as time and opportunity offered.

As an example of the units employed in field recording and mapping, and since we shall have need of such an example to clarify discussion at a later stage, the nine main vegetation groups used in surveying an area of Ndola district south of the Copperbelt of Northern Rhodesia are briefly summarised. This is woodland country in which there are limited areas of high relict forest. Associations of dominant tree species were therefore used as the chief indicators, together with soil colour and texture, in distinguishing the following major groups:

1. Red Earth Types:

   (*a*) Woodland of *Brachystegia spiciformis* and *B. longifolia* with evergreens in the understorey; on generally deep, brownish-red to lighter red clay-loams and loams.

   (*b*) Woodland of *B. floribunda, Julbernardia tomentosa*, and *J. paniculata;* on bright red to orange-red clay loams.

2. *Chipya* Types: High forest of *B. spiciformis, J. tomentosa, J. paniculata, Erythrophloeum Africanum*, and *Entandophragma caudatum*, with a luxuriant understorey of evergreens:

(a) On grey humic soils, varying marginally to more brownish or orange-toned sandy loams and loams;

(b) On strong chocolate-red or brownish red loams of the Red Earth class.

3. Copperbelt Loams and Sandy Loams: Woodland of *J. paniculata*, *B. floribunda*, *B. longifolia*, and *B. Boehmii*, with much *B. floribunda* locally:

(a) On light-coloured sandy soils, usually buff in tone;

(b) On loams of variable orange colouring;

(c) On yellow clay soils.

4. Pallid Sandy Soils: Woodland of *J. paniculata*, *B. longifolia*, *J. tomentosa*, and *Uapaca kirkiana*, with poor understorey; on pure white to pale grey or pale buff sandy loams.

5. Stronger Sandy Soils: Woodland of *B. longifolia* and *B. spiciformis* with less *J. paniculata* than the previous type and many evergreens in the understorey, including small *Marquesia;* on light buff to orange-toned sandy soils.

6. Museshe Types: Much *Marquesia macroura* (museshe) with *B. spiciformis* and *B. longifolia* and many evergreens in the understorey; on pale buff to more pinkish and orange-toned sandy loams and loams.

7. Musaka Types: *Brachystegia utilis* (musaka) in pure stand or with some *B. longifolia*, *J. tomentosa*, and *J. paniculata* and occasional evergreens; on light coloured, generally buff, sandy loams of shallow depth or with gravel near the surface.

8. Musuku-Museshe Types: Scrub woodland of *Uapaca kirkiana* (musuku) and *U. nitida* with widely spaced *Marquesia* (museshe) and *B. spiciformis*; on shallow gravelly soils.

9. Sheet-Ironstone Types. Woodland of *B. Boehmii*, *J. paniculata*, and *U. kirkiana*, sometimes with a little *B. floribunda*; on soils of varying colour with ironstone in the form of massive sheets, blocks, or pellets on the surface or immediately below it.

In addition to these general woodland and forest types, *dambo* grassland—seasonally wet drainage zones which occupy considerable proportions of the plateau woodlands—and hills with steep slopes impracticable or undesirable for cultivation, lithosols, major rock outcrops, open water surfaces, and extensive marsh areas, were distinguished and mapped. Intergrades—for example, between the Copperbelt loams and red earth or *chipya* types— were also distinguished where they appeared to be important and the vegetation-soil units were frequently subdivided into variants regarded as typical of the unit, better than the general run of the type (indicated by a positive sign) or poorer than the general run of the type (indicated by a negative sign).

This procedure made it possible to survey large areas rapidly and cheaply, and to classify the land in much the same way as the African cultivator would. The units employed differ from those used in the much later soil and vegetation surveys of the Copperbelt designed for a different purpose, in which soils and vegetation were considered independently. But whatever the unit employed in classification and mapping, whether vegetation-soil type, catena, soil complex, or series, it will rarely if ever consist of wholly cultivable soils. Even though allowance is made for major blocks of stony hills and permanent swamps, there still remains even in the best land or soil categories a proportion of land which for one reason or another cannot be used for cultivation.

CHAPTER II

CULTIVABLE AND UNCULTIVABLE LAND

1. VARIATIONS IN THE CULTIVABILITY OF LAND

The cultivability of land varies very greatly. Some regions can be cultivated over the greater part of their extent, others are wholly uncultivable. Baker (24) has estimated that of the 52 million square miles of land in the world outside the polar caps, not more than ten million is physically cultivable and capable of producing crops: but according to Bennet (27) technical and economic limitations are likely to restrict the area practicable for cultivation now or in the foreseeable future to something under six million square miles. Over the Continent of Europe the cultivable percentage of the great land divisions varies from 60 or more for the loess-covered plains of Hungary, the black earths of the Ukraine, and the glacial deposits, marine clays, and sands of Denmark, to 10 and less in the countries of the Scandinavian peninsula and the Baltic Shield. Of the 1,856 million acres of land in the United States not more than 610 million could be farmed even under the utmost pressure, according to Bennet's estimate, and much less is practicable for cultivation within the present technical and economic limits. Canada, with its great area of frozen soils and the bare rock, swamps, and acid podsols of the Laurentian Shield, has a smaller proportion of cultivable land. Canada's present farm area amounts to about 175 million acres, roughly 7.8 per cent of the total land surface, and less than half of this is in crop or summer fallow. Estimates of the total potential area suitable for cropping in Canada range from 350 million acres (15.8 per cent of the total land area) to 130 million acres (5.8 per cent), the higher figure representing physically arable land and the lower figure land which at present technical and economic levels would support a self-sustaining agriculture.

In the drier lands possibilities for irrigation and, ultimately, total rainfall and run-off set a limit to cultivability. For the Republic of South Africa, where the present cultivated area is about six million morgen,[1] including half a million under irrigation, it has been estimated that the total potential for cultivation is between seven and eight million morgen, including one million under irrigation. The total amount of rainfall run-off would probably be sufficient to irrigate two and a half million morgen, reduced to two million at the field edge, but this figure is unattainable owing to prohibitive costs and lack of storage sites (141). These figures indicated that of the total land surface of the Republic little more than 5 per cent can be cultivated at present technical and economic levels: but other estimates have put the proportion of cultivable land as high as 8 and even 10 per cent.

In desert countries the potential for cultivation depends on availability of water at low cost. More than 96 per cent of the land of Egypt is, and is likely to remain, uncultivable desert, uninhabitable except for very sparse populations of camel nomads. About six million acres are irrigated out of a possible nine million to which water might be brought, and an expanding population—which has increased from five to twenty millions in little more than a century—is squeezed into the narrow ribbon of the Nile valley and the delta at an overall density approaching 1,600 to the square mile. The settled area is only about the size of Belgium, the most densely populated part of Europe, and the population is twice as great. In the southern extension of the desert the proportion of cultivable land is still less. According to Hewison (80), the Northern Province of the Sudan, an area of more than 236,000 square miles has only about 500 square miles of cultivable land, and this is a narrow strip along the Nile varying from a few metres to four kilometres in width. Willimott (185) has suggested that in the comparatively well-watered Equatorial Province of the Sudan, west of the Nile, in contrast with the desert north, about 87 per cent of the total land area is "available for agriculture," although water supply remains a limiting factor in many parts. High cultivable percentages, of 60 and over, have also been suggested for Uganda but these appear to have been arrived at by deducting certain major uncultivable categories and assuming the rest to be cultivable, and it is not always clear whether the figures refer to land now practicable for cultivation or include swamp areas which might be made cultivable by drainage.

---

[1] One morgen = $2\frac{1}{6}$ acres.

2. ECONOMIC, TECHNICAL, DEMOGRAPHIC, AND SOCIAL FACTORS AFFECTING THE EXTENT TO WHICH LAND MAY BE CULTIVATED

These general examples will serve to illustrate the variability of this factor, the cultivable percentage of land, and the variety of meanings that may be attached to the term. It cannot be defined with precision except in relation to other factors, some of which may be liable to change. Thus, in commercial agriculture, the amount of land which may be cultivated profitably varies with production costs and commodity prices. There is a marginal zone within which cultivation expands and contracts as profit margins rise and fall. The "high-water mark" of prosperity of the sugar industry can be seen, for example, on the hills of Mauritius where the cane fields have moved up and down the slopes in response to economic change. Similarly, in subsistence agriculture there is a marginal area between clearly cultivable and uncultivable land. This area, though regarded as uncultivable—that is, not worth the labour of cultivating—by a people with adequate land will be brought into cultivation under conditions of acute population pressure. About twenty years ago a startling example of this was to be seen in the Fort Jameson district of Northern Rhodesia where, under intense population pressure, great areas of formerly wooded mountain and hill and *dambo* grassland country has been taken into cultivation. Catchments and *dambo* "sponges" had been stripped of their cover, cultivation had spread up the mountains over incredibly steep slopes almost to their summits, and the whole area presented an appalling picture of impending devastation. As soon as pressure had been relieved by addition of land and re-distribution of population these hill slopes were abandoned; fortunately, this occurred in time to prevent their permanent denudation, though indelible scars remain. Two later workers (132), commenting on the situation in this area some twelve years after the relief of acute pressure, remark that "hill cultivation is no longer practised and the trees have grown remarkably well," but "the scars are still to be seen in the Nyamfinzi and Mkwawe hills and elsewhere. They clearly indicate the desperate land shortage that must have existed."

There is, obviously, a wide divergence between the proportion of land cultivable for a people with advanced techniques who can command the capital needed for their application and a people who possess neither these resources nor the skill to use them. In considering the African systems of land-use, if we are to do so objectively, we must accept the limitations of traditional implements, skills, and customs, and adapt our conception of cultivability accordingly. Even when allowance has been made for major blocks of stony hills and permanent swamp, there still remains within almost every soil or land category a proportion of land which for one reason or another is impracticable for cultivation. The factors responsible may be physical, such as local steep slopes, areas of shallow soil over ironstone or along lines of outcrops, depressions subject to seasonal waterlogging, the presence of an impervious pan near the surface, or local occurrences of soils highly acid, saline, or deficient in some factor of fertility; or they may lie in the need to retain land for purposes other than cultivation; for timber, grazing, habitations, tracks, or even for the preservation of bush or forest products of importance to the economy or culture. Areas otherwise practicable for tillage may be unusable because of lack of surface water, or the incidence of diseases such as river-blindness and sleeping sickness and the prevalence of tsetse, or for mystical reasons which, however we may regard them, must be accepted if we are to make an objective assessment of the system. Sacred groves, rain shrines, and places dedicated to the spirits usually remain undisturbed even under conditions of acute land shortage. In one greatly overcrowded part of West Africa I came across a fertile valley with excellent seepage soils which had remained unused because any disturbance of the land would have caused offence to a powerful spirit. A group of sophisticated young men, converts to Christianity, who had recently returned to the village, wanted to use this land for vegetable gardens and they had the backing of the Agricultural Department. The rest of the village strongly opposed this impious proposal and the case was referred to the Chief's court, which recorded a judgment worthy of Solomon: "Let these ridiculous young men have their garden. If they die, it will not be our fault, for we have done our best to dissuade them. If they do not die, it will only show we have been mistaken in supposing this to be a sacred place."

Land known to be cultivable may not be cultivated because it is so situated that gardens cannot be effectively protected against destructive game animals. A remarkable example of this was to be found among the Tonga of the Zambesi valley in Northern Rhodesia whose traditional agriculture was focused on the alluvial deposits flanking the river and its main tributaries. In spite of shortage of traditional garden land and recurrent famines, they made little or no use of certain woodland and thicket types on karroo soils at some distance from the foci of settlement, mainly because of the virtual certainty of loss of crops by the depredations of game—especially elephant, but also baboons, buffalo, and pig. With the decrease of game, partly by deliberate control and partly by the increase of firearms among the Tonga, land of this category was rapidly exploited, so rapidly that in a matter of ten years or so most of it had been taken into cultivation and "bush" gardens exceeded those of the traditional types both in area and output. Other factors also influenced this development, but it appears that the main factor was the release of the land from the domination of the game.

Social organisation may also have an effect on the ability to use land and the extent to which it may be cultivated. A people organised on a centralised authoritarian basis can apply their combined labour to tasks far beyond the ability of small groups co-operating voluntarily. The *sishanjo* cultivation of the Lozi of Northern Rhodesia is a case in point; they once drained and cultivated, and to a lesser extent still cultivate, large areas of saturated sandy peats on the margin of the great Barotse plain, but the traditional system of tribute labour on which maintenance of the greater drainage channels depended was ended under British administration. Consequently much of this land has gone out of cultivation and must be regarded as uncultivable by the Lozi in existing circumstances.

3. ESTIMATION OF THE CULTIVABLE PERCENTAGE OF LAND

Assessment of the cultivable percentage proved to be the most puzzling and intractable of all the problems involved in the estimation of land requirements and Critical Population Densities of the traditional land-use systems. Cultivable land was taken to be such land as would normally be included in the cropping sequence and land rotation of the balanced system unaffected by pressure, but there was no ready means of assessing this factor for each of the vegetation-soil types. The first attempt to do so was based on a series of large-scale vertical aerial photographs of some of the African Reserves on the railway line of Northern Rhodesia, taken in 1939 as a preliminary to anti-erosion and agricultural development work. Conditions in this region were fairly well known at the time. Hence it was possible to select sample areas, about which it could reasonably be assumed that all land normally regarded as cultivable would have been cultivated recently enough to show on the photographs. After study of the whole range of photographs, a series of samples to which it was thought that this assumption could be applied with the highest degree of probability was selected, each sample being representative of one of the major vegetation-soil types of the area.

Unfortunately the photographs covered a very limited range of types and only the three following land classes could be used:

1. Acacia Tree-Grassland: *Acacia sieberiana*, or *A. polyacantha* in areas of moister subsoil, associated with species of *Ficus*, *Albizzia*, *Zizphus*, and other small trees, in *Hyparrhenia-Brachiaria* grassland; on buff to deep brownish-red or chocolate coloured colluvial loams.

2. *Combretum* Scrub-Woodland: Scrub-woodland, interspersed with areas of tall-grass, containing *Afrormosia Angolensis* and species of *Lonchocarpus*, *Pterocarpus*, *Dalbergia*, and *Terminalia*, with much *Combretum*, *Dalbergia* on fire-protected sites and open *Combretum-Terminalia* grassland in much-burnt areas; on light, friable sandy loams, greyish-brown to brownish-red in colour.

3. Southern *Julbernardia-Brachystegia* Woodland: Low woodland of *J. globiflora* with *B. Boehmii* on the poorer and *B. spiciformis* on the better variants, typically associated with wiry grasses such as *Loudetia*, *Schizachyrium* and *Andropogon* species; on soils ranging from pallid sands to pinkish-buff sandy loams.

Land intermediate between these types and grading from one to another was also distinguished by the covering vegetation. The cultivated land within each sample was then determined by planimeter measurements from the photographs, together with resting land in grass, bush or partly regenerated woodland fallow, and all land showing any sign whatever of having been cultivated at any time. Field observation was used as a check where this was thought to be necesssary and a ground scale for each photograph was determined in the field. They were on an approximate scale of six inches to the mile, but there was some variation due to differences in altitude.

The figures obtained from the 41 measured samples, each of which was about 12·5 square miles in area, are tabulated below; all land which showed any indication of previous cultivation, from examination of the photographs or on ground inspection, was included in the "cultivable" category. The vegetation-soil classes are indicated by the following notation:

A = Acacia tree-grassland.

c = *Combretum* scrub-woodland.

JB = *Julbernardia-Brachystegia* woodland.

A-C-JB = Mixed and intermediate types containing elements of all three classes.

C-JB = Mixed and intermediate types containing elements of these two classes.

CLASS	NO. OF SAMPLES	AREA MEASURED (ACRES)		CULTIVABLE PERCENTAGE	
		Total	Cultivable	Range	Mean
A	14	120,450	38,080	27–34	31·6
C	4	33,430	8,598	20–34	25·7
A-C-JB	7	63,070	13,875	19–23	22·0
C-JB	9	76,855	13,670	13–22	17·8
JB	7	62,570	4,520	5–11	7·2
	41	356,375	78,743	5–34	22·1

These figures probably reflect a maize standard of fertility, since this was the staple crop over most of the region from which the samples were taken. They suggest that of the total area measured, amounting to 557 square miles, only 123 square miles, or approximately 22 per cent, is cultivable for maize within the limitations of traditional techniques unaided by more advanced methods of reclaiming and enhancing the fertility of soils. Of the generally rich soils characterised by Acacia-grassland, only about one third is cultivable, while the more variable and usually poorer soils carrying scrub-woodland vegetation are cultivable for little more than a quarter, and the poor leached soils of the plateau class for less than one tenth, of their extent. The surprisingly low cultivable percentage of the most fertile land class is largely accounted for by seasonal waterlogging of large areas and the extent of cultivable land could, no doubt, have been much increased by appropriate drainage measures. Similarly, if we disregard the economic factor, part of the "uncultivable" sector of the scrub woodland and even of the plateau woodland could have been made productive by application of organic manure or inorganic fertilisers. But for a people who lack the skill, organisation and capital to carry out extensive drainage works, to whom the use of animal manure is unknown or objectionable, and who have no means of obtaining artificial fertilisers even if they have heard of them, land which might be made productive by these devices remains uncultivable.

At the time the estimates were made, the agriculture of the Tonga people, who occupy the Reserves covered by the photographic survey, was already in a state of transition brought about largely by adoption of the plough and a market for surplus maize. They own cattle, and a few cultivators were beginning to use manure while a very few were practising fairly advanced farming methods: but these changes were as yet on much too small a scale to affect the results significantly. The major changes which had taken place were extensive use of the ox-drawn plough and the partial substitution of maize for sorghum, a crop formerly more extensively grown as a staple especially on the lighter soils. The great majority of the Tonga were still cultivating subsistence acreages—they were still doing so when a survey was made five years later (10)—with little departure from the customary pattern, and demand for land had not yet pressed cultivation into the "marginal" zone to any marked extent.

The same method could not be applied elsewhere, since there were no aerial photographs of suitable areas, and estimates of cultivable percentages for other vegetation-soil types and systems were made by ground examination and survey of sample areas in regions where there appeared to be a balance between population and land; and also, for comparison, in overcrowded parts of the Reserves. These samples indicated a very similar range of variation. For example, the cultivability of the northern woodland types defined above (pp. 17–19) was estimated to range from 34 per cent for the red earth and *chipya* classes to as low as 5 per cent for the poorer variants of the pallid sands; and a general estimate of 22 per cent cultivable was arrived at for a surveyed area of 379 square miles, on the basis of the Lamba system of land-use with sorghum as a staple. Another survey of 956 square miles in the Fort Jameson and Petauke districts gave a general cultivable percentage of 25 for the Ngoni and Chewa systems of maize culture. Contrary to expectation, the field results suggested that the percentage of a vegetation-soil type which is cultivable under African systems of land use does not vary widely with variations in the staple crop. Later work by Peters[1] supported this finding for grain crop staples, but showed that it did not apply to cultures with cassava as a main crop.

Peters' investigations included an attempt to estimate a general cultivable percentage for Northern Rhodesia as a whole, excluding Barotseland, and he arrived at the conclusion that the figure must lie between 7.5 per cent and 13.5 per cent for the traditional systems of land-use. The figure could not be assessed with greater accuracy because much of the area had been mapped only on the basis of skeletal traverses; consequently the boundaries of the vegetation-soil types—and, in many cases, their cultivable extent— could be determined only as lying within certain fairly wide limits.

These attempts to assess the cultivability of land for the African systems gave, at best, uncertain results of poor reliability, and this uncertainty may well have resulted in material errors in the estimation of Critical Population Densities. They were, however, the best that could be contrived in the circumstances of the time and it was felt that this approach at least avoided the much greater errors that would have arisen from ignoring the factor or assessing it by deduction only of the major and more obviously uncultivable categories. Serious miscalculations have been made in the past, and continue to be made, as a result of over-optimistic assumptions regarding the cultivability of land or of failure to appreciate the significance of the factor, particularly in the demarcation of Native Reserves and the lay-out of settlement schemes. In the equatorial forest of the Congo basin one comes across vestiges of some of the earlier *paysannats*, established before the need for detailed preliminary survey was realised, which have failed and been abandoned

---

[1] D. U. Peters, unpublished reports. Much very valuable work by Peters remains unpublished because of his early and tragic death.

because they were sited on "uncultivable" soils; and de Schlippe (146) says of the Zande settlement scheme in the southern Sudan that "as no detailed survey preceded resettlement, holdings ran through river valleys and outcrops and included a proportion of agriculturally unsuitable land." Errors of greater magnitude have occurred where, as in the case of the Native Reserves of Northern Rhodesia and elsewhere, large areas were allotted without preliminary survey and investigation of the land and the limitations of the local systems of land-use.

It is difficult for people whose standards have been set by the uniformity of the farm lands of Britain—a uniformity produced by centuries of ploughing, manuring, marling, and liming—to realise the far greater variability of unaltered African soils formed under very different conditions of leaching and natural erosion. Disregard of this factor was one of the reasons for the failure of the Groundnut Scheme at Kongwa. It was not realised, until costly experience made it apparent, that soils naturally suitable for cropping are often limited and widely dispersed. All the bush clearing at Kongwa, and initially in the other areas, was done in blocks of one square mile, without regard to soil variation, and this resulted in the clearing at high expense of very large areas which later proved to be quite unsuitable for annual cropping.

Fallacious assumptions regarding cultivability continue to be made and this aspect of land-use requires much greater attention than it has received in the past. It should be possible to obtain much more conclusive data by isolating the several factors involved for separate investigation and by including in detailed soil surveys observations on variations in soil depth, slope, drainage, and other factors determining the local physical limitations of each soil class. With adequate staff and resources such data are fairly readily obtainable and are not infrequently collected in detailed farm surveys. Incidentally, it is instructive to note how much land often remains uncultivated even on intensively managed farms in the best environments.

CHAPTER III

THE LAND-USE FACTOR

1. DEFINITION OF THE FACTOR

The next factor we have to consider, what may be called the land-use factor, is the relationship between the duration of cultivation on each of the land or soil units used in classification and the period of subsequent rest required for the restoration of fertility. It is most conveniently expressed, for the purpose of assessing critical population densities, as the number of "garden areas" required, a "garden area" being the area in cultivation at any one time. For example, in the case of a soil capable of maintaining its fertility under alternate crop and fallow periods of equal duration only two garden areas will be required, while, at the other extreme, on a very poor soil allowing of only two years cultivation followed by a full period of woodland regeneration the requirement may be no less than sixteen garden areas. The land-use factor is 2 for the one type and 16 for the other.

2. CLASSIFICATION OF LAND IN ACCORDANCE WITH THE LAND-USE FACTOR

Vegetation-soil types or other suitable land units may be classified in accordance with the land-use factors applicable to the cultivable soils within them. On this basis, Trapnell proposed a classification of the main vegetation-soil types distinguished in the course of the ecological survey of Northern Rhodesia into five major land-use categories: Permanent or Semi-Permanent land, Re-cultivation land, Shifting Cultivation land, Partial Cultivation land, and Useless or Waste land (172). While this grouping fits well with the range of traditional systems found in Northern Rhodesia, with its great extent and high proportion of "shifting cultivation" land, some modification is desirable for more general application of the concept; in particular, the addition of a class of "Land Rotation Cultivation" soils (or "Recurrent Cultivation" land, as I have called it) is important.

We will, therefore, for purposes of general discussion, employ six major land categories defined in accordance with the manner in which the cultivable soils are commonly used:

1. PERMANENT CULTIVATION LAND

Land of this category contains the strongest and most fertile soils, for which the land-use factor, under customary usage, is 2 or less. They cover a wide range, including young soils on recently deposited volcanic ash, brown tropical soils of volcanic origin in the humid regions, young alluvium of rich moist valley land, hydromorphic and organic soils allowing of cultivation, strong red clays and loams, and some of the ferruginous tropical soils with relatively high mineral reserves and exchange capacity.

In traditional usage such land is not as a rule cultivated continuously for annual crops, except in areas rejuvenated by periodic flooding, as in the case of the Oualo lands of the lower Senegal valley where the waters of the river flood the broad flanking plains in July and subside four months later leaving a great area of moist and refertilised soil which is used for annual cropping by the Troucoleur people. On most "permanent" soils, where the systems have not been disrupted by population pressure, a brief grass fallow of one or two years is interposed after three or four years of cropping, to control weeds and preserve soil structure; or a longer period of cultivation, extending to as much as twelve years and sometimes even more on very strong soils resistant to erosion, is followed by a fallow period of equal or shorter duration. Comparatively long cultivation periods, ranging from four to ten years, appear to be characteristic of Northern Rhodesian systems on permanent soils of the Upper Valley and red earth classes and the Lower Valley and other alluvials, in contrast to East African systems such as those of Chaggaland, Elgon, Buganda, and Teso where the cultivation period rarely exceeded four years and was most commonly three years followed by a rest period of one, two, or three years. There is some evidence that the short fallow period of two or three years combined with short-term cropping is the better practice, particularly where cattle are kept. Caution in the use of grass fallows for grazing is very necessary—for, by destroying the cover and

inducing soil compaction and erosion, the effects of grazing
may be the reverse of recuperative—but such caution is
rarely if ever exercised.

The closest approach to continuous use of land is to
be found on soils of this category in the humid regions where
moisture and temperature conditions allow of the cultivation
of plantains as a principal crop. In such situations, as on
the volcanic soils of Chaggaland and Elgon and the rich
earths of the "fertile crescent" in Uganda, plantains and
bananas are used as perennial crops. Even so, the custom
was to allow part of the grove to go out of cultivation for a
short rest break at fairly long intervals.

2. SEMI-PERMANENT LAND

The "Re-cultivation Land" category of the Northern
Rhodesian grouping was devised for a range of fairly strong
and fertile soils, including weaker variants of the Upper
Valley class and red loams of similar character carrying
Combretum-Afrormosia and Pterocarpus-Combretum vegetation or Brachystegia spiciformis woodland, red earths and
allied red loams under Brachystegia-Julbernardia woodland
of varying composition, and Lake Basin and chipya soils
carrying Erythrophloeum-Pterocarpus vegetation or Mar-
quesia-Brachystegia woodland. On such soils "re-cultivation" systems were commonly practised; a cropping
period of from five to eight years was followed by a "scrub"
fallow of similar duration, a further period of cultivation and
a longer fallow lasting for at least twice the cultivation
period—for example, six years' cultivation, six years' rest,
six years' "re-cultivation" and then twelve years' rest or
more. The land-use factor for these soils therefore ranges
from 2·5 to 3, under this method of usage.

Former practice on the fertile soils of South Busoga in
Uganda appears to have followed a somewhat similar, but
more extended, pattern. A cycle of three or four crops
alternating with one year of natural fallow, during which
Panicum and Sorghum grasses covered the garden and
smothered weeds, was repeated two or three times and the
land was then left for a long period, commonly ten to fifteen
years, to regenerate under bush or elephant grass. The land

requirement was probably of the order of 2·5 and did not exceed 3 garden areas. But elsewhere in Africa soils of comparable strength and fertility are generally worked on simple systems of short-period cropping followed by a longer rest period, while the re-cultivation device is used in some of the traditional systems on land of other categories.

I have therefore included in the "semi-permanent" category all land on which soil fertility is maintained under systems employing more than two, but not more than three, garden areas. Such soils, like those of the first category, allow of a definite and more-or-less permanent relationship between the cultivating group and a particular parcel of land, approximating to our conception of a small family farm.

3. RECURRENT CULTIVATION LAND

For a great range of very different land types and cropping systems the land-use factor lies between 4 and 10, and most frequently between 4 and 8. Cultivation periods commonly vary from two to six years and rest periods from six to thirty years, in various combinations which give factors within this range of variation. Defined in this way, the category includes vast areas of land in such diverse and contrasting environments as the equatorial forest of the Congo basin, the moist semi-deciduous forests of West Africa, the Guinea savannah of north Ghana, the sands of the eastern coastal belt, and the dry woodland of East and Central Africa.

The environment and systems have no more in common than that the number of garden areas required for the maintenance of fertility falls within the same wide limits. The usual cycle is a simple alternation of cropping and fallow: for example, two years' cropping and six years' rest, or three to four years' cropping and twenty years' rest; but the device of "re-cultivation" is, or was, used in some systems on the basis of a cycle such as three cropping periods each of three years separated by two rest periods each of five years after which the cultivating group moved from the area of depleted fertility leaving the land fallow for twenty years or more. "Land Rotation cultivation," to use the new term signifying a more stable relationship between land and population than that associated with "shifting" cultivation, is common practice on land of this category: but, in some of the systems, cultivation and habitations "shift" from time to time as a necessity imposed by social and cultural factors rather than by the nature of the soil, or as an entirely voluntary move under conditions of abundant land.

Since the category includes so wide a range it may be divided into, say, three sections: land for which the factor, under the appropriate system of land-use (a) exceeds 3 but does not exceed 5, (b) exceeds 5 but does not exceed 7, (c) exceeds 7 but does not exceed 10. These will be referred to as short-, medium-, and long-term, Recurrent Cultivation soils.

4. SHIFTING CULTIVATION LAND

This leaves in the Shifting Cultivation category land for which the factor exceeds 10—soils so poor that one, two, or at most three years of cultivation must be followed by a very long fallow period, of the order of twenty to thirty years, for regeneration of woodland or the restoration of soil fertility. Such systems are practised in Northern Rhodesia on weak, leached, sandy soils and poor, raw clays of the plateau woodlands, weak variants of the Kalahari sands and certain classes of grey *dambo* soils in bush-group country and valley and flood-plain grasslands. The latter types, more especially the bush-group country, might be regarded as falling more appropriately into the next category.

5. PARTIAL CULTIVATION LAND

Some clearly definable categories of land, notably the extensive escarpment hill regions of Northern Rhodesia between the plateaux and the great valleys, are very largely impracticable for cultivation but contain widely dispersed and very limited sites or pockets of soil on which crops may be grown. The cultivable sites may be poor, allowing only of shifting or recurrent cultivation, or they may be of a higher order of fertility. Land of this category can therefore support only small, scattered, and generally isolated communities separated by a great extent of uninhabitable land;

and these communities may be settled with some permanence in well-watered and relatively fertile valleys, or they
may shift from one "island" site to another where the soils
require a post-cultivation rest of long duration.

6. UNCULTIVABLE OR WASTE LAND

This category consists of vegetation-soil types, or other
land units, which are wholly uncultivable under the traditional systems of cultivation, for reasons such as general and
extreme soil poverty or intractability, seasonal or permanent
waterlogging, or inability of the soils to retain moisture.
They may or may not be useful for other purposes such as
timber production, grazing, honey-hunting and other
collecting activities.

It includes a diversity of types: in Northern Rhodesia,
the halomorphic clays under *Colophospermum mupani* woodland in the great river valleys, some of the Kalahari sand
types of the west, *Diplorrhynchus* and other scrub-grassland
on Plateau and ironstone soils, *Philippia* scrub-grassland of
mountain summits, and the marshes and papyrus sudd of
such vast swamp regions as Bangweulu and Lukanga.

3. ASSESSMENT OF THE FACTOR

These divisions, though useful for purposes of discussion, are, of
course, to some extent arbitrary, and the classification of a land
type will depend on the unit used. If, for example, we were to
take the Lower Valley land of Northern Rhodesia as a single unit
we would probably classify it as Partial Cultivation land, so great is
the extent of uncultivable *mupani* woodland soils: but if we were
employing finer units we would distinguish Permanent and Semi-
Permanent alluvial land, chestnut-coloured sands under dense
Commiphora thicket, and the uncultivable *mupani* soils; or we
might further sub-divide the first two types into Permanent and
Semi-Permanent alluvials and Recurrent Cultivation land of
classes (*a*) and (*b*) and intermediate grades. The land categories
grade into one another, so that any dividing line is necessarily
arbitrary, and the more marginal soil variants are sometimes used
in different ways in different systems. Classificatory terms may
have little meaning, and may indeed be misleading, unless they

are used strictly in relation to clearly defined units and systems of land-use.

Few rotational experiments in tropical Africa have lasted long enough to assess the period required for restoration of fertility under natural fallow of long duration. Almost invariably, traditional fallow periods can be assessed only by enquiry and there is no yardstick of precise knowledge against which to measure the probable accuracy of the results. In the Northern Rhodesian work, the method generally used was based on detailed investigation of individual sample areas of regenerating bush and woodland. The date of the last cultivation was assessed as closely as possible for each sample and when sufficient samples had been accumulated a general picture of the sequence of regeneration from one crop cycle to the next was built up. Answers to enquiries were checked against tree ring counts and against strips of aerial photographs— taken in 1930—where these covered the sample areas. Compared with results obtained in this way, data from straightforward general enquiry tended to give underestimates of the longer fallow periods, probably because the informants could not remember and were unused to expressing long periods in terms of years. The African who knows his code of land-use does not as a rule think or express himself in the terms of the European, and the African who has acquired these terms is rarely an authority on traditional practice.

There was no great difficulty in distinguishing between customary rest periods and the shortened fallows of over-populated areas: in such areas complaints of land shortage and its effects were immediately volunteered. Situations which might have led to prolongation of the fallow much beyond the necessary limits were not encountered in the course of the detailed studies in Northern Rhodesia, since these were concerned with regions already overcrowded in relation to environments and agricultural systems or in process of becoming so: but it should not be difficult to recognise and make allowance for such situations where they exist.

The assumption that the minimum customary duration of fallow represents the period necessary for the return of fertility to a satisfactory level may not be universally valid, though it is probably true for the Northern Rhodesian and the great majority of traditional African systems. Jackson and Shawki (93) have described a system practised on static sand dunes in parts of the

Sudan, and typically close to the Nile north of Kosti, in which the period of retirement from cultivation appears to be determined by the growth and exploitability of gum arabic trees. Land is culti- vated—the main crops being bulrush millet and sorghum—for periods ranging from four to ten years, after which it is abandoned and becomes colonised by *Cenchrus biflorus* and *Acacia senegal* (gum arabic). The acacias are ready for tapping in about eight years and they remain dominant and are continuously tapped for a further six to ten years. This is followed by a phase of variable duration during which the trees degenerate and die out as a result of heavy tapping, and eventually the area is burned over in preparation for another cycle of cultivation.

Not only the land itself but the agricultural practices of its inhabitants must be carefully studied and clearly understood before any attempt can be made to estimate the land requirements of the traditional systems or to assess the way in which they have changed or are changing. We must first try to see the situations through the eyes of the African cultivators and put aside for the time being our own preconceived ideas, prejudices, and conceptions of good land-use, which derive from very different societies and environ- ments.

CHAPTER IV

THE NORMAL SURPLUS OF
SUBSISTENCE AGRICULTURE

1. The "Normal Surplus"

The last factor involved in the assessment of Critical Population Densities, the area cultivated per unit of population, is determined by human estimates of needs—in relation to basic requirements and the security of the group—and by physical considerations of climate, yields, and labour potential.

It would appear to be a reasonable—if not axiomatic—proposition that subsistence cultivators, dependent entirely or almost entirely on the produce of their gardens, tend to cultivate an area large enough to ensure the food supply in a season of poor yields. Otherwise the community would be exposed to frequent privation and grave risk of extermination or dispersal by famine, more especially in regions of uncertain and fluctuating rainfall.[1] One would, therefore, expect the production of a "normal surplus" of food in the average year.

2. Sales of African-Produced Maize in
Northern Rhodesia

This simple and obvious idea first occurred to me as the result of a study of a practical problem in Northern Rhodesia. The story goes back to the 1930s when world prices for maize fell far below the level remunerative for the European producer. Maize production was then in excess of local demand, which came mainly from the copper mines, and the stability—indeed, the existence—of the European farming industry of Northern Rhodesia was seriously threatened. To meet this situation marketing legislation was introduced. The grain price on the internal market was fixed and a Maize Control Board was set up to purchase and market all maize offered for sale, the final price paid to the producer being deter-

---

[1] Records for Cyprus, extending over 80 years, show that the wheat-growers of the Mesaoria, which is such a region, may expect three good seasons, four average seasons, two poor seasons, and one crop failure in each decade.

mined by the relationship between the quantity sold at the controlled local price and exported at the low world price. Some African cultivators in Reserves near the railway line, mainly the Tonga, were already selling considerable quantities of maize to traders and the remunerative local market was divided between European and African producers on what was thought to be an equitable proportion based on sales over the three previous years. The share of the African producers was estimated, on this basis, to be 58,000 bags (one bag = 200 lb of grain) and there was therefore considerable surprise and consternation when, in 1936, the first year of maize control, no less than 234,000 bags of maize were delivered by Africans.

The equity of the market division was, of course, called in question, but it appeared probable that a discrepancy even of this order could be explained on the assumption that the African producers, or the great majority of them, were in fact selling the normal surplus of subsistence cultivation. Data from sampling surveys indicated that the average "producing unit" might be regarded as a family group cultivating approximately six acres of maize and requiring about thirteen bags of grain to meet domestic requirements (12). By assessing the total number of "producing units"—about 17,000, as nearly as could be estimated—from population figures for the areas from which maize was then sold, and using the simple formula $P(6Y-13)$ to estimate the expectation of total sales, where P is the number of Producing Units and Y the mean Yield for the season in bags per acre, the following conjectures were formulated:

(a) For each increase of one bag per acre in excess of 2·17 bags per acre, the minimum domestic requirement, approximately 100,000 bags of maize would be sold by African producers.

(b) Annual deliveries would fluctuate within very wide limits, probably from a minimum of 20,000 bags to a maximum of about 340,000 bags, assuming a static producing population.

(c) Average deliveries over a long series of years might be expected to approximate to 85,000 bags, again assuming a static producing population.

These very tentative conclusions involved assumptions, based on very slight yield data, that the mean maize yield of any season would be unlikely to fall much below 2·5 bags per acre or to exceed

5·5 bags, and that the mean yield of the "average" season might approximate to 3 bags per acre. It was intended that they should be checked against the results of more adequate sampling and reliable field estimates of yields, but this could not be done on account of other preoccupations and the changes that came with the outbreak of war. It was not until 1943 that an estimate of yield was made from reasonably adequate field sampling, and then only in part of the Tonga country and for a different purpose. The purpose of this survey was to assess the maize yields obtained by paid demonstrators cultivating their own holdings on an improved system devised by the Agricultural Department, and to compare them with the general yield. Maize grown in the Demonstrators' gardens gave an average yield of 5·25 bags per acre, compared with an estimated general average of 2·75 bags per acre for that season (15). At this general yield level, on the basis of the original conjectures, expected deliveries would be 59,000 bags: actual deliveries in 1943 amounted to 60,000 bags (15).

The possibility that the original hypothesis and the conjectures deriving from it were not very far from reality, in spite of the inadequacy of the data, is supported by the fact that for fourteen years, from 1936 to 1949, and until there was a radical alteration of the whole picture, deliveries of African-produced maize fell within the predicted limits (Fig. 1.) Johnson (94) has described the period 1938–44 as one of declining production "following the low prices of the middle and late thirties." This must mean either that the Tonga maize-growers sold less of their surplus or that the number of farmers—in the sense of families cultivating significantly more than a subsistence acreage—declined. There is, however, no very convincing reason to suppose that the Tonga, accustomed to selling their surplus at "low" prices and with no criterion of price other than that paid to the European producer, to which the African price was related, suddenly reduced their sales; and the data collected by the 1945 survey (10) indicate an increase rather than a decline in the number of "farmers." In 1945 the great majority of the maize sellers were still subsistence cultivators deriving most of their cash income not from maize sales but from sales of livestock, poultry, and eggs, and from the wages of labour, to whom the selling of the maize surplus, when they happened to have one, was a convenient method of storage and any profit from it a gift of the season. It may, I think, be more accurate to regard

1936–49 as a relatively static period. Until the latter part of this period new ploughs, carts, and spare parts were in short supply and the marketing area remained much the same. The main factor determining the pattern of maize sales over the period was

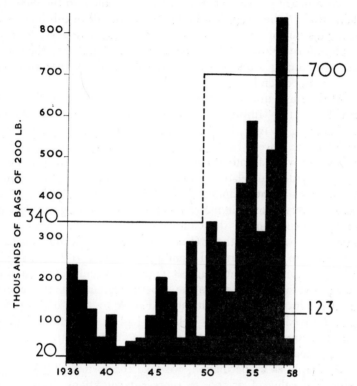

FIG. 1. Sales of African produced maize: Northern Rhodesia Railway lines areas only.

the effect of weather on the amount of surplus produced by a more-or-less static number of subsistence and semi-subsistence cultivators, and it happened that there was no very good season in the period 1938–44. One does not expect a six to turn up in every seven throws of a die.

The new pattern of the 1950s is to be accounted for by a number of factors, of which a great increase in the number of "producing units" was probably the most important. The marketing area was greatly extended, by the setting up of buying points and provision of transport. This not only expanded the original area but tapped the "normal surplus" of a large belt of fertile and undepleted maize soils in the northern Kafue basin, the country of the Lenje, Sala, and Soli peoples, and brought all of the main maize-growing areas of the railway line into the picture. Estimates by Johnson (94) indicate the magnitude of this increase. Basing his conclusions on 1954 population figures, he says, "a very rough estimate of the total number of farming families in the main maize-producing areas of the railway line may be hazarded at between 25,000 and 30,000."

At the same time a strong incentive to increased farming was provided by the "Improved African Farmers" scheme which had its beginning in 1947, the "new drive" starting in 1949, and by soaring maize prices. High prices provided a very strong incentive to "unimproved" farming, particularly in the newly incorporated areas of fertile and relatively abundant maize soils. Thus, while the number of contributors to maize sales increased rapidly, there was also a very significant increase in the average acreage cultivated per "producing unit"—the Cultivation Factor. The number of improved farmers in the railway line area, to whom acreage bonuses were paid, increased from 455 in 1950 to 1,830 in 1958, and if, as sampling data suggest (136), they cultivated on the average two-and-a-half times the subsistence acreage, this alone may have increased the Cultivation Factor by 8 or 9 per cent. "Unimproved" farming may well have had an even more significant effect on this factor, but there is no knowing; attention was concentrated on the improved farmers.

If, simply as a speculation, we take the formula $P(7Y—13)$, giving P a value of 27,500, to represent conditions during this period—though we might be justified in postulating a higher value than 7 for the Cultivation Factor, and we must remember that the factor values were probably rising throughout the period—the expectation of maize deliveries then falls within the limits 123,000 and 700,000 bags. Seven of the nine events conform to this expectation and two do not, the deliveries of the remarkable and contrasting years 1957 and 1958 when purchases amounted to 832,000 and 55,000 bags respectively (see Fig. 1.) The exceptions, however, serve to emphasise the point.

The forecasts or expectations of maize deliveries were based on certain hypothetical yield levels which might generally be expected, but exceptionally good and bad seasons are certain to occur in the long run. It happened that two such seasons followed each other. The first, 1956–7, was the near-perfect year, almost certainly the best for thirty years or more; while in 1957–8, according to report, "the season was the worst on record" (16). To explain the seemingly remarkable deliveries of 1957 it is only necessary to postulate the quite unremarkable maize yield, for such a season, of about 6 bags an acre—or less if one assumes a higher value for the Cultivation Factor at that time; while in 1958, one may reasonably assume, the mean yield approximated to subsistence level and the great majority of cultivators had little or no surplus. It was a very bad year but not a famine year; and, quite possibly, it was not the worst on record. On my own recollection, the 1932–3 season, when vast swarms of the red locust, then at the peak of the last great swarm cycle, destroyed almost entirely what drought had left of the crop, was probably a great deal worse. Curiously enough, this appalling season had also been preceded by an exceptionally good one, the surplus from which—it had not then been drawn into the money economy to any great extent—served to tide over the year of disaster.

The contrast between European and African deliveries of maize in the two recent years of climatic extremes is interesting and instructive:

DELIVERIES (*bags of 200 lb*)	1957	1958
European	1,176,000	543,000
African (railway line)	832,000	55,000

If the 1957 deliveries are taken as 100 in each case, European and African deliveries in 1958 were 46·2 and 6·6 respectively. African yields must, of course, have fallen to a greater extent (for the area of European production consists almost entirely, and the African area only partly, of good maize soils; while the technical skill, equipment, and "farming awareness" of the European are unquestionably superior): but the difference is mainly that to be expected between the saleable product of commercial farming, which is simply and directly related to the seasonal yield, and the surpluses of subsistence or semi-subsistence cultivation, in which the bulk of the crop in a normal year is used to meet domestic requirements. European and African yields probably fell to, roughly, 46 per cent and 36 per cent of those of the previous year.

3. THE ROLE OF THE BEER PARTY IN TRADITIONAL AGRICULTURE

Further evidence of the general existence of a grain surplus is to be found in the practice, almost universal throughout Africa, of the working "beer party." Beer-making played an essential part in the economies of most of the traditional systems of food-production, and the changes of recent years have not greatly diminished its importance. The more laborious operations, such as tree-felling, bush-clearing, opening new land, heavy hoeing, and harvesting, are still commonly carried out by collective work parties of kins-folk and neighbours, to whom beer—or, sometimes, game meat in hunting regions—is offered as incentive and reward. In effect, since agricultural production is individualistic, the majority of men in a group work collectively for each other in turns, the output of work varying with the quantity of beer provided. If much beer is offered much work will be done: but if the quantity is parsimonious or the quality poor the work output will be reduced in proportion. Women too initiate beer-parties, taking part when the work is hoeing, and this practice may be on the increase in regions of migrant labour. Such an increase, attributed to the absence of men, has been recorded among the Nsenga of Petauke (17).

De Schlippe (146) has described the role of the working beer party among the Zande of the southern Sudan[1] and pointed out that the practice tends to maintain some degree of social inequality. Households who act as generous hosts, because they happen to have a considerable surplus of cereals, will acquire the most exten-sive cultivations and are therefore most likely to produce a surplus again in subsequent years. He adds that "the incentive to thrift and foresight which is provided by prestige as well as by profit from work paid for in beer is very important."

4. OTHER USES OF THE NORMAL SURPLUS

There were other uses for the food surplus. It was used in the fulfilment of social obligations, to acquire prestige by the display of hospitality and generosity, and to honour important people,

---

[1] Turner (178) has described its operation in Ndembu society.

while in some societies it entered into barter trade and played a part in religious ritual. Lynn (106), writing in the 1930s of the Mamprusi in what is now Northern Ghana, says that their surplus of grain in a good year was "used lavishly in religious ceremonies"; so lavishly, it seems, that some enthusiasts found themselves short of seed by the start of the next season.

The obligation to offer customary gifts to political superiors, in acknowledgment of the right to hold or allocate land, sometimes amounted to a form of taxation which diverted part of the normal surplus to the maintenance of elaborate social and political hierarchies. This appears to have been true of the Chagga, who live on the moist southern slopes of Kilimanjaro in a region of highly fertile volcanic soils and reliable climate. Their chiefs once maintained elaborate courts, supported by customary gifts, where the heads of powerful clans—"nobles," as my Chagga informants called them—lived throughout the year, and to which any subject of the Chief might go in expectation of hospitality. This organisation was possible because soil and climate permitted a high population density, and ensured a surplus that did not vary greatly from year to year and could be collected within a relatively small area. In contrast with the Chagga, the Tonga—with their highly variable surplus, liable to vanish altogether—had no such organisation and, indeed, no political chiefs.

5. Hunger Months and Famine Years

The conclusion that fully agricultural peoples normally produced a surplus of food is not necessarily contradicted by the fairly frequent occurrence of "hunger months" in some African societies. No doubt, individual lack of foresight and too lavish use of the surplus were common enough: but where general and regular food shortages occur they are, I suggest, commonly associated with systems in which hunting and food gathering, pastoralism or tribute formerly made an important contribution to the food supply, or with fully agricultural systems in process of degeneration. The Bemba of Northern Rhodesia, who certainly have "hunger months," are a case in point. They preserve a strong hunting cult—as do the Ndembu, the Zande, and many others—which may well indicate the former economic importance of game meat. Bemba men will still point north to the country of the Mambwe, on whom they levied tribute, and say, "Our gardens were there";

and they have long been involved in the migrant labour nexus with its effects on man-power and production. The fact that, with the diminution of game, a hunting cult may no longer derive its importance from contribution to the food supply, but from the identification of hunting with masculinity and social status, explains its survival but does not disprove an economic origin.

People who are primarily pastoralists frequently cultivate too small an acreage to yield a normal surplus, and when the numbers of their livestock in relation to population fall below a certain level, recurrent food shortages are inevitable unless there is an adequate increase of acreage. This appears to be the situation of the Gogo of Dodoma in Tanganyika, a semi-arid region better suited to livestock than crop production. They are still described as "essentially pastoral," but the average household owns only about 8·25 livestock units, which is clearly well below the requirements of a pastoral economy, and they also cultivate. Rounce (144) has attributed the "prevalence of famine" in Dodoma partly to the small acreage cultivated "per adult": he says that four adults cultivate on the average only 4·5 acres, and one may hazard a guess, based on his figures, that this represents 0·7 of an acre or less per head of population, an area which may be too small to yield a normal surplus in this environment, particularly on depleted soils. Degeneration may also be regarded as a contributing factor, since there is serious over-stocking and over-cultivation and the fallow period has fallen below the level required for the maintenance of fertility. General population density is probably well above the critical point, in relation to the natural poverty of the environment and the weakness of the system—though there have been compensating innovations, such as conservation of crop residues for dry season feed (a Dodoma Native Authority rule specifies 100 bundles per household) and the use of manure: but the quality of manure is poor and, since it has usually to be transported in headloads, the quantity applied to the land is small.

People who relied partly on tribute or pillage are also very liable to find themselves short of food when these sources are no longer open to them. Such were the Ngoni, whose history Barnes has described as "essentially that of an armed nation on the march." Their settlements were on a military pattern, closely grouped, and this, together with their attitude to cultivation as an occupation fit only for women and slaves, necessarily implied a weak and inadequate agriculture. Priestley and Greening (132) estimate that as early as 1898 Ngoni lands in Fort Jameson were carrying a population three or four times greater than they could sustain in perpetuity under traditional methods of cultivation, and it is hardly surprising that food shortages appeared when tribute and raiding ended. The reverse of this situation is to be seen among the Matengo in the north of the Livingstone Mountains, between Songea and Lake Nyasa, who still cultivate about twice as much as they require for their own needs, a survival of the time when they had to provide not only for themselves but also for their Ngoni overlords.

For the people who lived wholly by their agriculture there were strong incentives and compulsions to cultivate more than the bare subsistence minimum, and among these the incentive of security was compelling. The food surplus was an essential safeguard and an important element in the economic and social structure of tribal societies. But this safeguard was never complete. In most years there was food to spare and in poor years a sufficiency that ensured survival, but, unless it had been preceded by an exceptionally good season, a year of catastrophe—by drought, flood, locusts, or other pests—meant famine, and, if not the destruction of the community, at least temporary dispersal and a reduction of its numbers. Twice in the last half of the nineteenth century the Lamba of Northern Rhodesia came near to extinction. In 1891, the year after Joseph Thomson's visit to Mushiri's country, the crops failed and there was famine, while the crops of the following year were destroyed by great swarms of the red locust. The plight of the Lamba was desperate, but in this crisis many were able to save themselves by fleeing to the Lenje country where the crops had escaped destruction. Of those who remained behind, in the hope of subsisting on wild fruits and famine foods, only a few survived. This was their second major catastrophe within fifty years. There had been an earlier locust famine in the decade 1850–60 so severe that the Lamba were almost wiped out (51). Many tribes must have suffered a similar fate and some may have perished. Even with the safeguard of the normal surplus, existence was precarious enough for the subsistence cultivator; without it, Africa would have been an even more sparsely populated continent when the Europeans first came there.

The existence of a surplus of the main food crop—cereals,

cassava, yams, or whatever it might be—or an abundance in the good seasons, does not, of course, imply that the diet was adequate or balanced throughout the year. The well-known diet deficiencies of Africa are common to the cultivating peoples. Except in the years of disaster, food was generally adequate in terms of calories, but there were, and are, in almost every agricultural society periods of "hidden hunger" due to vitamin and mineral deficiencies and a diet with too low a protein/carbohydrate ratio.

One of the earlier effects of European administration and settlement in Africa was to make the food surplus less essential as a safeguard and to attract it within the orbit of the money economy. Suzerain governments could generally be relied upon to provide famine relief in times of catastrophe and they did their best to control locust outbreaks—with final success, it appears, in the case of the red locust—and to mitigate their effects. The first markets for the surplus were administrative centres and mission stations whose small needs were easily supplied: but, as increasing demand came from industry, mining, and other enterprises employing African labour on a large scale, the very unreliable nature of the surplus—or, as it was usually expressed, the inadequacy of "native farming"—became apparent in the regions of unreliable climate. We must, however, leave this aspect of the matter aside for the present, since our main concern is with the factors influencing the area cultivated by subsistence producers following their traditional methods of land-use. The incentive to produce a surplus must be counted as one such factor, and it will be evident that climate, operating directly on crop yields and indirectly through its effects on staple crops and agricultural practices, may well exert a decisive influence. It may therefore be useful to prolong this digression a little and look briefly at some of the more contrasting climatic situations.

CHAPTER V

THE CULTIVATION FACTOR

1. CLIMATIC CONTRASTS IN EAST AND WEST AFRICA

The most extreme climatic contrast is that between the equatorial zone of the Congo basin and the arid region to the east of it which extends southwards from the "horn" through Kenya and Tanganyika (Fig. 2, in which the wet zone is represented by the distribution of equatorial forest and the dry region by areas where the chances of failure to receive a rainfall of 20 inches in one year are 30 to 100 per cent.)

The equatorial climate is characterised by heavy and continuous rainfall, generally 70 to 120 inches in the year, and constant heat, with temperatures of 80°F or more day after day; there is little relief from steaming conditions, dripping moisture, and the gloom of louring rain-filled clouds. At the opposite extreme, in the arid zone of dry heat and desert cold, rainfall is generally too low or unreliable to allow of cultivation as a means of life; it is predominantly the domain of the pastoralists. Both are regions of sparse population, but densities are higher in the equatorial zone where men may live by cultivation, and must indeed do so, since natural conditions are ill-suited to the rearing of livestock.

Between these two extremes lies a region of good rainfall, averaging about 45 inches, with a double maximum, the peaks generally occurring after the equinoxes of March and September. This fortunate region includes the highlands of the Central Province of Kenya (see Fig. 2. 1A), the "fertile crescent" of Uganda (see Fig. 2. 1B), and western Uganda and part of central Uganda (see Fig. 2. 1C). In the Kenya highlands, the two rainy seasons come in April–May and October–December (see Fig. 2. Nyeri) and falls of 40 inches in the year, reaching 55 inches on the slopes of Mount Kenya, are commonly experienced. The moister region about Lake Victoria has a rainfall of 45 to 60 inches in two seasons, March–June and October–November, but there is no really dry month in the year (see Fig. 2. Kampala). Temperature conditions are also very uniform, the proximity of the lake ensuring constant warmth. In western Uganda, with an annual rainfall of 35 to 40 inches, the two wet seasons are distinctly separated by the dry months of June and July (see Fig. 2. Kabale), but going north and east into central Uganda the two seasons tend to converge in the mid-months (see Fig. 2. Lira) and there is a dry

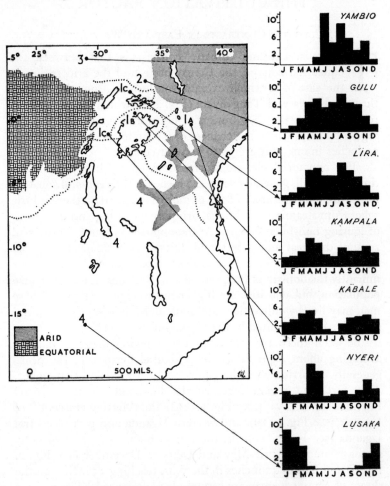

FIG. 2. Some Climatic Regions of East and Central Africa.

Compiled from a number of sources including *Au Service de l'agriculture congolaise*, INEAC, 1957; J. E. Griffiths, "Climatic Zones of East Africa", in *East African Agricultural Journal*, XXIII, No. 3 (Jan. 1958); *Report of the East Africa Royal Commission*, 1953-55; and from local records.

period in December–March, when, although showers occur, temperatures often exceed 90°F and evapo-transpiration is increased by high desiccating winds from the Karamoja plain. Vegetation dries and the grass burns. This type of climate grades into that of a zone which includes north and north-western Uganda and part of north-western Kenya (see Fig. 2, 2). Here the fall averages 40 to 75 inches, except in Karamoja where it is 20 to 40 inches, and the two seasons have practically converged so that most of the rain comes in the period April to September or October (see Fig. 2. Gulu).

Still further north, climate changes to what is sometimes known as the Sudanian type where there is a long dry season of four to six months when the sun is lowest in the sky, during which no rain falls, or no more than a trace, and temperatures are high throughout the year. This change becomes marked just north of the Uganda border, in the southern Sudan (see Fig. 2. Yambio). Northward again, there is a transition through zones of decreasing rainfall and changing vegetation to desert conditions.

South of the equatorial and East African climatic zones— starting, roughly, at 5° south latitude, but excluding the special climates of lake, mountain, coastal, and transitional regions—is a vast area dominated by what may be called the modified Sudanian type of climate, characterised by a marked dry season throughout the period May to October and violent alternations of seasons. Annual rainfall commonly ranges from 20 to 50 inches, spread over the months November or December to March or April, with the wettest months in the southern summer, December to February, and a single rainfall maximum usually in January or February (Fig. 2. 4 and Lusaka). The winter months, June–August, are dry, humidity is low and there is a considerable diurnal range of temperature with occasional frosts at higher altitudes, while the spring months are very hot and dry. Fire blackens the countryside, sweeping through woodland, bush, and grassland, at any time from July to November.

This type of climate extends over much of western and central Tanganyika, part of the southern Congo and most of the Rhodesias and Nyasaland. It has obvious disadvantages for the African cultivator, unaided by irrigation and with no implement but the hoe, in comparison with the East African and even the equatorial regimes; only one crop can be taken during the year, the planting

A.H.—5

season is short and the rains are uncertain. They may break late and delay planting, or they may fall in violent erosive storms or over such a period that weeds cannot be controlled, or there may be a mid-season drought or the rains may end early before the crop is ripe. The poor season of 1957–8 in the maize-growing area of Northern Rhodesia was due to a climatic pattern which included most of these irregularities: "Rains started late, fell excessively over a ten week period, then ceased abruptly early in March: much arable land was unplanted and weeding on the heavier maize soils was virtually impossible; lack of sunlight and water-logged conditions resulted in poor crop growth. Severe early flooding took place on the Barotse flood plain and the Kafue Flats causing serious damage to crops" (16). It was otherwise in the north of the country, where rainfall is usually heavier: "rains fell mostly at night, they were lighter than usual and there was a fair amount of sunshine in the growing period: good crops were reaped" (16).

It is a commonplace of elementary geography that the main types of African climate are duplicated geographically, so that going pole-wards from the equatorial zone in either direction a very similar succession of climatic and vegetation zones is found. This theoretical distribution is clearer in the west than it is in the eastern part of Africa in the northern hemisphere, where it is complicated by mountains, high plateaux, and deep rift valleys.

Even within the comparatively small area of Ghana a very marked sequence of climatic zones is evident (Fig. 3). The true equatorial forest climate is represented by a small area in the south-west where rainfall ranges from 70 to 120 inches, with a double maximum, showing as twin peaks in May–June and September–October: but rainfall, temperature, and humidity are high throughout the year and there is no dry month. The main forest belt of Ghana falls within the Guinea or sub-equatorial ecoclimate (see Fig. 3. 2) in which there is a definite dry season but humidity is sufficient to maintain moist semi-deciduous forest. Total rainfall in this zone is commonly 50 to 70 inches, with well-marked maxima in May–June and September–October and a short "dry" spell between (see Fig. 3. Kumasi).

North of the forest zone, in the region of the Guinea savannah, climate is more variable: changes throughout the year are related to the movement of the sun north and south of the equator and corresponding changes of the fronts between moist, rain-bearing winds from the south-west (the monsoon) and dry winds from the north-east (the harmattan). The monsoon penetrates farthest north in the northern summer, and consequently most of the rain

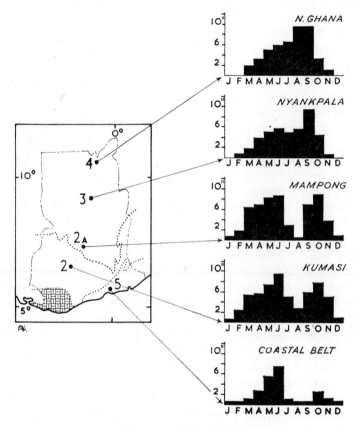

FIG. 3. Climatic Regions of Ghana.

falls in this period, while the desiccating harmattan penetrates farthest south in January and February. On the northern edge of the forest zone, where it changes to Guinea savannah, rainfall is still heavy and there are two well-marked wet periods (Fig. 3. 2A, Mampong)—here, it seems, man is a powerful ally of the harmattan in its annual assault against the forest: but as one goes north the rainfall peaks close up (Fig. 3, Nyankpala), and in the extreme north there is only one wet season followed by a severe dry season lasting from the end of October until the beginning of April (Fig. 3. 4, North Ghana). In this Guinea savannah of North Ghana the general aspect of the country is strikingly like that of northern Uganda, more than two thousand miles away on the other side of Africa, a resemblance which extends to the specific composition of the vegetation. Here are the same types of bush and tree-grassland, with some specific differences but many identical species of *Butyrospermum*, *Combretum*, *Terminalia*, *Ficus*, *Vitex*, *Acacia*, and the rest. The two regions also bear a very noticeable family resemblance to the acacia savannah and combretaceous scrub woodland of Northern Rhodesia, far away to the south. Although seasonal alternations of climate are more violent in this southern zone, the general pattern of the country is very similar to that of the northern savannahs and the generic composition of the vegetation is much the same, though the specific differences are, of course, much greater.

There is another area of climatic contrast in Ghana, the southern savannah of the coastal belt south and east of the forest (Fig. 3. 5), a hot dry region where the rainfall pattern shadows that of the forest but the annual total is only about 29 inches. The later rains are slight and the effective fall is reduced to a relatively short period (Fig. 3. Coastal belt). Humidity is high throughout the year but cloud cover is less and sunshine averages 6·75 hours per day compared with only 2·25 hours in the forest zone. Travellers flying from Kumasi to Accra cannot fail to be impressed by the sudden transition from the great forest, with its closed canopy above which rise the crowns of gigantic trees, to the dramatic contrast of this seemingly arid and treeless coastal region.

It will be evident that such differences in climate, differences in evaporation or evapo-transpiration, and in the distribution and reliability of rainfall, must have a profound effect on agricultural practices and on the area of land required to maintain the food supply of peoples who live by subsistence cultivation.

2. ESTIMATION OF THE CULTIVATION FACTOR: NORTHERN RHODESIAN SYSTEMS

The land under cultivation, or actual extent of the "garden area," must, of course, be ascertained by field sampling. At first sight this may seem a comparatively simple exercise but in practice it is not always easy to relate areas to populations in such a way as to arrive at a reliable estimate of the average acreage under cultivation per head of population at any one time. The human groups associated with specific garden areas are often complex and they may change fairly frequently either temporarily or permanently, particularly in regions of migrant labour. Figures are quite often given in published works and reports for the average size of a garden or the area cultivated by a "family," a "taxpayer," an "adult," or a "woman," and one is left to guess how many people these units represent.

In the Northern Rhodesian work, garden sampling was usually combined with sociological enquiries, a refinement made possible by the co-operation and assistance of social anthropologists of the Rhodes–Livingstone Institute. The procedure was to pick an individual at random, then to ascertain the relationship of the family group to which he belonged, and finally to measure all the land in cultivation by the family group at the time of sampling. This kinship segment, co-operating in the cultivation of and drawing subsistence from a measured set of gardens, became known as the "garden family" and was expressed in numerical terms by allowing one unit for each person, irrespective of age, obtaining the whole of his or her food supply from the garden, and an appropriate fraction for each person obtaining part of his or her supply. Changes in the composition of the group which had taken place since, and could not have been foreseen at, the time of planting were disregarded.

An example will make this clear. Suppose we arrive at a Tonga village and take the first inhabitant we meet as our starting point. He turns out to be the Headman, but that is immaterial. We learn from him that he has a garden he calls his own but he does not eat from it; his food comes from the gardens of his three wives. At the conclusion of our enquiry, assisted by all the villagers—after some initial shyness and suspicion they usually joined in with enthusiasm—we find ourselves with the following picture of the garden family and the way in which each of its members shares in the produce of the set of three gardens:

In the meantime we have gone to the gardens—accompanied by most of the village—and made further enquiries on the spot, so that no one can be in any doubt as to what gardens we are interested in; and when we think we have got a complete and

TONGA (HEADMAN'S) GARDEN FAMILY

*This table shows how each member of the garden family is related to the Headman as
senior of the group, and (in Col. 1) what proportion of his or her total food-requirement each individual receives (1) from the Headman's garden, and (2) from his
wives' gardens. In Col. 2 the total amounts are expressed as decimal fractions of
one person's total food-requirement.*

		COL. 1 Each	COL. 2 Total
(1)	Fed from Headman's Garden:		
	(a) Son, his wife, and 4 of their children	1/8	0·75
	(b) Son, his wife, and 1 child	1/2	1·50
(2)	Fed from Headman's Wives' Gardens:		
	(c) Headman	1/1	1·00
	(c) His 3 wives	1/1	3·00
	(e) 9 young and adolescent children of Headman and his wives	1/1	9·00
	(f) Family (a)	1/8	0·75
	(g) Family (b)	1/2	1·50
	(h) Daughter (husband away at work) and her child	1/2	1·00
	(i) Aged sister and her husband	1/1	2·00
	(j) Daughter of Headman's deceased brother (deserted by her husband)	1/1	1·00
	(k) Son-in-law (deserted by wife)	1/3	0·33
			21·83

accurate picture—to which everone has agreed, either because it
is accurate or, perhaps, because they have tired of the game by this
time—we measure the gardens.

Since the areas were usually very irregular in shape, this was
done by making a peripheral traverse with prismatic compass and
chain, plotting the traverses on squared paper and assessing areas
from the diagrams by a count of squares or by planimeter measurements.

In the case of the example, we find that the area of the Headman's garden, which lies by itself, is 2·47 acres, while the total
area of the wives' gardens, measured as one since they are conti-
guous, is 24·90 acres. If we regard the set of three gardens as one
sample, we now have an estimate of 21·83 units for the garden
family of twenty-eight people, of whom nine get part of their food
elsewhere and therefore belong to at least one other garden family,
and a figure of 1·25 acres for the cultivation factor or area cultivated
per head of population.

This process of sampling was repeated, and sometimes supplemented by complete village surveys, to give a sufficient number of samples for a satisfactory estimate of the cultivation factor, or at least as many examples as the available time would allow. The accuracy of the results again depended on the reliability of the informants but, though mistakes were inevitably made, it was believed that deliberate misrepresentation could be discounted, since, at the time the sampling was done—mainly in the period 1940–5—the people co-operated very willingly in the enquiries. The whole group or village population generally joined in with evident enjoyment and there was always someone quick to query any statement he considered inaccurate. But by 1948 such co-operation could no longer be counted upon, and recent investigators have encountered hostility, evasion, and deliberate misrepresentation. When political discontent is expressed as refusal to co-operate with the agents, or suspected agents, of Government, this method of enquiry may become valueless. In 1954–5, however, a social anthropologist working[1] and living in Ndembu society, carried out garden measurements for a group of villages near Mwinilunga and made an estimate of the cultivation factor for this group and system (178).

Data from four distinct and widely separated systems in Northern Rhodesia are summarised in the table below. They are:

(a) The system of the Plateau Tonga of the Southern Province, with maize as a staple;

(b) The Ngoni–Chewa system of the Eastern Province, with maize and sorghum as staples;

(c) The Lamba system of the Western Province, in which sorghum is the staple;

(d) The totally different cassava cultivation system, with subsidiary finger millet, of the Lunda–Ndembu, on Kalahari contact soils (Turner's figures).

	(a)	(b)	(c)	(d)	Total
Total population in samples (sum of garden families)	284	259	254	461	1,258
Total crop acreage	316	281	258	494	1,349
Area cultivated per head of population (acres)	1·11	1·08	1·01	1·07	1·07

[1] Dr V. W. Turner of the University of Manchester.

There was, of course, a good deal of variation between individual garden families, with differences in the composition, ability,
resources, health, and energy of the cultivating groups, but the
tendency to cultivate rather more than an acre per head of population, and the frequency of a figure of this order, was very striking.
Evidence of the frequency of such a figure is not entirely confined
to the Northern Rhodesian systems. A sample survey by the
Nyasaland Department of Agriculture has indicated that the
average acreage cultivated per head of population by the Tumbuka
of Mzimba is 1·08 acres. Similar figures for Southern Rhodesia
have been suggested by Robinson (142). He points out that in
the Chinamora Reserve, an area of 78,550 acres which carried a
population of 9,616 in 1950, the extent of food crop cultivation
was 10,400 acres while a further 904 acres of seepage land was
planted to vegetables for the Salisbury market—an average of
1·08 acres of food crops in cultivation per head of population.
The general figure for the Southern Rhodesia Reserves as a whole,
based on gross population and estimates of the total area cultivated,
appears to be of much the same order. It would seem that the
acreage cultivated per head of population has not increased significantly, in spite of the common use of the plough and the incentive of a cash market for surplus grain. This is probably
explained by the degree of population pressure, the need to retain
grazing land, the absence of industrial crops, and official dis-
couragement of relatively large-scale farming within the Reserves.
Other land is available in Southern Rhodesia—the Native Land
Purchase Areas—for Africans who want to become farmers in the
commercial sense.

The cultivated area is, no doubt, related to the calorific value
of the crop yield, as was indicated by Sir Daniel Hall many years
ago when he wrote: "It has been estimated that to produce food
containing 1,400,000 calories, i.e. a labouring man's allowance for
400–500 days, 0·76 of an acre would be required when cropped
with potatoes, a little more, 0·79, when cropped with maize, or 1·45
acres of wheat to be turned into flour" (73).

This figure of about one acre and a tenth in cultivation per
head of population occurred with such consistency in the Northern
Rhodesian sampling that it was thought it might be typical of
simple hoe-cultivation systems of subsistence agriculture under a
Modified Sudanian climatic regime. But there are important

exceptions. In the *citemene* (ash-planting) group of systems, the Cultivation Factor was found to be considerably smaller, for reasons which will become apparent when these systems are considered, while in the case of the peculiar semi-*citemene* system of the Swaka, higher cultivation figures were recorded. A marked divergence of practice was also noted within this latter system. The soils to which the Swaka have access are mainly of very low fertility; they are poor Recurrent Cultivation or, more generally, Shifting Cultivation types: but in the south of their area there is a limited extent of much stronger red loams characterised by the dominance of *Brachystegia Burtii* in various associations, representing Recurrent Cultivation land of a better type with variants approaching the Semi-Permanent category. Reconnaissance surveys made independently by Peters and the writer, and later sampling carried out conjointly, with the aid of aerial photographs, all showed a clear difference between the areas cultivated on the weak, pallid soils and the relatively fertile red loams.

SWAKA AGRICULTURE: AVERAGE AREA CULTIVATED PER
HEAD OF POPULATION

	On weak soils	On red loams
Peters' samples	1·80 acres	1·17 acres
Allan's samples	1·73 ,,	1·06 ,,
Joint sampling	1·67 ,,	1·09 ,,

On the red loams, the cultivated acreage, and cultivation practice also, approximated much more closely to the normal for a simple system of Recurrent Cultivation land-use.

3. EFFECT OF CLIMATE ON THE CULTIVATION FACTOR: DOUBLE RAINFALL, EQUATORIAL, AND NORTHERN SAVANNAH REGIONS

One would expect to find that subsistence producers cultivate smaller acreages in the two-season zones of reliable rainfall, where two crops may be taken from the same land, and in regions of equatorial and sub-equatorial climates where, in addition to multiple cropping, high-yielding staples such as plantains, yams, and taro may be grown. In the East African two-season zone both cultivation practice and cultivated acreages have been most profoundly affected by European contacts, development of industrial crops, and population pressure; and estimates of the crop acreages now cultivated may bear little relation to former customary practice. Furthermore, such estimates are usually presented in terms of crop acreage, which is often much greater than, and may be twice or even more than twice, the actual physical acreage under cultivation; and the relationship between the two is not always clear or readily determined. Nor is it easy to resolve the difficulties caused by the large extent to which inter-cropping is practised. Again, estimated crop acreages are sometimes related to population figures obtained from a census of a much earlier date, without allowance for what may have been a very significant increase in the interval.

The following figures, from the little direct sample data available, may, however, give some indication of the acreage required and probably cultivated under subsistence systems with annual crop staples.

	Acres per head
KENYA:	
South Nyeri (Kikuyu)	0·42–0·48
Machakos (Kamba squatters)	0·44–0·67
UGANDA:	
Adwaa (Lango)	0·65
Kasherengenye (Kigezi)	0·54
West Nile (Alur)	0·41

I am indebted to Colin Trapnell (173) for these data which he derived from the following sources. The South Nyeri figures were calculated from Humphrey's study of the Kikuyu lands (85), after deducting wattle acreages: the smaller figure represents actual land use at the time of Humphrey's study while the larger is an estimate of the proper requirement under traditional subsistence practice. The Machakos figures are for a Kamba community on a European estate, recorded by Pereira (128). In this case the higher figure is the estimated requirement in drought years, which probably approximates more closely to the customary subsistence acreage in this more arid area. The first two examples for Uganda were calculated from figures given in a report by Tothill (169), after deducting cash crop acreages, and the West Nile figure is from a study made by Langdale Brown in the course of an Oxford University expedition. Each figure represents the actual physical area cultivated and all refer to hoe-cultivation subsistence agriculture with annual grain crops.

It is not unlikely that a Cultivation Factor of about half an acre per head of population was usual for subsistence systems with a grain staple in the two-season zones of reliable double rainfall: but in regions where the rainfall of one of the seasons is less reliable the factor may have approximated to 0·75 of an acre, as it probably did in the drier parts of Teso in Uganda where the first rains are reasonably certain but the second rains are chancy and second rain crops often yield poorly. This figure was indicated to me as the former subsistence acreage by some of the oldest men of the Iteso, the few who claimed to be able to remember the conditions of thirty-five or forty years earlier. The first sample data for the area, collected by Courcy-Ireland in Amuria Saza in 1935–7 (43), indicate a higher figure, 0·91 of an acre of food crops per head of population: but by that time the transition to an exchange economy was well advanced and the plough had been in common use for a decade or more. At this time, as we have already noted, the neighbouring Lango of Adwaa, still dependent almost wholly on traditional hoe agriculture, were cultivating only 0·65 of an acre of food crops per head of population.

It has been estimated for part of Buganda that two acres of plantains will yield sufficient food for a family of eight people, even though a man eats the equivalent of seven pounds of fresh fruit a day, and it is possible that in these highly favoured regions where plantains and bananas yield heavily and may be grown virtually as permanent crops, the cultivation factor was less than half an acre per head of population. Such evidence as there is, however, suggests that it was more probably somewhere about the half acre level, including subsidiary cultivation of cereals, pulses, oil seeds, and roots.

Professor Monica Wilson says that "the area traditionally cultivated for subsistence by each Nyakyusa family consisting of a man, his wives and unmarried children, was probably about six acres, or half an acre for each man, woman and child" (187). The Nyakyusa live in the Rungwe district of southern Tanganyika in a high-rainfall mountain climate, with an annual fall averaging over 100 inches and they have, or had, an intensive system of plantain and banana culture with ancillary arable cultivation very similar to the systems of the Chagga of Kilimanjaro and the Gishu of Mount Elgon. So far as I could ascertain by enquiry among them, the two latter peoples also traditionally cultivated something of the order of half an acre of food crops per head of population: but in all three cases cultivation techniques and land distribution have greatly altered as a result of increasing shortage and the growing value of land.

The following data derived from the 1935–6 Uganda surveys (169) suggest rather higher food crop areas for plantain cultures in the "elephant grass country" of Buganda at that time, but they are not inconsistent with subsistence acreages of the half acre per head order.

ACREAGE CULTIVATED PER HEAD OF POPULATION

	Plantains	Arable	Total
Kabale	0·40	0·15	0·55
Kawoko	0·65	0·14	0·79
Kayuji	0·48	0·14	0·62
Mpita	0·49	0·23	0·72

The survey figures appear to refer to crop areas and, if allowance is made for double cropping, the net acreage in two of the examples may approximate to 0·47 and 0·55 per head, while in the other two cases, Kawoko and Mpita, in which the plantain and arable areas respectively are curiously high, the net figures may be of the order of 0·74 and 0·60 of an acre per head. The first three examples are for "hundreds" near Masaka in western Buganda and the fourth is from south Busoga.

Even today the net food crop area of Buganda as a whole may not be much in excess of the half-acre-per-head level, considered in relation to gross population—if we assume a population in the region of a million and a half and a food area of 868,300 acres, arrived at by deducting the great area of economic crops from the estimated net cultivated acreage for 1958 (19). This population figure is far from certain; the last census was in 1948 when Buganda had 1,302,200 people: but one may reasonably assume a considerable increase rate, since, though the fertility of the Baganda appears to be curiously low, the area attracts a flood of immigrants from Ruanda-Urundi and the outlying parts of Uganda.

Further work may show that a cultivation factor of about half an acre was common for subsistence systems in the forest regions of equatorial and sub-equatorial climates. Galletti, Baldwin, and Dike (60) found for Yoruba cocoa-farming families in eight localities where they carried out sampling that the mean area of food crops was 3 acres per family, the modal family consisting of a man, one or two women, and two to three children. This, again, is not inconsistent with a subsistence area of half an acre per head or even less, though there was much variation in the food acreage between areas of land shortage and relative abundance, and some cultivators were growing food crops for sale with hired labour. A few examples for Ghanaian cocoa farmers in the Eastern (Akim) Region, which I obtained during a visit to Ghana in 1959, seem to indicate that cultivators of less than half an acre for each consumer generally buy food while those with more are sellers. Unfortunately, only five examples could be investigated in sufficient detail to be reasonably certain of the accuracy of the figures.

CONSUMING GROUP		FOOD CROP ACREAGE		FOOD SITUATION
Kin	*Others*	*Total*	*Per head*	
11	2	2·5	0·19	Mostly bought
12	2	3·5	0·25	Some bought
10	6	8·0	0·50	Neither bought nor sold
10	2	17·1	1·42	Mostly sold
84	14	80·0	0·85	Some sold

The first three examples appeared to be fairly typical native Akim cocoa farmers, employing paid labourers who have been included in the consuming group since they obtained food from the food crop acreage. The fourth, also an Akim, had only a small acreage of cocoa and described himself as a "food farmer." He maintained that most of his income derived from the sale of food and that he invariably produced far more than his household and labourers could consume. The last example relates to a wealthy Ga "stranger farmer," with a great acreage of cocoa; he was the patriarchal head of a complex group of closely related families living and working on his estate. He said that he always had more than ample food, in spite of the size of his household, and sold a considerable quantity each year: but he thought more was consumed than sold. The impressions obtained from these samples were supported by general enquiry and the opinions of experienced Agricultural Officers who considered that, on the forest ochrosols of the Eastern Region and Ashanti, from 2 to 3 acres of food crops should provide ample food for a family of five.

Similar relatively small areas may suffice for subsistence in the equatorial forest region of the Congo. In 1958 the total area cultivated to African-grown food crops in the Province Orientale was estimated to be approximately 1,132,200 acres (154) in relation to a gross population of about 2,312,000. This indicates a mean area well below half an acre per head, when allowance is made for double cropping: but there is also a large area of oil palm which, though mainly exploited as a source of income, also makes an important contribution to the diet. Dumont (52) has suggested that the cultivated area may be limited by the physical capacity of the cultivators. After commenting on the relatively small quantity of cereals, the lack of calcium and of animal and even vegetable proteins in the diet of the forest people, he concludes that "the quality of the food is thus particularly deficient, and it cannot provide enough energy for the cultivation of an adequate area." His observations were, however, made in an area of high population pressure and land degeneration, a situation very unusual in the Congo forest region. I was told by Belgian officials that a "good man" could clear half a hectare—nearly an acre and a quarter—each year, a formidable undertaking even in secondary forest. My own impression, derived from the small section of the Bakumu I visited, was that while some men do achieve the half hectare, the average annual clearing is only about half this figure and the total food crop area, excluding oil palm, probably does not exceed 0·45 acre per head: but, where the system of production is unimpaired, this area yields a food supply adequate in quantity if not in quality.

There are some interesting data for north-eastern Ghana, starting with Lynn's classic studies of the 1930s (106) which set a model for later surveys. In all of this work measured acreages have been clearly related to the actual exploiting populations, rather than to indeterminate units such as "families," "cultivators," or that peculiar inhabitant of the Congo, the HAV.[1]

In the southern part of this region, comprising Western and Eastern Dagomba, the traditional system and land-use pattern of the Dagomba people has been little altered. There is no land shortage—except locally on a small scale and mainly about the large centres of population—and the food supply is ample so that there is an annual surplus. Conditions are, however, quite

[1] = "Homme adulte valide."

different in the northern districts of Mamprusi, Navrongo, Zuarungu, and Bawku where acute population pressure over a long period and, to some extent, the introduction of plough farming, have disrupted the systems and led to marked changes in the extent and range of cultivated areas. Incidentally, it should be noted that population pressure commonly causes an increase of the cultivated acreage, as a reaction to declining yields, and it is only in the later stages, when practically all the resting and marginal land has been absorbed, that subdivision and fragmentation become apparent.

The available survey data, in terms of the average acreage cultivated at any one time per head of the exploiting group—men, women and children, but excluding unweaned babies—are summarised below.

	Survey	Av. acreage cultivated per head
Dagomba	— Akenhead 1957 (5)	0·60
	— Masters 1955 (110)	0·71
Northern Tribes		
Mamprusi	— Lynn 1934–6 (106)	0·66
Kusasi	— Zebilla Survey 1936:	
	Quoted by Smith	1·02
	— Smith 1941 (151)	1·79
Fra Fra	— Atamore Survey:	
	Topham 1957 (168)	0·95

The data indicate that, in this region where climate is approaching the Sudanian type, with a well-marked dry season from November to March but with a wet season of good and relatively reliable rainfall (see Fig. 5, Nyankpala and north Ghana), the traditional subsistence acreage averages more than half but rather less than three-quarters of an acre per head. The figures for the northern tribes reflect the increase brought about by land degeneration and the use of the plough. The Dagomba may also have increased their cultivated acreage to a much smaller extent, in order to produce a larger surplus for sale, but this is less certain.

Chapter VI

THE *CITEMENE* SYSTEMS

1. Small-Circle and Large-Circle *Citemene*

It may simplify the discussion which follows if we now take note of the group of peculiar systems known in Northern Rhodesia by the term *citemene*, a Bemba word derived from the verb "to cut." The term is apposite enough since a feature common to all of the typical systems is the felling or lopping each year of a large area of woodland, an area several times greater than that on which crops are actually grown.

Felling is the usual practice in the case of the "small-circle" *citemene* systems,[1] such as those of the Lala and Bisa, and this is done in the early dry season, from May to August, the southern winter. Over the area of woodland selected for new gardens the trees are cut with the axe at breast height, all but the hardest and toughest trunks, which are left standing, and the branches are lopped from them and spread between the stumps to dry. After lying for some weeks, but before they are so dry that the leaves shed easily, the branches are collected and built into small stacks from two to three feet in depth scattered fairly evenly throughout the clearing. Stacking is a skilled operation and only a few forms of stack are used. These are prescribed by tradition. The commonest form is an almost perfect circle some twenty to thirty feet in diameter, but some are oval or pear-shaped while others take the form of long narrow strips, shorter strips, and rings about termite hills. The proportion in which the various types occur is determined by individual choice and the growth and density of the woodland, but the circle always predominates and in poor woodland it tends to become the only form because it is most economical of brushwood and labour. Plate 1 shows the land-use pattern resulting from this form of *citemene*.

The brushwood stacks are burned at the end of the dry season, when it is thought that the rains are about to break, and selection of the time calls for fine judgment. If it is done too early much of

[1] The Southern Citemene System, described by Trapnell (171).

the precious ash will be blown away and lost: if it is left too late and the rains have come the burn will be incomplete and the crop poor. The fact that the *citemene* peoples rarely make a mistake is a great tribute to their skill, judgment, and ability to forecast weather. After a good burn a fine even seed-bar is left. Sowing is carried out in December by broadcasting finger millet seed over the ash patches, another operation calling for considerable skill to ensure a stand which is neither too close nor too open. The crop receives, and requires, little attention after sowing until the grain ripens some five months later when it is harvested by the simple process of cutting off the heads with a small knife and packing them tightly in grain bins built within or close to the garden.

A striking feature of the "small-circle" systems is that the great majority of the ash patches are used only for a single crop, in spite of the great labour that has gone to their making. A few patches are planted with ground-beans or groundnuts in the second year but the area is usually insignificant. New ash gardens are made in the same way each year and the old ones abandoned for a long period of woodland regeneration.

The persistence of this seemingly primitive form of land-use among the Lala and Bisa is rather surprising, particularly as neighbouring and kindred peoples—the Lungu, Mambwe, Inamwanga, Bemba, Iwa, and others—have long practised systems in which many of the more obviously wasteful features of "small-circle" *citemene* are eliminated.[1] These systems differ from the primitive form in the following ways:

(1) the woodland is not felled but lopped, with the exception of the smallest trees which are usually cut at breast height, and the pollarded trunks are left standing;

(2) only one stack is made from the branches so that there is a single large circle, often about an acre, near the centre of the clearing.

(3) this large ash circle is used for a sequence of crops following finger millet in the first year.

Lopping is a dangerous operation, in the course of which men climb to the crowns of the highest trees, and there are many accidents each year, some of them fatal: but it may be assumed that the lopped trees regenerate more quickly, though we still have no

[1] The Northern Citemene System, described by Trapnell (171).

direct measure of the difference in the recovery rates of woodland after lopping and felling. The making of the large circle involves more labour, since branchwood has to be carried farther and with greater care to avoid loss of leaves, but it greatly reduces the marginal wastage which is a conspicious feature of the small-circle form and it allows of efficient fencing against the depradations of bush pig and other game. The difficulty of maintaining an efficient fence around the large area covered with small ash circles is, very probably, the main reason for virtually abandoning the garden after the first year. The relatively short fence needed to protect the single circle requires much less timber and labour and is far more readily maintained and preserved against fire.

The subsequent use of the ash garden is certainly a great improvement from the land-use point of view. Instead of being abandoned after the millet crop has been taken, the burnt land is planted for at least two, commonly three or four, and sometimes even five years to a sequence of crops. Finger millet is always planted in the new garden after the burn, but a number of catch-crops and some perennial sorghum or cassava cuttings may be planted with it. If the first crop is poor, finger millet may be planted again in the second year or the perennial sorghum allowed to take possession of the garden: but the most usual practice is to plant the whole area to groundnuts in the second year after burning off the stubble of the previous millet crop. In the third year the garden is often thrown into mounds on which beans are grown intermixed with other crops such as maize, cowpeas, gourds, pumpkins, and sweet potatoes. These mounds are usually cleaned and used for another crop of beans or, less commonly, broken down and spread to form a seed-bed for a second millet crop. There is much variation in the cropping sequence and many forms are found in every region where the systems are practised. In one variant, used by sections of the Bemba and Lungu, annual sorghums are grown, generally as an end-crop on mounds but sometimes as a substitute for groundnuts in the second year. Plate 2 illustrates the land-use pattern produced by many cycles of large-circle *citemene*.

In addition to the main ash gardens, all the "large-circle" *citemene* peoples cultivate subsidiary gardens with the hoe, and the "small-circle" peoples also make use of hoe cultivation and ancillary gardens to a considerable extent. Small separate gardens are often made for an early-maturing variety of finger-millet, to provide food before the ripening of the main crop, and village gardens are common to all forms of the "large-circle" system. The village gardens are used by the Bemba and Lungu for various forms of mixed cropping, while the Iwa, Inamwanga, and Mambwe have evolved or adopted an ingenious system of alternating maize and beans on mounds with finger millet planted on a seed-bed prepared by breaking down and spreading the mounds.

2. Origin and Distribution of the Systems

The simpler forms of pure *citemene* require no implement but the axe, an earlier invention than the hoe. The staple crop, finger millet, is probably of African origin, though it has also been suggested that it might be an ancient introduction from Asia, and no one has questioned the African origin of the ground-bean, the crop most commonly grown on second year circles in the small-circle systems. There is also some evidence, from aerial photographs in which the pock-marked appearance of land subjected to repeated cycles of small-circle citemene appears as a faint background to the land-use patterns of today, that the system was formerly more widely practised, and a number of otherwise normal hoe-cultivation systems show apparent evidence of former *citemene* practice, or include subsidiary *citemene* gardens. Indeed, it would be a simple matter to present an apparently evolutionary series ranging from small-circle through large-circle and semi-*citemene* systems to normal hoe-cultivation.

One is therefore tempted to regard small-circle *citemene* as a very early form of crop production evolved in the dry woodland areas of Africa as a supplement to hunting and food gathering: but, on the whole, it seems unlikely that this is so. *Citemene* practices appear to be restricted to a relatively small area—large in itself but small on the continental scale—along the Congo–Zambesi watershed, almost entirely in Northern Rhodesia and parts of the southern Congo—a region in which very poor soils predominate. In the course of a tour of much of East and Central and part of West Africa, made in 1959, I found no trace of true *citemene* practice north of this region, and no system of this type has been described from other parts.

In all bush and woodland systems trees are, of course, felled and burned, and special use may be made of ash patches created by the burn, but the main purpose of cutting and burning is to get rid of the timber, while in the *citemene* systems timber is cut, transported, and burned with the express purpose of creating fertility. A peculiar practice employed by the Dinka of the Sudan does, however, bear some resemblance to *citemene*. Trees are lopped and the branchwood with the leaves still attached is carried, sometimes for a considerable distance, and stacked to a depth of about two feet: but there the resemblance ends. Instead of burning the stack, the reduction of the branchwood is left to the action of termites. Termite action must be particularly rapid in this environment for by the end of the dry season the wood has been reduced to a surface mulch of dust and the land is ready for planting. By this means, it is said, even a badly depleted garden on which grass will not grow can be restored to fertility in a matter of a few months (93, 33). Other tribes follow a similar practice on a much smaller scale but seem to use only branches cleared from the cultivation site. The *hariq* cultivation of the Sudan makes use of heat, but it is grass that is burned and nothing is carried on to the land. This is a re-cultivation method applied to selected grass stands of particular composition under special circumstances and the main objectives appear to be the clearing of the ground and the reduction of subsequent weeding. It differs markedly from *citemene* practice also in that the vegetation is fired after the first heavy rains when a growth of new grass has already appeared. These and similar practices found elsewhere are obviously quite unrelated to the systems of the Congo–Zambesi watershed.

It seems probable that *citemene* is a device evolved by hoe-cultivating people who migrated into this region of the Congo–Zambesi watershed, a device designed to ensure high yields (and what is even more important in a subsistence economy, reliable crops) from land much of which would fall within the Partial Cultivation or Uncultivable category for a simple system of shifting hoe-cultivation. The Bemba, according to their own account (139), were formerly hoe-cultivators in Lubaland who learned *citemene* practice when they came into the woodlands they now occupy, and the Mambwe are strangely divided into *citemene* and hoe-cultivating sections. The southerly group within the woodland proper, the Maswepa Mambwe, practise an advanced form of large-circle *citemene* and sequence agriculture, while the methods of the northern or Aisa group are altogether different.

3. THE GRASSLAND SYSTEM OF THE AISA MAMBWE

These Aisa Mambwe live in country where there is much tall *hyparrhenia* grassland on sandy humic soils along the margins of the broad *dambo* system of the upper Saisi River. Grassland selected for cultivation is hoed up into large circular mounds as much as eight feet in diameter, in such a way as to turn the grass into the centre of the mounds where it is left to rot. A few cash-crops may be grown on some of the first-made mounds but the work of this initial season is little more than a preparation of the land for cropping. In the second year the weeds which have grown on the mounds are scraped down and left to rot between them and later, when the first rains have come, the mounds are pulled down and the humic soil containing the rotted grass is spread over the land between maize which has been planted earlier. Finger millet seed is then broadcast over the fine seed-bed prepared in this way, together with some perennial sorghum. In the third year the garden is mounded again but the mounds are not broken and finger millet is sown on them, or, occasionally, other crops. In the fourth season the process of spreading the mounds and planting finger millet on the flat is commonly repeated and in the fifth year a final crop of finger millet may again be grown on mounds. There is, however, a good deal of variation in the method of cropping during the last two or three seasons of the cycle, apparently determined by the amount of weed growth. If weeds are troublesome, particularly *Eleusine indica*, a grass closely related to finger millet and indistinguishable from it in the earlier stages of growth, the garden may be mounded in each of the last three seasons and maize and pulses may be planted on the mounds instead of finger millet. Whatever the variant used, the land is left at the end of the fourth or fifth season for a long fallow period and is not cultivated again, in the traditional system, until the weeds of the former cultivation have disappeared and the *hyparrhenia* grass is once more dominant.[1]

Subsidiary *citemene* practices are often associated with this main system. Very long grass which cannot readily be buried in the mounds may be cut and stacked about trees and stumps; any available brushwood is added to the stacks which are burnt at the end of the dry season to make ash patches on which gourds,

---

[1] Trapnell (171). See also Moffatt (119).

pumpkins, and other crops are grown. Furthermore, normal finger millet *citemene* is practised by the Aisa on a small scale where they have access to woodland, and forms transitional between the two systems have been noted among other sections of the Mambwe and the Lungu. It has therefore been suggested that this northern group was driven by the Bemba from woodland they once occupied into this small area of the Saisi basin under the scarp of the Abercorn plateau where they destroyed the trees and were forced to devise or adopt new methods of food production: but it is at least equally probable that the change was in the other direction. The Aisa seem to have no tradition of a former dependence on *citemene* and their grassland system bears a very close resemblance to the mound cultivation of the Fipa in the southern highlands of Tanganyika. It is not inconceivable that the Mambwe brought such a system with them and that it persisted where soil and vegetation favoured its survival and gave place to *citemene* in the woodland region of poor leached soils. A "backwash" of *citemene* practice among the grassland cultivators is no improbable occurrence and the existence of transitional forms is compatible with change in either direction.

4. Effects of *Citemene* Burning on the Yield of Crops

However that may be, it is certain that *citemene* methods give better and much more reliable results on the weak plateau soils of the woodland than hoe cultivation would do. Investigational work was started by Moffat in the Abercorn district as early as 1929 and by 1932 it was reported that "on the poor sandy soils of the plateau, there seems little doubt that the most reliable yields of finger millet are obtained under the *citemene* method" and "no method has given results of any promise except an adaptation of the fallow system as practised by the Mambwe" (11). The methods which had been tried included "ordinary farm practice," with the use of manure and fertiliser but at best they gave no better yields than *citemene* at greater cost, and Moffat[1] found that manure had a selective influence on the weed *Eleusine indica* and actually depressed the yield of millet. On the poorer woodland soils the Mambwe method as compared with the burn gave very uncertain and generally much poorer results. In an experiment at the

[1] Moffatt (119.)

Lunzuwa station "dug plots" prepared according to Mambwe methods were compared with "burnt plots" following normal *citemene* practice over five seasons in which three millet crops were taken. The results were as follows:

YIELDS OF FINGER MILLET
(IN LB PER ACRE)

Season	Dug Plots	Burnt Plots
1935–6	Negligible	1,618
1936–7*	—	—
1937–8	440	1,474
1938–9*	—	—
1939–40	585	1,200

* Beans and Groundnuts.

It had been discovered at an early stage that the effects of *citemene* cannot be explained by the fertiliser value of the ash alone, though this is considerable. On the eve of his retrenchment in 1933, the soil chemist had shown that ash from the burning adds large quantities of mineral plant food to the soil. "Phosphate and potash status was appreciably enhanced by the process of wood burning. The freshly burnt soil was more highly saturated with calcium, which accounts for its improved physical condition so noticeable in the field. Further, acid conditions have been corrected. The addition of bases which is responsible for the increase in pH value very probably tends to maintain the availability of the added phosphates" (159).

In 1940 an experiment was made at Lunzuwa to compare the effect of ash and burn alone and in combination in single and double doses. The effect of ash alone and burn alone was approximately equal, giving yields of 1,200 lb of finger millet grain to the acre, while a combination of ash and burn, the normal *citemene* method, yielded 2,200 lb per acre. Double quantities of ash and double intensities of burn gave only small yield increases—suggesting that the quantity of timber used in traditional practice may approximate to the optimum. In the absence of both ash and burn yields were negligible (13). This experiment has, I am told, been repeated recently with very similar results.

The reason for the beneficial effect of the burn, as distinct from that of the ash, has not yet been satisfactorily demonstrated, but some recent and fundamental work by Birch at Muguga provides a very interesting pointer. It had previously been supposed that decomposition of organic matter in tropical soils, and the consequent production of nitrates, takes place rapidly so long as the soil is moist and warm. The essence of Birch's discovery is that this process takes place very slowly in soils kept continuously moist and comes practically to a stop when the soil is dry: but decomposition takes place rapidly when the dry soil is wetted and a large flush of nitrate is then produced. Thus, in regions of wet and dry climate, humus decomposition is rapid at the start of the rains but quickly falls off as the wet season continues, becoming negligible in the following dry season and rising rapidly again with the coming of the next rains. Furthermore, the drier the soil before wetting the greater will be the flush of decomposition. This finding has a number of far-reaching implications and it is of obvious importance in relation to *citemene*; for, as Birch puts it, "intensified soil drying by maximum exposure to the sun or by the burning of vegetation on the surface soil will further enhance the amount of nitrate produced when the rains come" (28).

5. Weaknesses of the Systems

It may be that this is the mechanism through which the heat of the *citemene* burn exercises its main effect, but there is as yet no direct proof. Whatever the explanation, it seems clear that the ash-planting peoples, with no livestock and only the simplest equipment, have devised an effective means of conferring a high if transient fertility on soils of very low intrinsic value. Here we have one side of the picture. On the other side, to quote Birch again, "this enhanced production of nitrates can only take place at the expense of the humus reserve in the soil leading to its more rapid depletion with possible adverse effects on soil structure." These timber-burning systems require the annual exploitation of great areas of woodland which must subsequently be rested for a very long period to allow of recovery of the trees and restoration of the humus content of the soil.

The felled or pollarded woodland, fire-scorched after the burn, is an eyesore to which administrators and foresters are particularly sensitive; so sensitive that at one time an Order was made prohibiting the cutting of trees in the Bemba country. This was in 1907, when the British South Africa Company administered Northern Rhodesia. Curiously enough, the Order was at least partially effective. In the following year the Bemba grew very little millet and there was acute food shortage. Faced with the alternatives of supplying continuous famine relief or rescinding its decree, the Administration adopted the latter course. Agriculturists, or most of them, have learned to be more tolerant: but they are equally emphatic in their condemnation of the late burning of woodland. In the *citemene* systems, fire is necessarily excluded from the woodland until it is time to burn the brushwood stacks; then the flames run riot, sweeping with devastating effect through vegetation and leaf-litter which is tinder-dry at this time of year and blackening the surrounding countryside under a menacing pall of smoke. Late burning year after year not only retards the regrowth of the trees, it also destroys the woodland. This has been shown by burning experiments maintained continuously by the Northern Rhodesia Forest Department near Ndola since 1933, and another set at Lunzuwa in the Abercorn district started in the late 1930s. In the case of the former, a detailed study has been made by Trapnell (174) of the effect on the vegetation of a late or hot burn at the end of the dry season and an early or cool burn, repeated each year for more than twenty years, compared with complete protection. Contrary to previous belief, the *Julbernardia* woodlands do not represent a fire subclimax; the species of these genera that compose the main canopy dominants are, in fact, fire-tender and they are destroyed by repeated late burning.

How then has *citemene* survived? Probably because the woodland is not repeatedly late-burned. Only the areas around new cuttings are protected against fire until late in the season and elsewhere burning starts much earlier. Thus, any one piece of woodland is subjected to late burning only occasionally; in most seasons the burn comes comparatively early and sometimes it may escape the fire altogether for a season. *Citemene* has been going on for a long time, perhaps for centuries, and the woodland is still there. But it is possible that a long, slow process of degeneration is taking place even where population densities are well below the critical level, because of fire and the complete destruction of trees on the parts of the clearing where the stacks have been burned. On a recent flight over these regions, I had a strong impression of slow but inevitable degeneration; the woodland seemed thinner, more patchy, than it had been a generation earlier, and the scars of very old circles showed up clearly because of the poor growth of woody vegetation on them. I wondered if these circles ever had a chance of coming back to fully regenerated woodland.

It is obvious that these systems can survive only at very low population levels and that their continuance is possible, even at such levels, only under conditions of thinly dispersed or temporarily concentrated and shifting populations. We will consider later the Critical Population Densities beyond which degeneration, leading to ultimate collapse, is bound to set in.

Chapter VII

CRITICAL POPULATION DENSITY:
THE LAMBA SYSTEM

1. Main Gardens of the Lamba

We may now consider how the factors discussed in the previous chapters were used to assess the land requirements, or Critical Population Densities, of some Northern Rhodesian systems, taking as an example the agriculture of Mushiri's section of the Lamba people. They formerly occupied an area, probably of more than 2,000 square miles, on the southern side of the Congo-Zambesi watershed where it now forms the boundary between Northern Rhodesia and the former Belgian Congo: but with the development of mining and the growth of the Copperbelt their country was greatly reduced (Fig. 4). Ilamba, the original country of the Lamba-speaking people, is a much greater extent of about 25,000 square miles, partly in Northern Rhodesia and partly in the Katanga Province of the Congo.

A considerable range of agricultural methods is found within the larger group, with retention of *citemene* practices in varying degree in accordance with the dominant vegetation-soil types, and the following description refers only to the Mushiri section. The soils of the Copperbelt series in the region they occupy, although variable in character and fertility, are generally capable of yielding three or more satisfactory crops in succession without the application of *citemene* methods.

In preparing the main gardens the selected area of woodland is felled at breast height and the branches are lopped, carried with care to preserve the leaves, and laid in circular stacks, usually around anthills or stumps. In contrast with *citemene* practice, most of the cleared land between the stacks is then hoed over in preparation for planting, but the branch and brushwood stacks are burnt at the end of the dry season to form thick ash patches. A newly made Lamba garden of this type therefore consists of three distinct parts: the *fiteme* or ash patches, the *inkuule* or hoed portion between the ash patches, and the *cisumbu* or cut but uncultivated part which is rarely more than a quarter of the whole.

In the first year of cultivation the *fiteme* are hoe-planted to maize, among which sorghum seed may be broadcast, and underplanted with pumpkins and other cucurbits. Sorghum, the main

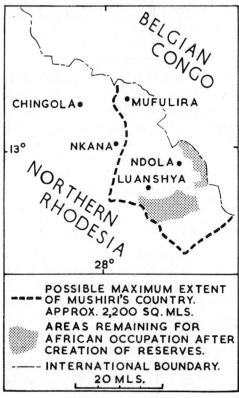

FIG. 4. Possible maximum extent of Mushiri's Country and area remaining for African occupation after the creation of Native Reserves.

cereal crop of the Lamba, mixed with a little maize, is broadcast over the *inkuule*, with the exception of some relatively small areas on the outer margin which are reserved for minor crops such as groundnuts, ground-beans, sweet potatoes, and cassava. Maize and pumpkins are planted on ant-hills, where fertility is higher, and ash patches for finger millet are quite frequently made round one side of ant-hills on the margin of the garden, while the unburnt land on the other side is hoed up into mounds on which sweet potatoes and sorghum transplants from the main crop are grown. Cucumbers of several types are underplanted in the *inkuule*.

Sorghum is broadcast only in the first year, and the Lamba say this is necessary to check regrowth of grass. In the second year the whole garden, including the *fiteme, inkuule,* and minor crop area of the previous year, is hoe planted with sorghum and a little maize, while extensions for the minor crops are made in the *cisumbu.* There is, however, a small but interesting exception to this general rule: finger millet on ash patches is usually followed by ground-beans or groundnuts, as in small-circle *citemene* practice, and any branchwood left over from the first year is collected and used to make small ash patches on which pumpkins and other cucurbits are grown.

In the third year the *inkuule* is often mounded to check weed growth and the whole garden, including the minor crops area of the second year, is planted to sorghum, while further extensions, which may bring the whole of the *cisumbu* into cultivation, are made for the subsidiary crops.

Cropping is continued for three or, more usually, four years on the weaker soils which are typical of the area, but may be extended to eight years or more on the strongest and most fertile types. When land is judged to have become too infertile to yield another cereal crop, an end-crop of sweet potatoes and cassava on mounds is frequently taken.

2. GARDEN EXTENSIONS

The main gardens are extended at more-or-less frequent intervals. Ideally, the traditional system of garden extensions implies the preparation of a new area each year and the retirement of an equivalent area of the old garden, but it is doubtful if extensions are usually as regular as this in normal practice. The illustration (Fig. 5), a simplified diagram based on a detailed study of the land used by a small Lamba family over eight seasons, may approximate more closely to the normal under present-day conditions of labour shortage in the villages.

A garden of five acres (A) was planted in 1932 and used for three consecutive seasons. In 1935 a small extension (B) was made to the north while the poorest part of the old garden was abandoned.

In the following season a large extension (C) was made to the east, expansion in any other direction being impossible owing to neighbouring cultivations, and in 1937 a much smaller one (D) was

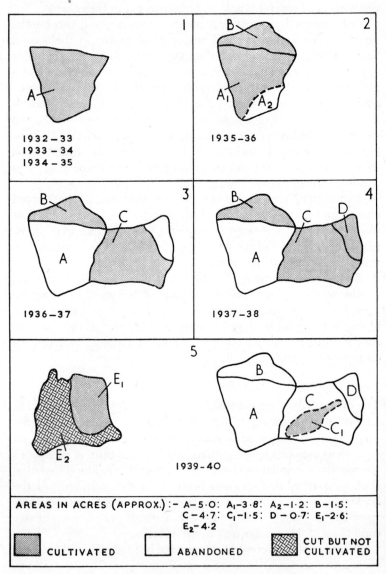

FIG. 5. Extensions of a Lamba Garden.

added. These extensions were coming on to poorer and poorer soils, the best bit of this particular block of woodland having been used for the initial garden and the first extension. This will be evident from the fact that while most of (A) and all of (B) gave four satisfactory crops only three such crops were obtained from (C) and two from (D). Beyond this, in the only direction open, lay "uncultivable" land. By 1939 it was imperative to make new gardens and a block of woodland (E) about half a mile from the previous cultivation was selected and felled. The season was difficult, the labour force inadequate, and only part of the new land (E1) could be hoed and planted in that year. This area was too small to ensure the family's food supply, so part of the old garden (C1), the part judged to be most fertile, was sown with sorghum for a fourth year. The gamble would probably have come off in a good year but the 1939–40 season was a very poor one: the crop on the old land failed completely and the yield from the new garden was far below expectation. Consequently, the members of this family were among the many in the area who required famine relief in 1940.

The table below summarises the land-use pattern over the eight seasons.

	CLEARED LAND (ACRES)						TOTAL		GARDEN FAMILY (No. of members)	ACREAGE CULTIVATED (per head)
	CULTIVATED				UNCULTIVATED		Resting	Cultivated		
Season	1st	2nd	3rd	4th						
1932–3	5·0							5·0	4	1·25
1933–4		5·0						5·0	4	1·25
1934–5			5·0					5·0	4	1·25
1935–6	1·5			3·8			1·2	5·3	5	1·06
1936–7	4·7	1·5					5·0	6·2	7	0·90
1937–8	0·7	4·7	1·5				5·0	6·9	7	0·96
1938–9		0·7	4·7	1·5			5·0	6·9	7	0·96
1939–40	2·6			1·5	4·2		10·4	4·1	5	0·82

For the first three seasons the garden family consisted of the husband, his wife, and their three children. In the fourth season this was increased by the addition to the consuming group of a third child, and in the following year by a young brother and sister of the husband who had been placed in his charge because he lived near a school. An evident attempt was made to enlarge the cultivated area to meet the needs of the larger group, but this was only partly successful owing to the disruption of the old mechanism of reciprocal help. Not only was a high proportion of the able-bodied men absent at work, but very many of the villages had been moved into the Reserve and had opened gardens in the same year. Consequently their peak demands for labour tended to coincide and there was little or no free labour of kin or neighbours to be called upon.

This was one of the main causes of the 1940 food shortage. The "famine" villages were, almost invariably, those caught in the vulnerable stage of preparing new gardens and with too small an area of cultivation to ensure the food supply in a very poor season.

3. SUBSIDIARY GARDENS

In addition to the main gardens, most Lamba families have a few *fiteme* for finger millet, usually in woodland a considerable distance from the village and main gardens: they may be relics of former *citemene* practice. These very small gardens are generally made in woodland on the poorer soils, or even old ironstone soils, regarded as uncultivable by any other means. They are similar to small-circle *citemene* gardens. Branchwood from the felled trees is laid in circular stacks, and sometimes in strips between them, and burned to make ash patches on which the finger millet seed is broadcast. Pumpkins and gourds are sown on the outer margins of the circles and some sesame, an oil seed, and tephrosia for fish poison may be added. A few circles are sometimes planted to ground-beans or groundnuts in the second year but otherwise the garden is abandoned after one crop has been taken.

Another traditional form is the ridge garden for Livingstone potatoes (*Coleus esculentus*). These are made in the marginal grassland of *dambos* and take the form of long beds or ridges about four feet wide separated by trenches some two feet in depth. Two crops of Livingstone potatoes are taken, the second being a volunteer crop, and the garden is then abandoned. Formerly extensively employed, this form of cultivation was falling into disuse prior to 1940 when it was revived to some extent under the stimulus of food shortage.

Another type of small subsidiary garden, known as *fipoka*, is made by hoeing up the humic topsoil of fertile sandy-clay *dambo* soils on the upper part of moist seepage areas, very often on the lower side of an ant-hill. These probably originated, and are to some extent still used, as pre-rains gardens for maize and other subsidiary crops, but such sites are now more commonly devoted to the production of European vegetables for sale in the mine townships.

The Lamba make little use of village gardens, but small mounded gardens for cassava, sweet potatoes, and tobacco are sometimes made on old village sites where these are near at hand, and the usual collection of useful plants, including a few plantains grown in rubbish pits, pawpaws, "relish" plants, castor, and tephrosia, is to be found in or on the margins of inhabited villages.

In contrast with the large area of main gardens, the subsidiary gardens amount in the aggregate to only a small fraction of an acre per head of population and they are of little significance in the estimation of land requirements.

4. ORIGIN OF THE CONCEPT OF CRITICAL POPULATION DENSITY

The conception of land requirements, as applied to traditional systems, originated from the investigation of the food situation in Mushiri's Reserve in 1940, an investigation which was undertaken as a result of contradictory reports from District Officers, one alleging and the other denying the existence of famine conditions. It was a relatively simple matter to demonstrate the existence of near-famine conditions, by sampling grain bins throughout the area at a time when they should have held about six months' supply of food and seed sufficient for the next planting. Approximately 30 per cent of the villages did not have enough grain for seed, 40 per cent had their seed requirement and food for three months or less and the remaining 30 per cent had a bare sufficiency or a small surplus. If the total grain supply had been evenly distributed throughout the population it would have been enough to provide food for only about six weeks, after deduction of the seed requirement and an allowance for normal wastage. The immediate causes of this situation were also fairly easy to diagnose as an adverse season for sorghum (the staple crop of the Lamba), because of excessive rain, and the shortage of labour in the circumstances already described. Much more alarming than the immediate problem—which was, of course, solved by the issue of famine relief and seed—was the outlook for the future. Conditions throughout most of the area were such as to justify a prediction of recurring food shortages and the ultimate collapse of the system of food-production, possibly within a decade. It was evident that the Reserve was greatly over-populated in relation to the system of land-use and that a continuation of this situation could result only in progressive deterioration of the soil and accelerated erosion.

Rapid introduction of any system of permanent farming, at a rate commensurate with the need, was out of the question at that time. The Reserve consisted of a triangle about 242 square miles in area between two confluent main drainage lines, the Kafubu and Kafulafuta streams, with a central watershed of practically uncultivable pallid sands and an extensive area of sheet ironstone. Fertile vegetation-soil types were represented only by small pockets of degraded chipya and eroded red earths, and the arable soils consisted almost entirely of light weak variants of the Copper-belt loams intersected by many *dambos* extending from the central watershed sands to join the wide flanking *dambos* of the two main streams.

There was at that time no knowledge or experience of the possibilities for permanent cultivation on these unpromising soils. The working out and adequate trial of improved systems, capable of supporting relatively high population densities and within the means of the Lamba, would have required many years even if the resources for doing so had been available; and in the uncertain event of success, the introduction and general adoption of the new system among a people who could see no need and had no will for change, would again require a considerable period of time. Furthermore, the Lamba had very few livestock, far too few to provide manure sufficient for the maintenance of soil fertility, and the great majority had none at all—not even a sheep or a goat. They had no trained oxen, no carts, no ploughs, and no means of obtaining these. Ahead was the prospect of long years of war and decreasing supplies of fertiliser and farm equipment. In the meantime, it might reasonably be predicted, the land of the Reserve, and with it the people, would be reduced to the final stages of degradation, and the ultimate problem would be one not only of introducing a new system but of rehabilitating the people and reclaiming the devastated land.

On the other hand, the existence of great areas of unused and empty land—a circumstance which strongly influenced the attitude of the Lamba—offered a ready, if temporary solution by redistribution of population on a planned basis, provided that the land requirements of the Lamba system could be worked out. Resettlement on such a basis would avert the danger of catastrophic collapse of the food production system and allow time for the gradual improvement and development of agricultural techniques.

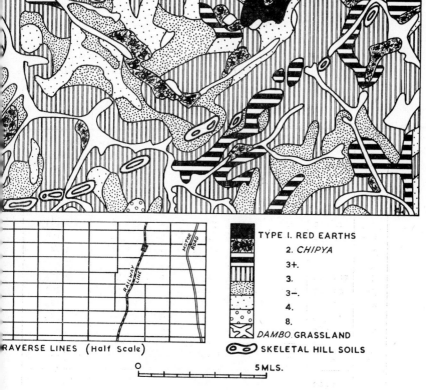

TYPE I. RED EARTHS
2. *CHIPYA*
3+.
3.
3−.
4.
8.
DAMBO GRASSLAND
SKELETAL HILL SOILS

TRAVERSE LINES (Half Scale)

0   5 MLS.

FIG. 6. Section of a vegetation-soil map of the Lamba re-settlement area Ndola District, Northern Rhodesia.

5. Estimate of Critical Population Density for the Lamba System and Environment

The first attempt to estimate the land requirements of hoe-cultivation systems of land use in Northern Rhodesia was made as a contribution towards the solution of this specific problem. The Reserve and, later, some 400 square miles of vacant Crown Land to the south were surveyed and mapped, on the basis of the Vegetation-Soil units already described (pp. 17–18).

Part of the southern area, about 155 square miles in extent, is reproduced (Fig. 6) to show the complexity of the environment and to illustrate the type of map on which the assessment was based. The traverse grid from which the map was constructed is also indicated: the east-west lines of this grid were invariably one mile apart while the interval between north-south lines was generally two miles, but in this section the railway line and a main road crossing the area have been used as traverse lines.

The following table summarises the data obtained from the survey of the uninhabited area south of the Reserve and shows the

V.-S. TYPE	TOTAL AREA (*Acres*)	YEARS (*a*) OF CULTI-VATION & (*b*) OF REST (*a*)	(*b*)	C.P.	L.U.	AREA REQUIRED PER HEAD (*Acres*)	TOTAL CARRYING CAPACITY (*Persons*)
1	4,380	—*	—*	33–4	3	9	487
1 —	1,160	—*	—*	25	3	12	97
2	12,980	6–12	6–12	33–4	2	6	2,163
2 —	1,650	—*	—*	25	3	12	138
3 +	15,430	—*	—*	25–30	4	15	1,029
		5	20				
3	125,900	3	21	25	8	32	3,934
3 —	43,610	2–3	22–8	15–25	11	55	793
4	22,450	2	22–8	8–12	13	130	173
4 —	11,380	2	22–8	5	13	260	44
7	1,260	—	—	—	—	—	—
9	190	—	—	—	—	—	—
D	2,010	—	—	—	—	—	—
	242,400			22			8,858

* Re-cultivation.

factors used in estimating its human-carrying capacity, on the basis of what was thought to be traditional Lamba practice.

The first column lists the Vegetation-Soil types found within this area, in accordance with the criteria previously defined, with an additional category (D) of seasonally waterlogged grassland, ranging from small "pans" and depressions to larger areas of seasonal swamp. It will be noted that Vegetation-Soil types 5 and 6, which had been distinguished in a region further to the north, were not represented in this area, or not on such a scale as to be worth mapping as separate units.

Column 2 gives the total area of each of these types, as determined by planimeter measurements from the map, including a proportion of *dambo* and hill lithosols, since these were measured with the surrounding or adjoining main type. The area of each occurrence of a type was recorded separately, for later use in the event of planned resettlement of population.

Columns 3*a* and 3*b* show the cultivation and rest periods for each Vegetation-Soil type, in accordance with traditional Lamba practice as far as this could be ascertained. The former were based on information provided by Lamba informants who professed to know "the things of the soil" and on observations of current practice in areas of varying population density, while the fallow periods were derived from information and reconstructed garden histories, with the use of tree ring counts as a check on stated periods of regeneration. The information supplied by different informants was generally very consistent, but there were occasional divergencies. For example, in the case of the 3+ Vegetation-Soil unit some informants said that re-cultivation had been the normal practice while others maintained that such soils were usually cropped for five years and then left for a long regeneration period approximating to twenty years. The factors for the heavily-wooded red soils and *chipyas* proved most difficult to assess because these sites had been little used by the Lamba in the past when they had more than ample land, probably because of the heavy labour involved in clearing and subsequent cultivation. Where there is ample land and free choice the preference is for the better variants of type 3 and the more lightly wooded *dambo* fringe *chipyas*: but under conditions of land-shortage in the Reserve these heavily timbered types had been cleared and cultivated, or over-cultivated, and it was apparent that the Lamba would rather make use of them than return to land after what they considered to be an inadequate period of regeneration.

The fourth column gives the Cultivable Percentages (C.P.) allocated to each Vegetation-Soil type, for the Lamba system with sorghum as a staple. The surveys, of which the example is part, were made in country formerly occupied by the Lamba from which they had been removed some fourteen years earlier. Woodland previously used for cultivation could generally be distinguished by the habit of the regrowth, and this enabled observations on the extent of previously felled and unfelled woodland to be made in the course of the traverses. These records were used, in conjunction with observations on the extent of cultivation in the Reserve and the "yardstick" obtained from aerial photographs (p. 24), to assess the "cultivability" of each of the Vegation-Soil units. *Dambo* areas and hill soils unfit for cultivation are included in the uncultivable sectors.

Column 5 shows the Land-Use factor (L.U.) for each of the Vegetation-Soil types, estimated from the data in columns 3*a* and 3*b*. It will be noted that approximately 53 per cent of the area falls within the category of Recurrent Cultivation land, while about 40 per cent is in the Shifting Cultivation and Uncultivable categories and rather more than 7 per cent in the Permanent and Semi-Permanent Cultivation categories.

The Cultivation Factor is not shown since it was assumed, as an approximation, to be unity—one acre of land in cultivation per head of population at any one time. Three sets of samples were taken, consisting of:

(*a*) a random group within the Reserve,
(*b*) a complete village in the Reserve,
(*c*) a small Lamba settlement outside the Reserve with access to ample land.

Sample	NO. OF GARDEN FAMILIES IN SAMPLE	TOTAL POPULATION IN SAMPLE	AREA OF MAIN GARDENS (ACRES)	
			Total	Per head of population
a	23	127	120·4	0·95
b	8	40	44·0	1·10
c	18	87	93·6	1·07

The relatively low figure given by the random samples (*a*) is, of course, due to the high proportion of cultivators in the Reserve who had made new gardens in the previous year and whose cultivated acreage was therefore lower than normal. On the other hand, the village group (*b*), of which a complete survey was made, had retained their old gardens for a fifth year of cultivation and the figure obtained from these samples probably approximates to the maximum, while the third group may represent a more normal distribution of old and new gardens. Although the evidence pointed to a slightly higher value, the Cultivation Factor was taken as one acre in view of the very approximate nature of the other estimates.

For a single Vegetation-Soil type, the area of land required per head of population may be expressed by the formula 100L.U. × C/P, when L.U. is the Land-Use Factor, C the Cultivation Factor and P the Cultivable Percentage for the type. Column 6 shows the total area of land required per head of population, calculated on this basis, and Column 7 gives the final estimate of the carrying capacity of the area for the Lamba system of land-use.

According to this estimate, the mean cultivable percentage for the whole area of 379 square miles is about 22, and the total carrying capacity is 8,860 people; or, to put it in another way, the Lamba system of land use may be capable of supporting a general population density of 23 or 24 persons per square mile in this environment. The term "Critical Population Density" was coined as a descriptive label for this concept of the human-carrying capacity of an area in relation to a given land-use system, expressed in terms of population per square mile, and it was defined as the maximum population density the system is capable of supporting permanently in that environment *without damage to the land.*

In formulating the estimate we have taken only the main gardens into consideration and the final conclusion involves the assumption, which appeared to be fully warranted, that all requirements for subsidiary gardens, domestic timber, grazing, and the collection of wild fruits and other natural products which contribute to the Lamba economy could be met from the "uncultivable" sector and the woodland fallows of long duration. As has been noted, certain *dambo* types and poor woodland soils are in fact used for subsidiary gardens, though these have been grouped as "uncultivable" in estimating requirements for main gardens.

Using the same method of survey and assessment, the Critical Population Density for the 242 square miles of Mushiri's Reserve was calculated to be about 18 per square mile, the difference between this figure and the estimate for the southern area being due to the greater prevalence of very poor woodland soils and old ironstone types within the Reserve. In 1940, when the first estimates were made, the actual density of resident population in the Reserve was about 44 per square mile, and there was reason to believe that during most, if not all, of the previous decade this area had been carrying a population of at least twice the estimated Critical Density.

6. CRITICISM OF THE ESTIMATE

The original estimates were, necessarily, of a very tentative nature and the values attributed to the factors are open to criticism and revision, more especially the "cultivable percentages" which were based on little more than observation and conjecture. Sixteen years later—in 1956—some interesting critical observations were made by Wood, following a survey of conditions in the Ndola Resettlement Area (191). The story of resettlement will be told later: at the moment we are concerned with the concepts and conjectures on which it was based.

Wood concluded that the general Cultivable Percentage for the area was probably not less than 36, compared with the 22 per cent of the original estimate. He arrived at his figure by deducting 10 per cent for *dambo*, allowing a cultivability factor of 45 to 50 per cent for all the remaining land, and deducting a further 5 to 10 per cent for "probable wastage due to haphazard cultivation." On the other hand, he postulated a much higher value for the general Land-Use Factor, based on forestry data then available which indicated that a period of about forty-four years must be allowed for full regeneration of most of the types found in the resettlement area, to the point of maximum regrowth of the trees. The accuracy of the original estimate of the Cultivation Factor was, however, confirmed by Wood's measurements of 4,660 acres of main gardens, which, related to his count of the exploiting population, gave a figure of 1·05 acres in cultivation per head.

On this basis of estimation, the general Land-Use Factor approximates to 12, the land requirement is about 35 acres per head, and the Critical Population Density is of the order of 18 or 19 to the square mile rather than the 23 or 24 per square mile obtained from the original estimate for the same area.

This approach, however, involves the very debatable assumption that the period required for soil regeneration and for full woodland regrowth, from the aspect of forestry, are the same—or, in any case, that the Lamba behave as though this were so. It is natural to assume, at least for forest and woodland soils, that the vegetational climax is the ultimate step of restored fertility, but there is a good deal of evidence that this is not necessarily the case. The great forest of the Congo Basin may require well over a century to return to the full climax after clearing and cultivation, but the work of INEAC has shown that soil fertility is restored, at least to a satisfactory level, in the relatively short space of fifteen, or even twelve years; and it is considered that this *forêt secondaire* is better suited for cultivation than *forêt primaire*. The Makonde thicket system of southern Tanganyika and the *baphia* scrub cultivation practised on certain of the Kalahari Sand soils of Barotseland are comparable examples of relatively rapid recovery of fertility at a sub-climax vegetational phase in the dry, deciduous woodland zone. Certainly, the earlier enquiries among the Lamba yielded no suggestion that they regarded a regeneration period of more than forty years as necessary even for the poorest of the cultivated woodland soils, or that they were unaware of the variations of soil strength and fertility within their complex environment. On the contrary, they showed a clear appreciation of these differences and adaptions of practice in accordance with them. It is, of course, possible that traditional knowledge had been lost or fallen into disuse and that practice had changed in the intervening years: but there is a more probable explanation. The later study was made in the Resettlement Area when population was relatively sparse, and at a level of probably not more than half the critical density. The inhabitants had free choice of well-regenerated woodland and were cultivating only a few of the preferred types, as I observed when I revisited the area in 1959. This circumstance may well have given a misleading impression of uniformity of practice and, quite possibly, of cultivability. Misconception may also have arisen through the frequent use of the term "full woodland regeneration" in the sense of recovery of the vegetation to a stage recognisable as woodland rather than bush or scrub—meaning, generally, regeneration of twenty years or more and not necessarily a full restoration of the timber potential. I have been guilty of this very loose use, or misuse, of the term. So have the Lamba. This, I think, is what they mean when they speak of *iyamba*—woodland fit to be cut for main gardens, but not necessarily woodland fully mature in the forestry sense.

It may well be, at least in some cases, that the fallow periods which have become established in traditional practice do not restore fertility to the maximum potential of the soil, but that the customary cycle of cultivation and regeneration results in a balance at a somewhat lower level of fertility; a level which is, nevertheless, "satisfactory." David Peters seems to have been working towards this conclusion in the course of the survey of land-usage in Barotseland which ended with his death. His study of over-cultivated woodland gardens on the Kalahari sands bordering the Barotse Plain led him to suspect that levels of fertility might have risen to 60 or even 70 per cent of the maximum within one-third of the time required for full regrowth of the woodland, and that soil regeneration was even more rapid where a good stand of *baphia* scrub had colonised the gardens within two or three years of the last cultivation.

A further point which may be of some significance is that the condition of the woodland in the Reserve, as it was observed in 1940, some twelve years after the concentration of population, accorded better with expectation based on the lower figures for cultivability and regeneration. Movement of villages extended over a few years, but the majority of transfers seem to have taken place in 1928. The Reserve was, of course, already occupied but the population density was almost certainly below the critical level. If we assume a more-or-less balanced initial population, a general Cultivable Percentage of 36 and a regeneration period of forty-four years, we may reasonably suppose that at the time of concentration some 50 per cent of the "cultivable" woodland was aged over twenty years, dating from the end of the previous cycle of cultivation, and that this was mostly in the range 22–44 years. Doubling the population, and consequently the consumption of land, would have the effect of reducing the woodland at such a rate that by the end of twelve years, or three cycles of cultivation, about 25 per cent would remain in the age-group exceeding twenty years. We should expect to find that most, if not all, villages still had before them at least one further cycle of cutting in woodland of this age-group. If, on the other hand, we adopt the lower figures, we must suppose that a much smaller proportion of the cultivable woodland, not more than 20 per cent, was aged over twenty years at the time of concentration, and that little of this was much older than twenty years. Allowing for the difference in the age of the woodland at the start and for the lower Cultivable Percentages, we should expect that a doubling of population would result in more rapid degeneration of vegetation, at a rate which would reduce most of the cultivable woodland to scrub regrowth of four to ten years' regeneration by the end of three cycles of cultivation.

The conditions observed in the Reserve in 1940 cannot be expressed in terms of comparable simplicity because cutting had been very uneven, owing to the unplanned siting of immigrant villages and voluntary concentration near urban settlements. Consequently, a few villages still had before them a further cycle of cutting in *iyamba*—in this case, woodland of about twenty years' regeneration—but the great majority were clearing gardens in scrub of ten years' regrowth or less, and in the more congested areas the cycle had been reduced to two years' cultivation following a short-scrub fallow of four or five years. Untouched woodland remained over the considerable extent of old ironstone and pallid sandy soils, which the Lamba had made no attempt to cultivate even under the utmost pressure of land shortage. These conditions were more in accordance with expectation based on the lower estimate of cultivability.

7. ADDITIONAL CONSIDERATIONS

The outlook of the African subsistence cultivator and of the European agriculturist on such matters as productivity and this crucial question of "cultivability" are very different. The subsistence cultivator is concerned with security against famine. His object is to ensure, in so far as he can, a certain minimum return for his labour, a return which will guarantee an adequate food supply. Until he has absorbed the doctrine of the money economy, and ceased to be a subsistence cultivator, he is not greatly interested in productivity much above this level, or in procuring a very large

surplus which he cannot store. This attitude explains the preference of some peoples, including the Lamba, for soils which,
though less fertile than those they tend to neglect while land is
ample, are yet capable of giving safe and satisfactory yields with
less labour—or with more of such pleasant work as tree-cutting
and less of the dreary, back-breaking drudgery of the hoe. In
some regions the urge for security may influence this choice, since,
in seasons of prolonged and continuous rainfall, the weeds on the
soil of higher fertility are more likely to win the battle with the hoe.
Or the wishes of women may be a decisive factor, for hoeing is
mainly their concern while tree-cutting is the work of men.

It is claimed that when the richer lands of Southern Rhodesia
were set aside for European occupation they were little used by
Africans, who preferred to cultivate the lighter soils. This may
well be true, for there is reason to believe that population densities
were, in general, below the critical point at that time: but these
richer soils represented a reserve of land which would certainly
have come into use with increasing numbers. A similar preference
is shown by the Zande of the southern Sudan. De Schlippe (146)
notes that they avoid elephant grass formations, despite their
fertility, because they are too difficult to clear with the small
Zande hoe, and he points out that "if one can clear with the same
effort three times as much poor land and get only half the yield
there is still a net gain."

This selection of the weaker soils means, of course, more
frequent garden-making, since the fertility of these soils falls
rapidly under repeated cultivation. Results of a rotation experiment conducted at Yambio (1949–53) indicate the rapidity of this
decline in the case of a soil traditionally cultivated by the Zande
for two or, exceptionally, three successive years (Fig. 7). The
fertility of the light soils of the *Julbernardia-Brachystegia* woodlands in Northern Rhodesia (plateau, sandveld, or Class III soils)
appears to decline in much the same way, though rather less
steeply (Fig. 8, III [a, b, c].) The figure shows hypothetical
"fertility gradients" for a number of Northern Rhodesian soils,
based on the few available data for maize yields after continuous
cultivation for known periods without manure or fertiliser (10,
132, 25). They indicate, of course, the approximate yield levels
which might be expected in a "normal" season. The soils of Class
I include those of the acacia tree grassland and the stronger red

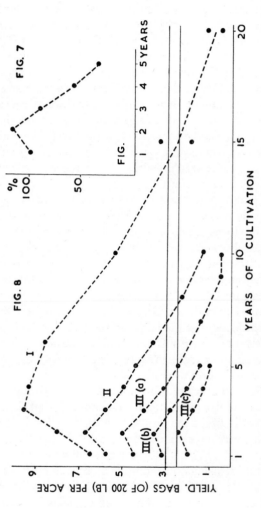

FIG. 7. Yambio Experiment.

Decline of fertility under cultivation. Average of four indicators—height of cotton, and yields of cotton, groundnuts, and finger millet—expressed as percentages of the first three years' averages.

FIG. 8. Hypothetical figures to illustrate decline of fertility of some Northern Rhodesian soils under continuous cultivation to maize without manure or fertilisers.

earths and clays, while the Class II or transitional soils are mainly those associated with the *Combretum* scrub-woodland types of vegetation.

The minimum return for which the subsistence cultivator looks may be something of the order of 500 or 600 lb per acre, in terms of grain yields. If this is so, the better variants of the Class III soils (IIIa) will be worked for four years, while less fertile variants (IIIb) will be worked for two or, exceptionally, three years. The least fertile variants (IIIc) will not be cultivated at all in traditional practice though they are not uncultivable in any absolute sense and may even give satisfactory yields in a good season, or with the use of advanced techniques. To the subsistence cultivator who has no knowledge of these techniques, or who lacks the means of employing them, such soils are "uncultivable" in the sense that their use involves a risk he dare not take.

On the same criterion, the Class II or transitional soils will have a "life" of six or seven years while that of the strong Class I soils may extend to as much as fourteen or fifteen years. Recultivation practices were commonly employed on soils of the former type but the soils of Class I were not, as a rule, worked to the limits of their cultivable life. They were usually cultivated for five or more years and then rested under a natural grass fallow for an equal or shorter period. Ballantyne (25) has suggested, on the basis of analytical data, that the fall in fertility of these soils under continuous cultivation is a result of loss of soil structure and that the regular interposition of the grass fallow rebuilds structure lost during the previous period of cultivation.

The ecological criteria used in the earlier work distinguished, in effect, types of country associated with soils of different character. We have already discussed the proposition that any land type distinguished in this way must contain an uncultivable sector of considerable extent, including not only the more obviously uncultivable variants and intrusions but also a less obvious range of soils which are impracticable for cultivation for a variety of reasons. The variations of fertility even over a long-cultivated and highly farmed field of seeming uniformity are often surprisingly great, a fact well-known to anyone who has conducted uniformity trials or who is aware of the difficulties imposed on agricultural experimentation by soil irregularities and the elaborate techniques which have been devised to overcome these difficulties. In selecting his arable land, the European cultivator who works a large and regular area with tractor ploughs and equipment, must, to some extent, take the bad with the good. He relies on his techniques to raise the level of the less fertile variants and to even out, in a considerable degree, the inequalities of soil. The hoe cultivator, who relies wholly on intrinsic fertility, is much more selective. He makes his first choice on a basis of ecological criteria, but the land is then subjected to a minute examination, since every inch is turned over by hand with the hoe. Wherever a change in the character of soil or vegetation indicates lower fertility, below the level judged to be satisfactory, the hoe will be turned away and the operation continued in another direction, so as to avoid the area of unsatisfactory or doubtful soil. This, of course, often results in very irregular garden shapes and an appearance of "haphazard" cultivation.

Thus, if one looks at the same piece of land from these different points of view, that of the subsistence cultivator with no resources but the hoe and his traditional knowledge, and that of the agricultural "improver" with his conditioned outlook and background of advanced techniques and resources, the two estimates of cultivability are bound to vary very considerably. At the time that the assessments of cultivability were made from aerial photographs, a number of sample areas were examined on the ground and the cultivable proportion estimated by eye. These estimates were invariably from 30 to 50 per cent higher than the figures later deduced from photographic measurements. In the earlier work we were attempting to assess what African cultivators, given ample land and left entirely to their own devices, would in fact do, rather than what we thought they might or should do. The concepts of cultivability used in the original estimates of Critical Population Density derive from this approach, but it is not contended that they are more than first approximations of a very tentative and uncertain character. More recent estimates, however, do not appear to rest on much greater factual knowledge and it is doubtful if they attain a higher degree of probability, regarded strictly from the aspect of the limitations imposed by traditional resources and practices.

The extent to which local conditions and the purpose of an enquiry may affect the assessment of cultivability is illustrated by Priestley and Greening's estimate in 1954–5 (132) for an area of about 218 square miles forming part of the Ngoni Reserve in Fort Jameson district. This region is still greatly over-populated and it

includes what has become known as the "devastated area." They
arrived at a figure of 49 per cent of cultivable land, by subtracting
the total area of hill and *dambo* and deducting 10 per cent from the
remainder as an arbitrary allowance for "roads, villages, streams,
gulleys and small localised areas not cultivable for one reason or
another." This estimate was used in assessing the degree of over-
population, but it was regarded by its authors as "too optimistic,"
for it involves the assumption that "even ferruginous rubbles and
the poorest types of Marginal Sands are cultivable"; and, they add,
"if there were no shortage of land we would have little hesitation
in condemning such soils as uncultivable."

These soils, and a good many other variants, would almost
certainly be regarded as uncultivable by a people free from the
inexorable pressure of acute land shortage; and they would most
certainly be so regarded by a people such as the Ngoni, whose
maize culture, in a region of predominantly plateau soils, depends
for success on very careful selection of land.

Nevertheless, Priestley and Greening arrived at an estimate for
the carrying capacity of the area of only 3,940 people, or 18 per
square mile, an estimate somewhat lower than that based on the
earlier criteria. This, again, is due to the use of very high values for
the Land-Use Factors—of a magnitude probably without parallel in
Africa—which appear to be based on forestry rather than agricultural experience. The difference between the earlier and later
estimates of Critical Population Densities for traditional systems
are not great, though the latter tend to be lower: the divergence lies
in the values attributed to Cultivable Percentages and Land-Use
Factors, and this can be resolved only by greater factual knowledge
derived from direct experiment and experience over many years
and a great variety of soils.

CHAPTER VIII

EASTERN PLATEAU AND VALLEY SYSTEMS OF NORTHERN RHODESIA

1. TRADITIONAL PRACTICES OF THE NGONI-CHEWA

The traditional agriculture of the Ngoni-Chewa people, who live in the Fort Jameson district of Northern Rhodesia was based on the use of what may be called "cultivation mounds." I use the past tense in referring to this system because although remnants of it survive, customary practice has, in general, been profoundly altered, first by acute land shortage and, later, by innovations introduced by the Agricultural Department, notably the substitution of contour cultivation ridges for mounds.

In traditional practice, when a new garden was prepared from well-regenerated woodland, the land was lightly hoed over, in such a way as to cut the surface into sods. The dried sods were later broken up with the hoe and the grass roots shaken out and placed in small heaps scattered evenly over most of the garden area. A little earth was then drawn over each of these heaps. In October, towards the end of the dry season, the heaps were burnt, leaving small patches of ash mixed with incinerated soil. These patches were known as *vikuse*. Maize was planted together with cowpeas and pumpkins on the *vikuse*, and as a pure crop at a wide spacing over the ash-free soil between them. This planting was done in November, shortly before the main rains, and in December, when the maize had reached a foot or so in height, the process characteristic of the system was begun.

The weeds which had grown between the *vikuse* were hoed down and placed in heaps: earth was then drawn away from the *vikuse* and thrown over the heaps to make a series of small mounds throughout the growing crop. Mounds completed before the end of December were planted with groundnuts and later ones with beans and, very frequently, sweet potatoes.

In the second season, maize was planted on the mounds, which now replaced the *vikuse* of the first season. Then, in December, when weeding had become necessary, new mounds were made in the same way as before, by scraping down the weeds and placing them in heaps and drawing earth from the old mounds over the heaps, with care to leave sufficient soil about the roots of the growing plants. These new mounds were sown, like the first series, with groundnuts and beans or sweet potatoes.

This process of double cropping with pulses and maize on cultivation mounds was repeated throughout the life of the garden, a period which commonly varied from three years on the poorest to as much as ten years on the strongest of the cultivated soils. It was not only a device to check grass and weed growth, like the initial sorghum broadcast of the Lamba, for it involved the deliberate use of weeds as green manure. The cultivators regarded the making of the mounds as a preparation for the maize crop of the following year, which would enhance fertility and ensure better and more certain crops.

Although the staple crop was maize (as, of course, it still is), finger millet was also grown as a subsidiary cereal, mainly for the making of beer. In preparing the main gardens some areas were left unhoed. On these, chopped branches from trees felled in clearing the site were neatly stacked and burnt, at the same time as the burning of the *vikuse*, to make ash-beds for the millet. In the second year finger millet might again be grown on ash-beds prepared by burning logs, left-over branchwood and trash from the crop. This was not *citemene*, in the true sense, since only timber from the cultivated area was used: but the Ngoni-Chewa also made use of small subsidiary gardens of true *citemene* type, to supplement and extend the supply of millet. These were generally made on the flanks of wooded hills, by cutting over and carrying branchwood from an area about eight times as great as the cropped area; and they were used for only one year.

Grazing needs restricted the use of *dambo* grassland for subsidiary cultivation: but moist, humic seepage sites of high fertility—known as *fipoka*—were commonly drained by constructing large mounds or ridges and used for early crops of maize, beans, peas, and pumpkins. They are still so used, but within marketing distance from Fort Jameson they have been given over increasingly to the production of European vegetables, and excellent strawberries. These little gardens are, of necessity—and traditionally were—protected against cattle by strong and tall timber fences.

There was practically no development of village gardens in this system: but, as we have noted, old village sites are now increasingly used for cultivation and are prized for their fertility, to the extent that a village may move merely to release the site. This is probably a "modern" development induced by acute land and food shortage: it may, perhaps, be regarded as an extension of the traditional practice of planting tobacco and, more rarely, a little maize, pumpkins, and other crops on old kraal and village sites abandoned for the normal reasons.

2. THE SENGA SYSTEM AND ITS AFFINITIES

The use of small mounds, in the general manner described, is the salient feature of the two main systems of the Eastern Province of Northern Rhodesia, the Eastern Plateau and Eastern Valley systems of Trapnell's description: but the former comprises a sequence of minor forms which succeed and grade into one another from north to south with decreasing cultivation of finger millet and changes in minor crops. Among the Tumbuka and neighbouring Chewa in the north the whole of the first-year garden is sown with finger millet which is grown on hoed land and not by *citemene* methods. In the central region about Fort Jameson, as we have seen, this crop was restricted to burnt areas in the main garden and small supplementary gardens of *citemene* type. South and west of this region the burnt area of the main garden takes the form of small, often diminutive, circles which are frequently planted to maize and other crops instead of finger millet. With this decrease in the cultivation of millet goes a change in the interplanted crops: beans, the main interplanted crop of the Tumbuka, is replaced southward by groundnuts and, as drier conditions are approached, by sweet potatoes. The change to drier conditions is also marked by the appearance of sorghum, first as an end-crop on old lands and then as a second cereal staple.

The Eastern Valley System of Petauke district, which is practised by the Senga and some of the Ambo and Kunda peoples, was regarded by Trapnell as a form derived from the Eastern Plateau System under the influence of contact with the neighbouring sorghum culture of the Luangwa valley. In preparing the main garden, the timber is stacked rather roughly in small piles throughout the cleared area and the land between them is hoed over. After burning the timber, maize is sown throughout the garden, even on the ash patches, though a little finger millet is retained on some of them. On the main area, between the ash patches, the crop is widely spaced to allow for the cultivation mounds which are made, as in the Plateau system, at the time of the first weeding in December. These new-made mounds are, however, usually planted only with sweet potatoes. Subsequent cropping is determined by climate and soil. A further crop, or more, of maize is taken where conditions allow of this, but in the lower-lying areas of high temperature and uncertain rainfall, sorghum (almost invariably with some intermixture of maize) is planted in the second and subsequent years. The supply of maize is, however, maintained by annual extensions of the main garden. These extensions are sown with groundnuts in the first year and sometimes in the second year as well, followed by maize and, subsequently, sorghum. Separate gardens for groundnuts alone are also made, on light-textured soils.

Subsidiary streamside and *dambo* cultivation is practised: but, as in the case of the Plateau system, there is practically no use of village gardens.

The Eastern Valley system therefore differs in three main respects from what may have been its parent form: the development of groundnut culture; the use of sorghum as a second cereal staple; and the reduction of finger millet almost to the vanishing point. Malting varieties of sorghum largely replace finger millet as a beer crop.

3. Carrying Capacities and Critical Population Densities

An attempt to estimate the carrying capacities of large areas in the Fort Jameson and Petauke districts, on the basis of the Eastern Plateau and Eastern Valley Systems of land-use was made during the earlier War years and mainly in 1940–2. The problem was essentially similar to that of the Ndola district, but much greater populations and land areas were involved. Here, too, the land set aside for Native Reserves had proved inadequate under customary forms of land-use. By the time of the outbreak of War, much of this land was in an advanced state of degeneration, in spite of years of agricultural extension work and demonstration. The systems of food production were in decay and the food supply was becoming increasingly precarious. Surrounding the Reserve there were great areas of empty land, some of it of very high agricultural value, from which population had been removed some ten to fifteen years previously. To add to the complexity of the situation, this was not Crown Land: in consequence of a series of accidents of history it formed part of the land concession of the North Charterland Exploration Company.

It is hardly surprising that there was growing discontent among the people in the overpopulated reserves and that appeals for recruits for the forces and co-operation in the War effort met with no very enthusiastic response. In these circumstances the immediate relief of the intense population pressure within the reserves was seen not only as a measure urgently needed to save the land from destruction but as an emergency war-time operation of high priority.

It was clear that "measures to improve agricultural methods— except, possibly, improvements involving free issue of fertiliser annually in great quantity—could not alone remedy the situation in a reasonable time, if at all" (14). In any case, fertilisers, and all the other equipment needed for agricultural development, were then in very short supply. The staff position was critical. Aerial survey was, of course, out of the question at that time, and there was no earlier photographic cover. Even the simplest and most essential equipment, such as prismatic compasses, cyclometers, and chains and levels, was hard to come by. Topographic maps were sketchy or non-existent.

The assessment of land distribution and potential was made in the manner described for the later Ndola survey, but because of shortage of staff and equipment, the need for urgency, and the great areas involved, cover was less complete. Traverse lines were usually from one to three miles apart and in one direction only, but close grid-survey was used in important areas of high potential, while some very poor regions were assessed by means of sample traverses only.

The following major Vegetation-Soil classes were distinguished and mapped.

1. *Combretum-Afrormomum* and *Pterocarpus-Combretum* vegetation:
   (*a*) on upper valley soils
   (*b*) on allied chocolate-red loams.

2. *Brachystegia spiciformis* woodlands:
on marginal upper valley soils.
3. Undifferentiated *Brachystegia-Julbernardia* woodlands:
on red earth and allied red loams.
4. Eastern *Brachystegia-Julbernardia* woodlands:
 (*a*) on plateau soils
 (*b*) on escarpment hill soils.
5. Central *Julbernardia paniculata-Brachystegia* woodlands:
on plateau soils.

The general distribution of these land classes in the Fort
Jameson and Petauke districts, as determined in the course of the
survey, is shown on the *Vegetation Soil Map of Northern Rhodesia*
(sheet II) (176). They are defined in Trapnell's accompanying
memorandum and more fully described in the *Report of the Ecological Survey of North Eastern Rhodesia* (171).

These main classes were subdivided for the purposes of land
assessment into types regarded as more or less fertile, durable
under cultivation and resistant to erosion, in accordance with such
indicators as the growth and specific composition of the grass
cover, the composition of the understorey in woodlands, the
texture and colour of the surface soil, and the opinion of African
cultivators. The first three classes contain erosion-resistant soils
of very high fertility and staying power which were believed to be
capable of sustaining permanent cultivation, in the sense that
fertility could be maintained at a satisfactory level by means of
fallow periods equal to or shorter than the periods of cultivation.
These included very rich chocolate or chocolate-red loams and
clay-loams of strong structure associated with *Pterocarpus-
Combretum* vegetation and *B. spiciformis* woodlands, and local
areas of heavy black loams characterised by *Acacia* vegetation and
a tall growth of *Hyparrhenia*. Light-textured soils associated with
similar forms of vegetation, which, though often of high initial
fertility, appeared to be susceptible to fairly rapid depletion and
erosion, were graded as Semi-Permanent, or as short-period
Recurrent Cultivation soils in the case of variants judged to be
least fertile.

Land of the plateau classes, while generally poor, showed a
wide range of variation in agricultural value, as assessed on a
maize standard of fertility. The eastern plateau soils carrying good

Brachystegia Burtii-Julbernardia paniculata woodland are, in general, more fertile than those of the other plateau regions of Northern Rhodesia, but they vary considerably in texture and quality, ranging from fine-grained loams of relatively high fertility to coarse-grained sands. Poorer plateau land, generally of very low agricultural value, is characterised by woodland types containing little or no *B. Burtii*. These variants include fairly extensive areas of pale, highly leached sand soils carrying scrub-woodland of *Brachystegia stipulata* and *Protea*, often with a compacted ironstone horizon near the surface and subject to seasonal waterlogging. The plateau land classes were, therefore, subdivided into types, in accordance with what was judged to be their potential for the traditional systems of land-use, as short-, medium-, and long-term Recurrent Cultivation land, Shifting and Partial Cultivation land, and agriculturally useless variants.

Although the Fort Jameson and Petauke districts have some of the best soils in the territory, the general estimate of the human-carrying capacity of the vacant areas turned out lower than had been expected, owing to the much greater extent of plateau land and the occurrence of vast masses of escarpment and other hill types, uncultivable or impracticable for cultivation, and extensive

FORT JAMESON RESETTLEMENT AREAS
(1940–1)

Area Surveyed (Sq. miles)	E.C.C.*	E.C.P.D.†
123·6	1,860	15
30·5	500	16
63·9	1,350	21
172·3	3,970	23
224·5	5,565	25
84·7	2,440	29
152·4	4,600	30
73·1	2,480	33
30·6	1,135	37
955·6	23,900	25

* E.C.C. = Estimated Carrying Capacity (persons).
† E.C.P.D. = Estimated Critical Population Density (persons per square mile).

areas of other almost useless land. For the nine unoccupied regions in the Fort Jameson district, the estimate of Critical Population Density, on the basis of Ngoni-Chewa traditional land-use, worked out at 25 per square mile.

In the Petauke district similar surveys and assessments were carried out over areas amounting in the aggregate to 1,054 square miles. The total carrying capacity of these areas was estimated, on the basis of the Eastern Valley practice of the Senga, to be about 20,500 people, or approximately 19·5 per square mile.

CHAPTER IX

THE CARRYING CAPACITY OF *CITEMENE*

1. THE LALA OF SERENJE

As one would expect, the *citemene* systems practised on the generally poor soils of the Northern and Central Plateau woodlands of Northern Rhodesia are not capable of supporting populations even of the very moderate densities suggested for the Lamba and the Eastern Plateau and Valley systems. There is reason to believe that general Critical Population Densities for these systems of ash-planting, in the regions where they are still practised, are of the order of 4 to 10 people per square mile.

The first study of small-circle *citemene*, from the point of view of land requirements, was made in 1944 among the western Lala of Mkushi district (9), but this gave a picture of a system in a state of rapid decay and transition brought about by movement into Reserves. In the following year, Peters, who had participated in the first survey, made a very careful and complete study of what might be regarded as the parent system—that of the eastern Lala on the Serenje plateau (129), an area of nearly 6,000 square miles straddling the Congo-Zambesi watershed between the Lake Bangweulu depression and the rift valleys of the Luangwa and Lukasashi. Here the situation had not been complicated by land loss, but a condition of general land shortage was suspected and it was very evident that acute land shortage, in relation to the system of land-use, existed in some areas.

The calculation of Critical Population Densities for this and other *citemene* systems is somewhat complicated by the fact that the people who practise them do not rely wholly on the crops from their ash gardens: they invariably cultivate a range of subsidiary gardens as well.

Six forms of subsidiary gardens are commonly cultivated by the Lala of the Serenje plateau:

  1. Second-Year Ash Circles. A few of the small ash circles in the main *citemene* garden are planted in the second year

with ground-beans or, less frequently, groundnuts or cow-peas.

2. Sorghum Gardens. These are subsidiary gardens cut in woodland and prepared in much the same way as the *citemene* gardens, but this system of use and cropping is altogether different. Maize, sorghum, and sweet potatoes are planted on the ash circles, instead of finger millet, and the land between the circles is mounded and used for crop-ping. The mounds are sown with sorghum, usually inter-mixed with cowpeas, groundnuts, and cassava, except for a few which are reserved for sweet potatoes and beans. Here, the practice of mounding is to be regarded as a device for ensuring more certain yields from soils which are, intrinsi-cally, of very low fertility. The shallow layer of richer top-soil is concentrated in the mounds, giving a compact volume in which the root system of the plants may develop: but the process requires a high output of labour in relation to the meagre return.

3. Maize and Bean Gardens. Very small gardens are made on *dambo* margin sites adjoining large termite hills. The long grass at the base of the ant hill, and any timber on or near the site, is used to make a few ash circles. Mounds are made about the ant hill, and the circles and mounds are sown with maize and beans.

4. Cassava Gardens. Small gardens for cassava are also made in *dambo*-fringing woodland, or on the dry upper slope within the *dambo*. The crop is planted on mounds, at a rate of five or six cuttings to the mound, and a few plants of maize or sorghum and cowpeas may be added.

5. Seepage Gardens. Maize and beans are grown on seepage sites in *dambos* and by streamsides, where such sites are available. As a rule, the grass and turf on the site is hoed up in a circular pattern and allowed to dry before burning in August. Maize, planted in the moist soil during August, is generally reaped in December as green cobs. Beans are then planted as the maize is harvested. Another method sometimes employed, probably on sites of lower fertility, is to flatten the grass and cover the area with transported branches which are burned to give a *citemene* effect.

6. Livingstone Potato Beds. Long beds, very similar to the

form described for the Lamba, are made on the upper
flanks of *dambos* and planted to Livingstone potatoes, sometimes with a border of cassava.

The problems involved in the estimation of land requirements
and Critical Population Densities of the *citemene* forms of land-
use are, in some ways, less complex than those of the soil selection
systems of hoe cultivation. In so far as the main gardens are concerned, only two land categories are of major significance; woodland which is suitable for *citemene*, and land which is unsuitable.
A reasonably good assessment of the proportion of any woodland
area suitable for *citemene* may be made by careful stereoscopic
examination of aerial photographs, but where photographs are not
available estimation is more difficult and may be liable to considerable error. Such estimates as have been made, with the aid of
complete or partial photographic cover, for large areas of the
northern and central *Brachystegia* and *Julbernardia* woodlands
vary from 50 per cent suitable for *citemene*[1] to rather more than 70
per cent.[2] The variation is probably something of this order, and
over these plateau regions as a whole the proportion of the total
land surface which is suitable for *citemene* may be about 60 per cent.
The unsuitable land includes *dambos* and stream courses, which,
with their thinly timbered margins, frequently account for 10 or
11 per cent of the land surface, and much more variable areas of
scrub woodland, open bush, tree-grassland and other grassland
types, "pans" and swamps, and hill slopes with rubble or skeletal
soils. Small-circle *citemene* may, however, be practised on slopes
too steep for hoe cultivation, provided there is soil and timber.
Even a proportion of bare rock outcrop is no deterrent.

The Land-Use Factor is, of course, determined by the length
of time required for the trees to regenerate to such a stage that they
are once more suitable for cutting and will yield as much fuel as
was consumed in the previous burn. This period is very difficult
to assess: it varies greatly with the effects of fire and the extent to
which the woodland is exposed to late burning. The long-term
experiments at Lunzuwa, in the Abercorn district, have indicated
that under a careful regime of early burning, lopped trees may
recover in twenty years, or a little more: but, under uncontrolled
conditions, felled woodland may require as much as thirty-four or

[1] Mambwe Reserve V, Moffat (119).   [2] Eastern Mkushi, Peters (129).

even forty years. There is, however, no certainty that a full period of woodland recovery is necessary for the maintenance of a *citemene* system, or that such a period is commonly observed in traditional practice. I formed the impression—admittedly, in areas more favourable to tree growth than the Serenje plateau—that *citemene* can be, and commonly is, sustained at lower levels of regeneration than full recovery of the woodland to maximum growth, and that periods of the order of twenty-two to twenty-five years may suffice in some areas. The survey of land-use in the Mkushi district (9) indicated that the western Lala had in the past recultivated woodland after regeneration periods of twenty-two to twenty-five years, at a time when they were not short of land or timber. Alder's later work among the Lungu of Abercorn (6) suggests a somewhat similar period. He found that the periods of woodland regeneration averaged "at least 21·4 years."

From the point of view of the *citemene* cultivator, the decisive factor may be the extent of woodland required to maintain a given area in cultivation and the amount of labour involved in the alternatives open to him. The following figures from Peters's data for the Lala of the Serenje plateau illustrate, for this environment, the relationship between the age of woodland and the area under crop.

Regeneration period (years) of trees cut for *fiteme*:	9–12	13–16	17–20	Over 20
Burned area as a percentage of the total area cut:	4·41%	6·26%	7·31%	9·57%

The cutting of woodland of less than twenty years' regeneration is, of course, abnormal and it is done only under pressure of extreme necessity. Probably, most *citemene* peoples would regard as satisfactory for a further cycle of cutting woodland allowing of at least a 10 per cent burn, and it may be that this stage of regrowth is reached after twenty-five years or less in favourable environments and after thirty years or more in poorer areas such as the Serenje plateau. (Of Peters's "over 20" samples, 7 out of 11 represented regrowth of more than thirty years.)

From his study of the Serenje Lala, Peters found that the area of ash circles actually cropped to finger millet amounted to only 0·15 of an acre per head, taking account of the fact that about 15 per cent of the population belonged to families who had no *fiteme*,

though they doubtless provided labour for and shared in the produce of the *citemene* gardens. The maintenance of this crop area,
together with the provision of timber for fencing, requires the
annual consumption of 1·66 acres of regenerated woodland. This
area of 1·66 acres may therefore be taken as the equivalent of the
Cultivation Factor—the area of land in use at any one time.

Peters erred on the safe side, if he erred at all, in allowing a
period of full woodland regeneration, in the sense of regrowth of
the trees to maximum height after felling at breast height. This
period he found to be about thirty-five years, by means of annual
ring counts made on sample trees of full growth. Soil type appeared to have little effect on the rate of regrowth, but it did vary
noticeably with site and, especially, soil depth. On this basis, he
took the Land-Use Factor, or number of garden areas required,
to be 36, which implies a total requirement of approximately 60
acres of woodland per head of population for the maintenance of
the *citemene* gardens. To this must, of course, be added the amount
of woodland suitable for *citemene* which is consumed in making
other forms of gardens, and, from his sample survey, Peters found
that the area of such gardens in cultivation at any one time amounted
to an average of 0·25 of an acre per head of population. Allowing
a normal cultivation cycle of four years for these gardens and a
regeneration period of thirty-five years, he added a further three
acres to the total woodland requirement.

The proportion of the plateau covered with woodland suitable
for *citemene*—the "Cultivable Percentage"—was taken as 60 per
cent of the total land surface. Peters was far from satisfied with
this estimate, since it had been based on a single strip of aerial
photographs along the watershed, the only photographs available,
and on eye observation and traverse records elsewhere: but it was
the best approximation that could be made at the time and in the
circumstances.

If this factor is applied to the previous data—and if it is assumed
that ample land for other garden forms, such as *dambo*-fringe, ant
hill, and seepage sites, can be found within the large area unsuited
to *citemene*—the total land requirement works out at 105 acres per
head of population. Peters therefore concluded that, "in view of
the limits of accuracy of the survey results, all that can be said with
certainty is that the carrying capacity lies between 5 and 7 persons
to the square mile, but in view of the agreement of these survey

results with the present densities of population (which varied from 5·6 to 11·0 per square mile in the seven chieftaincies and averaged 7·3 per square mile over the plateau as a whole) the carrying capacity may, with a very small chance of error, be taken as approximately 6 persons per square mile."

He was, however, careful to point out that this Critical Density could be maintained in perpetuity without damage to the land only under conditions of ideal population distribution and with the use of all land suitable for *citemene*. In fact, some suitable land remained unused even under conditions of shortage, because of distance from water or habitations or for less tangible reasons, while density of population and intensity of land-use varied very considerably. Peters also formed the opinion, after further study of the situation, that his 60 per cent of "suitable" woodland contained a high proportion of "marginal" land. This is, of course, a subjective concept difficult or impossible to define. I have suggested that *citemene* peoples regard as suitable land woodland which is capable of giving at least a 10 per cent burn. Marginal land might, then, be defined as woodland giving less than a 10 per cent burn but practicable for *citemene*, though at an output of energy greater than the cultivator is normally prepared to expend. What happens in practice is that the cultivator re-cuts "suitable" woodland at shorter intervals, in preference to cutting "marginal" woodland, until the former has degenerated to the condition of the latter. The move to marginal land then takes place. From his observations on the use of marginal land, Peters thought it probable that "to avoid this shortening of the cutting cycle in favourable places the population using this agricultural system must not exceed in density 4 to the square mile. Only under a system of control of cutting areas, which would have ensured equal use of favourable and marginal areas, could the carrying capacity have been raised to about 6 to the square mile.'

This amounts, in effect, to a revision of the estimate of land suitable for *citemene* from 60 per cent to 40 per cent, leaving 20 per cent in the marginal category—a surprisingly high proportion. Such a proportion might, however, be accounted for by the existence of large areas of degenerated woodland. To quote Peters again: "What is certain is that the shortening of the cutting cycle occurred on parts of the plateau many years ago and *before* it was made necessary by a general density of resident population exceeding 6 to the square mile." I agree with this statement, though I think it requires some qualification. The state of the woodland certainly indicates a former cycle of degeneration, but it is probable that this came about through increase of population beyond the critical point for a system which then relied to a greater extent on *citemene*, a system which may have had a carrying capacity of no more than 4 per square mile. The Lala reacted to this situation in two ways, after woodland degeneration had become well advanced: by decreasing their *fiteme* and increasing the size of their hoed gardens, and by sending out a plethora of population which migrated westward into uninhabited or sparsely inhabited woodland which was then a sort of no-man's-land between the Lala and Swaka peoples. This relieved the pressure on the Serenje plateau and prevented further degeneration, but continuing growth of population, probably at an increasing rate, checked recovery of the trees and maintained a proportion of the woodland in the marginal category.

2. THE WESTERN LALA

The evidence for this migration from Serenje was obtained in the course of my study of the Mkushi Lala. Many of the men who were middle-aged or elderly at that time (1944) claimed to have come as immigrants from the Serenje plateau, as young men or as children with their parents, and there was some evidence that a westerly movement of the Lala had continued as late as the 1920s. It appeared from this information that there had been something like a mass migration starting, perhaps, in the 1890s and continuing for a decade or more before tailing off. Furthermore, the villages founded by the earlier immigrants had no tradition of mound cultivation of sorghum. They knew of it, of course, but they maintained that it had never been their practice and therefore the work was much too hard for them. On the other hand, this form of mound cultivation was practised by some of the more recent immigrants and by villages along the Serenje border which had maintained close contact with the eastern section. It may be that the early immigrants left the Serenje plateau before the general adoption of mound-cultivated sorghum and cassava gardens and that they brought with them a more purely *citemene* tradition, with subsidiary cultivation of minor garden forms only—second year ash circles, seepage sites, ant-hill maize patches and Livingstone

potato beds. The Critical Population Density for such a system
might well be something of the order of 4 people per square mile.

Until 1929, when Native Reserves were established in the
Mkushi district, the general level of population density was probably well below this figure. At that time there may have been about
9,000 people occupying an area of more than 3,000 square miles.
Demarcation of Reserves reduced the available land area to about
1,400 square miles, so that the general density of population was
more than doubled. This would have resulted in acute shortage of
timber and failure of the system of food production within a matter
of about fifteen years, even if an ideal redistribution had been
achieved and population had remained static. But the boundaries
of chieftaincies remained unaltered and movement into the
Reserves resulted in a chaotic maldistribution of populations which
continued to increase at a rate exceeding 1·5 per cent per annum,
judging by the district counts. The situation which arose is
described in some detail by Allan (9). Excluding the escarpment
hill zone, where the small valley-living populations were not
affected, population density over the Reserves as a whole had risen
to 9 per square mile, and to 12 and 18 respectively in two of the
major chieftaincies. Maldistribution was more extreme than the
general figures indicate, because people who had been moved from
the Crown Land tended to concentrate just within the boundaries
of the Reserves, creating an outer rim of high density approaching
or exceeding 20 to the square mile. In these conditions, over much
of the area, the woodland available for *citemene* was used up in a
very few years.

Unlike the Serenje Lala, those of Mkushi could not adapt
themselves gradually to a changing situation, and migration no
longer offered a solution. But they also reacted in two ways: by
altering the system of food production and by agitating for more
land. In the more congested areas there was a dramatic reduction
of *citemene* and a haphazard, almost panic, adoption of hoe cultivation. In the following table, figures obtained from my sample
survey are contrasted with Peters' data for Serenje. My survey was
made under conditions of population density approximating to 18
per square mile, and the table indicates the extent of the change.

Not only had the Mkushi Lala reduced the number of their
fiteme, but the intensity of the burn had also been reduced and
yields had fallen. According to the yield indications I obtained,

Area Cropped per Head of Population (Acres)

	Serenje Lala*	Mkushi Lala
Finger millet *fiteme*	0·170	0·121
Second year ash circles	0·008	0·028
Sorghum gardens	0·120	0·636
Maize and Cassava gardens	0·115	0·047
Moist gardens	0·015	0·038
	0·428	0·870

* Figures for families with fiteme. They therefore differ from those previously used which were adjusted to allow for families without ash-gardens.

the finger millet gardens could not have supplied even half the grain requirement. The people had attempted to compensate for this by extensive hoe cultivation of sorghum, in a manner which clearly indicated that these gardens had only recently originated, or acquired a new importance, among a people who were previously mainly *citemene* cultivators. There was little evidence of soil selection. Gardens were sited apparently at random, often on land which peoples with an established system of soil selection agriculture would certainly have regarded as "uncultivable"— that is, not worth the labour of cultivating. Crops were usually grown on the flat even on the poorest soils, and total failures of sorghum planted on unsuitable land were frequent. The food supply from this source was highly precarious. This was the general case, but some of the people were obviously finding their way towards a system of soil selection by trial-and-error, and even by deliberate experimental plantings, while others were making increasing use of mound cultivation. The extent of change varied greatly. *Citemene* gardens were universal, but some families exceptionally fortunate in woodland had as many as 40 ash circles per head and still derived most of their food from these gardens, while others had no more than 6, and the general average was about 12 ash circles per head of population.

In such a situation of disruption and transition the concept of Critical Population Density has little meaning, since there is no fixed basis for estimation. Three possible solutions presented themselves in theory: the ideal solution of "good farming"; the other extreme, reversion to the original system of land-use with its very high land requirement; and, thirdly, the adoption of some intermediate system such as appeared to be evolving, as a basis for planned redistribution of populations. In the circumstances of the time the first solution had to be regarded as an impracticable ideal; all the considerations mentioned in connexion with the Lamba problem applied here with even greater force; while reversion to the most primitive form of *citemene* on a large scale would have been a retrograde step, though there was probably almost enough unused land to allow of this.

The situation might, of course, have been left as it was in the hope that a new, balanced, and stable pattern would emerge: but population densities were already too high, in relation to the general poverty of soil, to justify any such hope, and it was virtually certain that the Lala would continue their *citemene* practice to the last tree. Almost inevitably, the result would have been wholesale destruction of the occupied land, degeneration of the abandoned and unprotected woodland under the effects of unchecked late fires, starvation in the midst of potential plenty, and growing social and political unrest.

The estimation of land requirements was therefore based on a somewhat theoretical system involving production of rather less than half the grain requirement by *citemene* methods with the remainder from hoe-cultivated sorghum, in accordance with what appeared to be the current trend. It was assumed, of course, that a reliable system of soil selection for sorghum would develop, but this assumption did not seem too optimistic in view of what could be seen to be happening, and of the fact that some of the southern Lala, in contact with the Senga and probably influenced by their culture, had long practised such a system.

The land requirements of the *citemene*-sorghum system in the Mkushi environment were estimated to be 46 acres of woodland suitable for *citemene* per head of population and an additional total area of 26 acres per head of population for sorghum, calculated on the basis of long-term Recurrent Cultivation. This estimate was very tentative, since the data on vegetation-soil types and their distribution were derived only from sample-line traverses totalling 80 miles and from the general information which Trapnell and Clothier (175) obtained in the course of their ecological survey. The proportion of the land surface covered with woodland practicable for *citemene* was estimated at 72 per cent, by means of measurements from the available aerial photographs, and the proportion of land which might safely be cultivated to sorghum was judged, from the traverse data, to be about 20 per cent.

The total land requirement was, therefore, taken to be approximately 90 acres per head of population—64 acres of land in all for *citemene* and 26 for sorghum. It was assumed that in an area of this magnitude ample land would be found for all forms of subsidiary gardens. This might well be regarded as an overestimate since the two major garden types were treated separately and the total land requirement was obtained by adding the requirements of the two, a treatment which is applicable only if the "uncultivable" part of the land required for sorghum is unlikely to be used for *citemene*, even though a good deal of it may be suitable. In current Lala practice the two forms of cultivation were completely separate, the sorghum gardens being in a belt about the village and the *citemene* gardens some distance away, leaving a good deal of "waste" woodland—which provided domestic fuel and timber and other collected produce—within the sorghum belt and between it and the *citemene* areas. The higher land allowance was therefore regarded as more appropriate to the system as it would be applied in practice, without a very strict degree of imposed control. A lower land allowance without such control would, it was judged, result in over-cutting of the *citemene* areas rather than utilisation of the fragmented areas of "waste" woodland.

The figure of 90 acres per head of population, or 7 people to the square mile, was therefore taken as a general guide for planning redistribution of populations. There was, of course, the risk that any considerable addition of land would be followed by reduction, or disappearance, of the sorghum gardens and increased *citemene*, but it was hoped that this tendency might be offset by associating villages or other groups with well-defined land areas, so that the limits of the land available to them would be obvious from the first, and by simple Native Authority rules designed to discourage extensive *citemene* and to foster hoe cultivation.

The plan of resettlement covered most of the Mkushi district and included the Swaka people whose traditional agriculture differs from that of the Lala.

3. THE SWAKA SEMI-*CITEMENE* SYSTEM

The Swaka, whose country lies between the land of the Lala and the Lamba, practise a form of agriculture in which hoe cultivation of sorghum is combined with *citemene* production of finger millet in a single system. Sorghum is the main crop and finger millet a relatively unimportant subsidiary.

The opening procedure is much the same as for small-circle *citemene*. A large area of woodland is felled at breast height and the branches and brushwood are stacked and burnt in small circles, rings about ant hills and long, narrow strips that often join one ant hill circle with another. But at this point there is a marked departure from normal *citemene* practice. An area towards the centre of the clearing, varying from a half to a quarter, but commonly a third, of the whole, is hoe cultivated between the ash patches and planted to sorghum. This hoed area is called *inkuule* by the Swaka, while the remainder of the clearing, on which finger millet is grown in accordance with normal *citemene* practice, is known as *chonde*.

Citemene practice is also applied, to some extent, in the cultivation of sorghum, for some of the brushwood from the *chonde* is carried on to the *inkuule* and used to increase the burnt area within the sorghum garden. The extent of this practice varies with soil fertility; the poorer the soil the greater the quantity of brushwood taken from the *chonde* to enhance the fertility of the sorghum garden. Areas of *chonde* from which all the brushwood has been taken are normally left unused.

Small areas of groundnuts, sweet potatoes, and cassava are planted within the *chonde* and on the margins of the *inkuule;* and, as in normal small-circle *citemene*, some of the ash-circles are planted with ground-beans or groundnuts in the second year. Less commonly, and mainly where wild pigs are numerous, the root crops are grown in separate village gardens.

Most of the Swaka practise a system of annual extensions. The *inkuule* is extended each year by taking in part of the previous year's *chonde* while part of the old *inkuule* which has completed the normal period of cultivation is abandoned and fresh woodland is cut to extend the *chonde*. In this way an annual supply of finger millet is ensured. Figure 9 shows the appearance of a typical Swaka garden in the inter-crop period after one harvest has been taken; the *inkuule* extension has been prepared and the cutting of *chonde* is in progress.

An interesting change of procedure was noted towards the south of the Swaka area, where stronger and more fertile soils make their appearance. On these soils the method of annual extensions

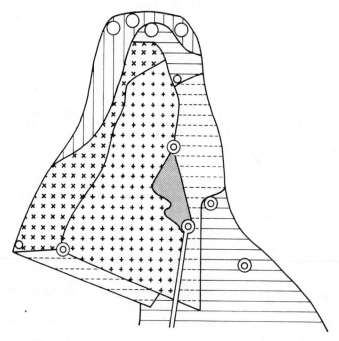

A SWAKA FAMILY GARDEN (FROM A DETAILED SURVEY)

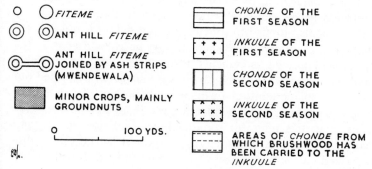

○ ◯ *FITEME*		▬ *CHONDE* OF THE FIRST SEASON
◎ ◉ ANT HILL *FITEME*		⊞ *INKUULE* OF THE FIRST SEASON
◎—○ ANT HILL *FITEME* JOINED BY ASH STRIPS (MWENDEWALA)		▥ *CHONDE* OF THE SECOND SEASON
▨ MINOR CROPS, MAINLY GROUNDNUTS		▨ *INKUULE* OF THE SECOND SEASON
○———— 100 YDS.		▤ AREAS OF *CHONDE* FROM WHICH BRUSHWOOD HAS BEEN CARRIED TO THE *INKUULE*

FIG. 9. A Swaka Garden.

is not generally used: fresh woodland is commonly cut only every five or six years, when a new sorghum garden is required; *citemene* production of finger millet is still further reduced and the system of land use approximates more closely to soil-selection, though a vestige of ash-cultivation persists.

Such, in broad outline, was the basis of Swaka land-use when, in 1943, it was studied by D. U. Peters and the writer as part of the survey of agricultural conditions in the Mkushi district. Garden sampling, which was carried out mainly by Peters, showed a very marked difference between the area cultivated per head of population on the poor soils of the north and on the belt of stronger soils in the south. Most of the area is covered by Central *Julbern-ardia-Brachystegia* woodland on Plateau soils generally of a poor recurrent cultivation type, but in the south there is an extension of the Eastern *Brachystegia-Julbernardia* woodland, characterised by the dominance of *B. Burtii* in various associations, on stronger and brighter coloured soils, representing recurrent cultivation land of a better type with variants approaching the Semi-Permanent class. The figures obtained from ten random samples in the former and seven in the latter category, supplemented by measurements from aerial photographs, are summarised in the table below.

In this system, semi-*citemene* cultivation of sorghum virtually replaces finger-millet *citemene*, though the tradition of ash-cultivation persists even in the region of better soils. The figures show clearly the minor significance of finger millet. On the poor soils it provides, probably, less than one-tenth of the grain requirement and on the better soils it has practically disappeared as a food crop.

It appeared, from the accurately measured field samples supplemented by general observation and rough estimates, that the area of woodland felled to provide a cultivated area sufficient for one person amounted, on average, to very nearly four acres in the typical system. Measurements taken from the few available aerial photographs on which family gardens could be picked out with reasonable certainty give a higher average figure of 5·39 acres of woodland per head, but the difference was thought to be due to the inclusion in this figure of some areas of extension cutting and recently abandoned *chonde*, since these could not be clearly distinguished on the photographs from woodland which had contributed to the current cycle of cultivation. The figure of four acres

SWAKA AGRICULTURE (1943)
AREAS CULTIVATED (PER HEAD)

			CROP	AREA CULTIVATED (Acres)*	
				(a)	(b)
Inkuule	—		— Sorghum	1·395	0·930
	—		— Cassava	0·065	0·046
	— Or in village gardens		— Sweet potatoes	0·037	0·028
Chonde	— Ash patches		— Finger millet	0·28	0·009
	— Margins of ash patches		— Pumpkins, gourds	0·019	0·009
	— Second-year ash patches land in *in-kuule*		— groundnuts — ground- beans	0·037	0·019
Ant-hill gardens	—		— Maize	0·084	0·046
Dambo-margin beds	—		— Livingstone potatoes	0·009	0·005
		Total cultivated		1·674	1·092

* (a) on poor shifting-cultivation soils. (b) on B. Burtii red loams of higher quality.

of woodland per head for each cycle of cultivation was taken as representative of general practice.

The cultivation period varied with the soil type, but was fixed and definite for each type, indicating a well-established tradition of land use. On the poorest cultivated soils (Type 4a) only two successive sorghum crops were sown, though a small "volunteer" crop might be harvested in the third year. On somewhat better plateau soils (Type 3), three full crops were taken; while on the stronger land under *B. Burtii* woodland the cultivation period was five years (Type 5b soils) and six years on the best examples (Type 5a). In every case, and for each of the types, it was stated unequivocally that the land would normally be left after cultivation for a "full" period of woodland regeneration, and there could be little doubt that this had been general Swaka practice in the past. They were not, in fact, using the best soils to the full extent of their potentiality, but this was of no great practical importance in relation to the problem since these soils are of very limited extent and accessible only to a small minority.

On the basis of these data for the typical system, and assuming a period of about twenty-five years for woodland regeneration, and a proportion of woodland to total land area of 72 per cent, the following tentative estimates of land requirements were made.

LAND-REQUIREMENTS OF THE SWAKA SYSTEM

VEGETATION-SOIL TYPE	ACREAGE REQUIRED PER HEAD (*approx.*)	CARRYING CAPACITY OR CRITICAL POP. DENSITY PER SQ. MILE
4 *a*	62	10
3	56	11
5 *b*	33	19
5 *a/b*	30	21
5 *a*	28	23

It appeared that the semi-*citemene* system of the Swaka might be capable of supporting populations of about 10 per square mile on the poor soils which comprise most of the region and of 20 per square mile on the better soils, without permanent damage to soil or woodland. This conclusion involved the assumptions that even on the poor soils some 27 per cent of the land would be cultivable for sorghum, with the addition of the *citemene* burn, and that the total land area allocated for the main field type would include suitable sites for the minor garden forms. It involved, also, the more questionable assumption, in the case of the poorer soils, that a rest period of twenty-five years is adequate for regeneration of soil and woodland.

4. LAND PROBLEMS IN THE SERENJE AND MKUSHI DISTRICTS

As in the case of Western Lala, the work was no more than a rapid reconnaissance survey designed to give a reasoned answer to the vexed question of the adequacy or otherwise of the Reserves set aside for the Swaka and Western Lala, a question which has been argued and debated rather inconclusively for some years.

Prior to 1929, the Swaka were occupying an area more than 3,500 miles in extent and the mean population density was certainly less than 4 per square mile. Two Reserves were set aside for the Swaka by the Northern Rhodesia (Native Reserves) Supplemental Order in Council of 1929. The combined area was 1,435 square miles and it is improbable that the population for which they were designed exceeded 13,500 at this time. If a more or less ideal redistribution of population had been possible it is unlikely that any serious or general land shortage would have arisen until population growth upset the balance. But, again, the surviving boundaries of chiefs' areas remained inviolate and movement into the Reserves resulted in extreme maldistribution of population followed by rapid breakdown of the system of food production in a number of areas.

DISTRIBUTION OF SWAKA POPULATION AFTER CREATION OF RESERVES

CHIEF'S AREA	AREA (*sq. miles*)	POP. 1943	POP. PER SQ. MILE
NKole	71	2,409	33·9
Chitina	726	5,800	8·0
Maoma	8	1,330	—
Mukonchi	470	4,580	9·7
Chikupili	160	1,903	11·9
	1,435	16,022	11·2

The loss fell mainly on NKole and Maoma. The former lost the greater part of his original land and his people crowded into the remaining fragment of the chieftaincy, creating a general population density at least three times the critical figure, with considerably higher densities in the western half. The immigrants did not, of course, move into full-grown woodland but into woodland at various stages of recovery from previous cultivation cycles. By 1943 tree growth had become greatly degraded throughout the whole area and in the western half little remained but scrub of a few years regrowth. The area of the Chieftainess Maoma had been reduced to an absurdity, a mere eight square miles, and her people never did move into the Reserve.

In the other three chiefships the general population densities did not appear to exceed, and certainly did not greatly exceed, the critical level: but there was some serious local congestion. In Chitina's area the incoming population had concentrated in the west and north-west, giving rise to a density of 28 per square mile, while an area of about 60 square miles in the east remained almost uninhabited. Between these two regions, population densities ranged from 4 to 6 per square mile. Immigration had also caused serious congestion and over-cutting in the south of Chikupili's area, while densities remained low in other parts: but Mukonchi's population was comparatively well-distributed, apart from a tendency to over-occupy the fertile soils of the *B. Burtii* woodland which make their appearance in this area.

At the time of the survey additions had already been made to all of the chiefs' areas, with the exception of Maoma, or had been recommended by the Administration. The main practical purpose of the survey was, therefore, to assess the adequacy of these additions.

On the basis of the indications obtained from the field studies it was possible to say with some confidence that the enlarged areas were, in theory, adequate to allow of continuing practice of the typical Swaka system, at 1943 levels of population.

POSSIBLE POPULATION DENSITIES FOLLOWING ADDITIONS
TO SWAKA RESERVES

CHIEF'S AREA	ADDITIONAL (*sq. miles*)	TOTAL AREA (*sq. miles*)	POSSIBLE POP. DENSITY PER SQ. MILE
NKole	211	282	8·5
Chitina	182	908	5·3*
Maoma	—	8	—
Mukonchi	165	635	7·2
Chikupili	122	282	6·7
	680	2,115	7·6

* Population somewhat reduced by the creation of Nafulama's chieftaincy.

These additions of land did not, of course, wholly solve the problem. Planned resettlement was clearly necessary, in order to bring about a rational distribution of population. NKole's people

had already migrated, practically *en masse*, into the extension
recently added to their part of the Reserve, creating immediate
overpopulation there while leaving the old area almost empty and
exposed to the full sweep of destructive late fires. Chitina's people,
on the other hand, had made no move because occupation of their
new area meant not only a fairly long move but an unpopular one,
away from the railway line and main roads into "wild" country to
the east. The need for resettlement was fully realised, but everyone
felt that someone else should do the moving. In Mukonchi's and
Chikupili's areas the situation was fairly satisfactory but the
problem of Maoma remained unsolved. Her people had moved
towards but not into the reserve and were concentrated in an area
of some 80 square miles of Crown Land at a density approaching
17 per square mile. If they had moved into the Reserve area
available to them, population density would have reached the
catastrophic figure of 167 to the square mile.

The Mkushi problem was a relatively simple one, at least in
terms of a temporary solution, for a great deal of land was available,
or likely to be available within a short time, as the result of a new
policy regarding the unoccupied lands outside Native Reserves.
These were to be divided into two categories: Crown Land,
intended for European settlement, and Native Trust Land to be
set aside for the use of the African peoples. A Commission set up
to implement this policy had already recommended the creation
of well over 3,000 square miles of Trust Land in the Mkushi
district; an area which, when added to that of the Reserves and
their extensions, provided more than enough land for the existing
Swaka and Western Lala populations on the basis of their current
methods of land-use.

This situation gave rise to the question—should all of the Trust
Land be allocated for immediate use? Two considerations favoured
this action: the natural wish of the people and the better control of
woodland, bush, and grass fires which occupation ensures. On the
other hand, judging by the estimates of Critical Population
Densities, the whole of the land would not be required for at
least thirty-five years—assuming a population increase rate as high
as 2 per cent per annum, with no improvement in agricultural
methods—and it might not be required for considerably longer.
The availability of an area much in excess of requirements would
discourage progress towards less extensive land-use and encourage

a reversion to small-circle *citemene*, at least among the Lala, and possibly among the Swaka as well. Indeed, any land addition would be likely to have this effect to some extent.

On a balance of considerations, it was thought best to hold part of the land in reserve until such time as it would be allocated with the greatest benefit to the people as a whole.

The solution recommended and finally adopted, was to make some further land additions in such a way as to reduce the population density of each of the chiefs' areas to a figure thought to be well below the critical point, reserving the balance of the available land—an area of well over 1,000 square miles—against future needs. The pattern of land distribution then became as follows:

AREA AVAILABLE (SQ. MILES)

	ORIGINAL RESERVES	ADDITIONS	DENSITY OF POP. PER SQ. MILE*
W. Lala:			
Kanyensha	320	375	6·0
Shaiwila	510	605	5·3
Kaundula	78	163	6·0
Mulungwe	344	—	3·8
Nafulama	—	179	3·8
	1,252	1,322	5·8
Swaka:			
NKole	71	211	8·2
Chitina	726	182	5·7
Maoma	8	160	8·0
Mukonchi	470	165	7·0
Chikupili	160	122	6·7
	1,435	840	7·0

*After resettlement.

The problem of re-distribution of population within the enlarged chieftaincies was dealt with by agreement with the Chiefs and Headmen as to the villages which should move and the sites to which they would move, designed to obtain a distribution pattern approximating as nearly as possible to the ideal. The Chiefs also agreed to make simple Native Authority Regulations providing for the control of *citemene*, particularly among the Lala, and for the protection of the unoccupied land held in reserve and the prevention of overcrowding on the very limited area of better soils. The restriction on *citemene* merely limited the number of ash patches which might be made by a family each year, with the object of increasing the average size, thus reducing wastage and initiating a transition towards the large-circle form.

It was hoped in this way to establish a balance which would endure for at least twenty years and which might, with increasing knowledge and experience, be maintained indefinitely by gradual alteration and improvement of the systems. No doubt it would have been preferable to start at once on a programme of radical improvement, or at least on experimental work designed to that end, but the need had to be weighed against the small resources then available and the urgency of other problems. One of the objects of the attempt at estimating Critical Population Densities was to enable the relative urgency of agricultural problems to be assessed, so that the available resources might be utilised to the best advantage. This approach was, however, somewhat over-shadowed by the post-war urge for immediate and universal development.

The problem of the Serenje plateau, which Peters studied after the completion of the Mkushi survey, was obviously of greater urgency and difficulty though it had attracted less attention. The Serenje Lala could not draw attention to their plight by agitating for the return of land, for they had lost none. The problem could, however, be broken down and somewhat simplified by defining areas of greatest urgency. A region of 100 square miles about Lake Lusiwashi, carrying a population density of 17 to the square mile, was in an advanced state of woodland degeneration; this area, the most densely populated part of the most densely populated chieftaincy, that of Maila, clearly called for priority attention.

Peters proposed to combine immediate measures of ameliora-tion, starting in the Lusiwashi area, with a programme of long-term improvement following local trials and experiment. The ameliorative measures he suggested consisted mainly in restricting the burnt area of each *citemene* to a single patch—in effect, an immediate adoption of the northern or large-circle system—

combined with complete protection or early-burning of the woodland to ensure more rapid regeneration, enlargement, and improvement of the subsidiary gardens and the development of a system
of annual extensions.

Restriction of the burned area to a single circular patch would,
by reducing marginal wastage, have the effect of lowering the
woodland requirement for the average *citemene* from 18 acres to
13 acres, still permitting the same cropping area; while early-
burning and complete protection would, he estimated, reduce the
period required for woodland regeneration from thirty-five to
twenty-five and twenty years respectively. The combination of
these two measures, if applied completely and effectively, might
therefore reduce the total land requirement to about 60 acres per
person, allowing for some increase in the area cut for subsidiary
gardens; and, conversely, increase the Critical Population Density
to something of the order of 10 people per square mile. In addition,
food supplies and saleable produce could be increased by use of the
ash gardens for at least a second year on the poorer soil and for a
longer period on the better variants.

But, even within a limited area, it would not be easy to bring
about a rapid change from small-circle to large-circle *citemene*, as
Peters pointed out—although the latter system is widely practised
and used by neighbouring peoples. The extra labour of carrying
the branches to a single site would act as a deterrent, more
especially in the absence of a very high proportion of the active
labour-strength as migrant workers. As has been noted, the
natural tendency was in the opposite direction; towards smaller
and more widely scattered ash circles, as degeneration of the woodland progressed.

Control of fire is no less difficult. Complete protection in the
neighbourhood of gardens is practised throughout most of the dry
season, and it is not until the burning of the stacked branchwood
shortly before the rains that the destructive force of fire is released
to devastate the woodland. It might therefore seem no very
difficult matter to achieve complete protection of the woodland as
a whole, but experience has shown this to be an impracticable
ideal so long as the African's view of the matter remains unchanged.
Attempts have been made to eliminate bush fires by legislation,
but they were no more successful than the ban on *citemene*: fires
were started, either by accident or intent, the culprits were rarely

or never found, and the decrees could not be enforced.   In *citemene* regions there are additional and peculiar difficulties. These are almost insuperable in the case of the small-circle form, and even the large circle would require very careful fire-guarding and supervision to prevent the spread of fire from the burning stacks.

Early-burning, a satisfactory and more practical alternative, has been enforced over limited areas, but its effective application requires a vigilance and persistence not commonly displayed by African administrations, native or alien. Nowhere can it be said with confidence that the practice has become fully accepted and integrated into local custom. The early burn disrupts normal hunting routine and its introduction is therefore resisted wherever hunting has an economic or high prestige value; while in *citemene* regions there is the risk of premature burning of branchwood, which usually lies spread throughout the clearing for drying at the time the burn should be made.

These changes, if they could be rapidly accomplished in spite of the initial difficulties, would do no more than slow down the rate of degeneration in the more highly congested areas and provide a temporary solution elsewhere. Peters therefore pointed out the need for local experiment on which to base long-term improvements and proposed a programme including:
(*a*) trials of crop sequences following first-year finger millet on the ash gardens, using the traditional sequences of the more advanced forms of *citemene* as a basis; (*b*) investigation of the possibility of devising a wholly new system of short-cycle *citemene* or semi-*citemene*, by substituting for indigenous tree regrowth plantations of quick-growing exotics, such as *Gmelina arborea* or *Cajanus indicus* or some other fallow crop; (*c*) trials of methods of ameliorating the extensive *dambo* soils and of utilising seepage sites for rice, wheat, and vegetables; (*d*) planning and demonstration of simple irrigation systems, for which there is considerable scope on the Serenje Plateau, and trials of wheat and potatoes as irrigated crops; (*e*) variety trials of sorghum and cassava on the main soil types.

He also advocated the introduction of cattle, partly to supply manure for the *dambo* and irrigated gardens, though the natural stock-carrying capacity of the region is low, and the breeding of small stock and poultry. In addition, he proposed the development of a fishing industry on Lake Lusiwashi, seventeen square miles of crocodile-free but little-used waters, and the introduction of fish-farming throughout the plateau.

By these means it would be possible, though only through persistent effort and with considerable expenditure and capital investment, to expand and improve food supplies and to establish a trade, at least in poultry and dried fish, with the Copperbelt. Rapid and complete disappearance of the *citemene* system was not envisaged: indeed, it was foreseen that it might have to be continued indefinitely as the only practicable way of producing crops over large areas which, if not used for *citemene*, would not be cropped at all—and in order to maintain a partially deforested belt along the southern limit of the plateau as a barrier against the encroachment of tsetse. The objective as envisaged by Peters was the improvement of *citemene* and, at the same time, its gradual reduction, with increasing use of *dambo* and irrigated land.

5. LARGE-CIRCLE *CITEMENE*

In large-circle *citemene*, as it is practised by the Maswepa Mambwe and other peoples under undisturbed conditions, the ash gardens provide the main food supply. Extended use of the ash gardens, for two or more years after the initial finger millet crop has been taken, is an important feature of the system, and subsidiary dug gardens, though always used and almost invariably mounded, are relatively small. Sampling data collected by Alder (6) in 1957 within the relatively sparsely populated and well-wooded Lungu Reserve No. 2 of Abercorn district will serve to illustrate the areas normally cultivated by the Mambwe and other related peoples of this region. The population-land balance of this Reserve had not been affected by land alienation and only to a small extent by economic change and other disturbing factors. In 1958 the general population density, according to the district count, was less than 6 per square mile, and it may be assumed with some confidence that land-use practice did not vary greatly from the traditional pattern.

AREAS CULTIVATED PER HEAD OF POPULATION: LUNGU RESERVE NO. 2

First year ash gardens: finger millet	0·290 acre
Sequence cultivation: ash gardens in second and subsequent years	0·420 ,,
Subsidiary dug and mounded gardens	0·170 ,,
	0·880 ,,

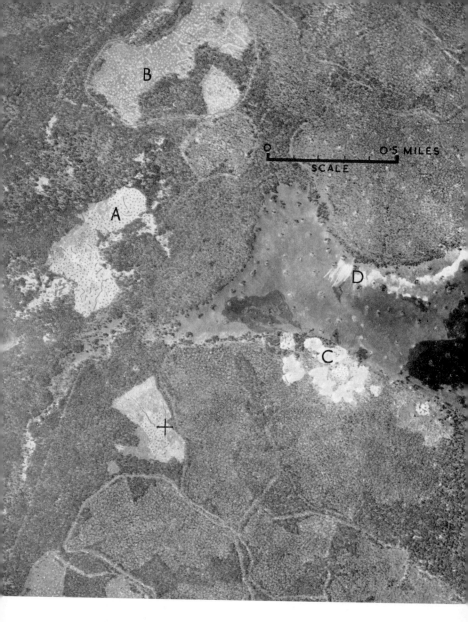

Plate I

Small-circle *Citemene*. Serenje District, Northern Rhodesia

A = Gardens in course of preparation, showing brushwood circles and lines. B = Gardens of the previous year, showing ash circles and lines and timber for fencing. C = Subsidiary hoed gardens. D = *Dambo* margin gardens. Old *citemene* gardens in various stages of woodland regeneration and traces of the burnt fences can also be seen.

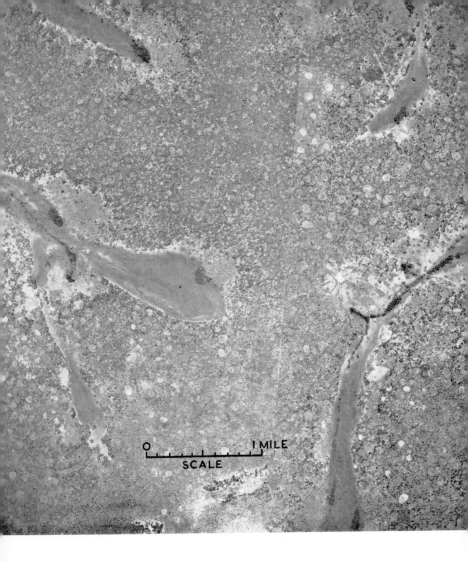

PLATE II

THE PATTERN OF LARGE-CIRCLE *CITEMENE*

An area of excessive population in Kasama District, Northern
Rhodesia, showing circles in current use and traces of many
previous cycles of cultivation.

Reproduced by permission of the Air Ministry. Crown Copyright
Reserved. Royal Air Force Photograph.

The amount of woodland used to make the ash garden is less than in small-circle *citemene*, because the concentration of the burned area into a single large circle greatly reduces marginal wastage. Trapnell estimated the total area of the clearing to be about 6·5 times the garden area in more thickly wooded country and about 10 times the area in poorer woodland, while Moffat and others have estimated that the proportion ranges from 5:1 to 10:1. The amount of woodland required for *citemene* each year is therefore likely to be of the order of 1·5 to 3·0 acres and to average a little over two acres per head of population. Assuming that the trees regenerate after lopping in a period of twenty to twenty-five years, the total requirement of woodland suitable for *citemene* may be expected to vary with the quality and regenerative capacity of the woodland from 30 to 80 acres per head of population.

The density and vigour of tree growth varies considerably over the great extent of the northern plateau, and so does the proportion of woodland to total land surface. Alder, (7), who made a careful study of the Woodland Factor in the Mambwe problem area, Reserve No. 5, found that *dambo* and streamsides and thinly wooded flanking zones accounted for 10 per cent of the whole area, and open bush and tree-grassland for a further 38·2 per cent. He therefore concluded that only about 50 per cent of the area of this Reserve could be regarded as suitable for *citemene*. This is, however, a watershed region, situated between the Tanganyika, Congo, and Zambesi drainage systems, which has been subjected to severe over-cutting, and a relatively low proportion of woodland is to be expected. The available data suggest that the proportion of woodland over the Northern Plateau as a whole may vary from 50 per cent, or rather less, to as much as 75 per cent, with a general average in the region of 60 per cent.

To anyone who has flown over this country, or travelled through it by car, and seen the great stretches of what may look like almost continuous woodland, the estimates may seem surprisingly low. But, apart from the *dambos*, which widen out towards the watersheds and often form extensive fish-tail heads, and the thin woodland, tree-grassland, and patches of open grassland, again most prominent on the watersheds, there are large areas of steep hills and outcrops impracticable for *citemene* although they are well-wooded. Another rather less obvious factor must also be taken into consideration. *Citemene* itself reduces the proportion of usable woodland, particularly the large-circle form. On the burnt areas the trees are destroyed, and regeneration must come from the roots, if they survive the burn, or from seed; a process for which a long period—at a guess, fifty years—must be allowed.

On the basis of these considerations, it is suggested that the general Critical Population Density for the more typical forms of the large circle *citemene* system may be about 8 to the square mile, but regional variations from 4 per square mile in the poorer wood-land and hill regions to, perhaps, 16 per square mile in the most favourable sites may be expected.

It should be noted that this tentative estimate has been based on the area cropped by what was probably a "donor" people who supplied food to the dominant Bemba. They may have grown an unusually large area of millet in the past and this custom may have been retained with the development of a cash market for the inflated "normal" surplus. The demographic picture does not, however, suggest that these systems are capable of supporting populations much in excess of 8 per square mile over any large area: general population densities per square mile over the main *citemene* regions (based on 1958 population figures) are approxi-mately as follows:

Kasama	8·8	Mporokoso	4·5
Abercorn	8·2	Chinsali	3·9
Isoka	7·0	Mpika	3·0
	Luwingu	6·2	

Within the smaller areas of the Bemba Chieftaincies in Kasama, densities vary from 4 per square mile (Chimbola) to as much as 15 per square mile (Mwamba). In the less populated districts ample land for *citemene* remains and it is hardly surprising that Serenje Lala from the cut-out areas of Maila's chieftaincy (17 per square mile) have been moving into the neighbouring country of the Bisa chief Mpumba (3·6 per square mile) in Mpika district. This migration, it seems, went on for some years without much notice being taken: then Mpumba objected, though not on grounds of land shortage, and movement is now permitted only on transfer of political allegiance to the Bisa chief. In Kasama and Abercorn, on the other hand, although there is as yet no sign of a general collapse of *citemene* there are considerable areas of local over-population in which degeneration of the woodland is proceeding at a rate which, if continued, must lead to the collapse of the system within a few years. Most of this local congestion has come about naturally, by increase of population or attraction to areas of economic opportunity, and some is probably no more than temporary overcrowding; but in Abercorn district the familiar story of the Reserves was repeated.

6. LAND PROBLEMS IN THE ABERCORN DISTRICT

In 1930 Native Reserves were demarcated in the Abercorn district, and the subsequent movement of the Mambwe into these restricted areas resulted in the immediate creation of population densities far beyond the critical point for the system of land-use. The general population density in the Reserve to which the *citemene*-cultivating Mambwe were confined reached a figure of 17, or perhaps even 20, per square mile, where previously there had been no more than 6 people to the square mile. Although the Mambwe reacted, like the Lala before them, by reducing their *citemene* and enlarging the hoed gardens, degeneration of the woodland in this region of rather poor tree growth soon reached spectacular proportions. By 1938, lopping had given way to felling, regeneration periods had been reduced to a totally inadequate level, the ratio of cut to burnt area had fallen as low as 1 : 16, and the standard of subsistence was falling rapidly.

In 1938 measures were taken to check this destruction of tree growth and prevent a rapid and complete collapse of the system of food production. Land adjoining the reserves was obtained from its owners, the British South Africa Company, and a scheme of control was devised and carried out by Unwin Moffat, then Senior Agricultural Officer in the region. The essence of the scheme was the distribution of villages as evenly as possible over the old reserves and the newly acquired land, so that a demarcated cutting area could be allocated to each village, of sufficient size to allow of the continuation of *citemene* without destruction of the woodland. Better methods of cutting and care of the regenerating trees were introduced, and imposed as a condition of the grant of more land, the most important being the practice of early burning. This is a deliberate light and partial burning of the grass and undergrowth as soon as possible after the rains, an operation requiring considerable care and some skill. If it is carried out at the right time, the early burn cleans up the ground litter of dry grass and other debris, without doing serious damage to living vegetation, and so protects the regenerating woodland against the fierce late fires.

It was hoped that with this care and protection the trees would recover from *citemene* lopping in less than twenty years. At the same time, tree-cutting was controlled and restricted by demarcating for each village the woodland area to be cut each year, with the object of encouraging the tendency towards larger village gardens and the substitution of hoe cultivation for *citemene*. The area which might be cut in any one year was based, initially, on an average allowance of 7 acres of woodland per family, or approximately one acre and three-quarters per head of population, and the proportion of woodland suitable for *citemene* was estimated—without the aid of aerial photography—as 60 per cent of the land area. Assuming the accuracy of the postulates, the modified and controlled system should have been capable of supporting population densities of 10 to 13 per square mile. The scheme was accepted readily enough by the Mambwe and their Native Authorities, mainly because it offered the inducement of more woodland, and within four years of the start 230 villages with a total population believed to be about 17,500 had been resettled.

Although it gave a respite of more than twenty years and prevented a catastrophic breakdown of the system of food production, the *citemene* Control Scheme failed in its full purpose. Within twenty years of the beginning of the scheme, two-thirds of the villages had used up their woodland and were re-cutting areas previously used, the average period of regeneration being about 16·5 years. The trees had not regenerated to a satisfactory level and this second cycle of cutting marked the beginning of a process of degeneration that could be checked only by further reduction of *citemene*.

Carefully controlled burning trials, which were laid down at three experimental centres in 1937–9, had given results approximating fairly closely to expectation; but the same degree of control could not be exercised over an area of some 2,000 square miles, particularly in face of the difficulties created by staff shortage during the War and the political climate that followed. Resistance to control assumed a political and emotional content, which was intensified after the creation of the Central African Federation, and defiance of Native Authority regulations became a vehicle for the expression of political discontent. Early burning and other measures were neglected or indifferently carried out, and over the area as a whole conditions were such that the trees could not recover in less than twenty to twenty-five years, according to Alder's estimate. It seems probable, also, that the proportion of woodland had been overestimated in the beginning and the initial population underestimated, while a temporary shift of policy during the War had further disturbed the balance. In the three years 1943–5, much larger cutting areas were allocated, presumably in the interests of immediate food production.

The circumstances arising from wartime conditions and the political situation thereafter were, of course, unexpected, but other complications and difficulties had been foreseen. It was realised that the annual allocation of woodland was less than the Mambwe would wish to cut and that population increase would necessitate a further gradual reduction of *citemene*. But it was expected that these changes would be balanced by progressive alteration of the system; initially by better use of the ash gardens in the second and subsequent years and by the extension of hoe cultivation. Sampling figures which Alder (7) gives for the controlled area and for an uncontrolled area, Lungu Reserve No. 2, in which the population-land balance had not been disturbed, indicate that this expectation had been only partially realised.

AREAS CULTIVATED PER HEAD
OF POPULATION (ACRES)

	CONTROLLED AREA	UNCONTROLLED AREA
First year ash gardens: finger millet	0·26	0·29
Sequence cultivation: ash gardens in second and sub-sequent year	0·35	0·42
Subsidiary dug and mounded gardens	0·28	0·17
	0·89	0·88

In the controlled area, it seems, the extent of the ash garden has not been greatly reduced, but less rather than more use is made of this garden in the second and subsequent years. This suggests a reduction of the intensity of the burn, due to restriction of the cutting area and poor quality of timber, resulting in lower yields and a shorter period of fertility. On the other hand, there has been a significant increase in the size of dug gardens, to the extent that the gross acreage cultivated in the controlled and uncontrolled areas is much the same. In spite of this, one may suppose that the productivity of the former is considerably lower, on account of the smaller area and poorer yield of the main garden.

7. KINSHIP OBLIGATIONS AND THE POPULATION-LAND PATTERN

This supposition is supported by striking differences in the size and composition of garden families in the two areas, revealed by Alder's demographic survey.

GARDEN FAMILIES: AVERAGE COMPOSITION

	IMMEDIATE FAMILY			DEPENDENT KIN		TOTAL
	Men	*Women*	*Child-ren*	*Adults*	*Child-ren*	
Controlled	0·46	1·00	2·25	0·15	0·14	4·00
Uncontrolled	0·48	1·00	2·61	0·46	0·63	5·18

Alder investigated the reasons for these differences, with the assistance of Watson (of the University of Manchester), a social anthropologist who was working in the district at the time.

More of the men were absent from the controlled area at any one time, working or seeking work in the distant centres of employment, and they had taken more of their women and children with them: but the most striking difference was the much greater number of dependent kin attached to families in the uncontrolled area. Since the Mambwe social pattern is patrilineal, unlike that of the Bemba, these dependent kin consisted mainly of relatives of the male heads of households. They were sisters and brothers of the household heads, mothers, widowed or deserted daughters, sisters-in-law, and their children. Where choice was possible these people had attached themselves to families in the uncontrolled rather than the controlled areas, pre-

sumably because of the greater availability of land and food sup-
lies. After examining Alder's data, Watson concluded that "there
are fewer dependents in the controlled area because the gardens
are not so big; but garden families with big gardens attract
dependents wherever they live."

Some sixteen years earlier I had observed the same phenomenon on an even more striking scale in the overcrowded Reserves of
the Fort Jameson district. The data, which have been lost or
destroyed, indicated a very large accretion of dependent kin by
families with gardens on the stronger soils of continuing fertility.
"A very heavy burden had been thrown on the limited soils of
high fertility and resistance to erosion, the only soils left in the
original area capable of carrying moderately good crops. These
soils, then in continuous cultivation, were feeding twice as many
people as they would normally do" (9). It is the productivity rather
than the size of the garden that is the determining factor.

This mechanism may have been a factor of importance in
preserving the population-land balance of the traditional systems,
by ensuring a flow of population from local areas of overcrowding;
but its continued operation is a major threat to the stability of
improved farming systems, since it leads to "hidden subdivision"
of land holdings even though they may in theory be held on an
individual tenure. We will consider this aspect of the matter, and
also the outcome of the wartime resettlement schemes in Northern
Rhodesia, in a later section.

CHAPTER X

SPECIAL ENVIRONMENTS

1. THE AISA MAMBWE AND THE FIPA

We have already noted the curious division of Mambwe agricultural practice, the use of *citemene* methods by the Maswepa section and of an altogether different system by the northern or Aisa group. The grassland system of the northern Mambwe is associated with relatively high population densities. In 1928, before population distribution was disturbed, the general population density in Reserve No. 4 of the Abercorn district, where the system is practised, was probably about 30 to the square mile. By 1938, at the time of the ecological survey, the figure was approaching 40 per square mile and there was no more than an inkling of impending trouble, though Trapnell (171) was doubtful if the area could maintain this population for long "in view of the brief fallows now given [1938] and the number of cattle." The present general density of resident population is rather more than 53 per square mile, with large regional variations; and according to Alder (8), there were besides, in 1960, about 58 cattle per square mile.

It is difficult to say what the Critical Population Density of the original system may have been or how far general degeneration of this system has proceeded as a result of population increase. Marked symptoms of degeneration are evident in areas of population densities exceeding 60 or 70 people per square mile, where local numbers almost certainly exceed the regional carrying capacities: but the process of change has been greatly complicated by other factors such as the absence of men needed for the heavy work of mounding, the pressure of a growing cattle population, the introduction of the plough and the recent emergence of a class of "individual settlers" who are "farming" relatively large acreages.

The Aisa Mambwe maintained in the past, and still do, that soil fertility can be preserved under their system by eight years of fallow following four years of cultivation, but this may be a minimum period of fallow applicable only on the best soils of highest regeneration capacity such as are preferred for cultivation. Without a greater knowledge of the soils of this area, and particularly of their regenerative capacity under traditional treatments, estimation of human carrying capacity must be, in a considerable degree, speculative. All that can be said, from the history of the Reserve and the estimates that have been attempted, is that the Critical Population Density of the grassland system in this environment, uncomplicated by labour and cattle problems, probably lay somewhere within the wide limits of 30 to 70 people per square mile and was much higher than that of any *citemene* system.

It is not surprising that the system attracted early attention and that it was hoped it might be a natural successor to the more advanced forms of *citemene*. Trapnell thought that the agriculture of the Northern Mambwe might be regarded as "in some sense the culmination of the more developed form of the woodland systems": but he added, "the essential process of the grassland system, that of spreading mounds for millet, may have originally been derived from sources outside this country and it is not, therefore, to be regarded as a simple legacy from the developed form of the Northern Citemene System."

There is a fairly close resemblance between Mambwe grassland agriculture and certain East African systems, including that of the Fipa in the Southern Highlands of Tanganyika, though there are some differences in practice and in minor crops and the traditional form of mounds. The Fipa, who live in high grassland or tree-grassland country at altitudes of 5,000–7,000 feet, start the preparation of their main gardens in February–March by cutting the long grass and laying it in piles. Sods are then cut with the hoe and inverted on top of the grass heaps to make mounds which are commonly about three feet wide, two to two-and-a-half feet high, and from a foot to two feet apart. The incorporation of all the grass in the mounds resembles Matengo practice, which will be considered later, and differs from that of the Mambwe who usually cut and burn the longer grass, together with brushwood and trash, to form small ash circles on which early millet is sown. This may be a relic of *citemene* or it may be an adaption to conditions in which decomposition of bulk organic material is less rapid.

The Fipa, like the Mambwe, usually grow beans on the initial mounds, though sweet potatoes and cassava are sometimes planted and, very occasionally, chickpeas or wheat. Deliberate use is also made of weeds as green manure, as in Mambwe practice.

In the following season, generally in late November when the rains have set in, the mounds are broken and the humic soil, in which the well-rotted grass and roots have become incorporated, is spread over the garden to form a fine seed-bed for finger millet. Maize is quite commonly planted earlier, and the whole process is remarkably similar to that of the Mambwe. After the harvest of this first millet crop the land is mounded for the incorporation of weeds and crop residues and a second crop of finger millet is taken in the third season. In the fourth season the garden is often mounded again and planted to maize, beans, groundnuts, and groundbeans, or a crop of groundnuts is planted on the flat. The cultivation sequence may end at this point or it may be continued for a further year or more before the land is left for recovery of the grass-land to its previous state, but I have little information on cultivation periods and less on the fallow periods customarily employed in this environment.

It is possible that the Mambwe, who may be a people of East African origin, brought with them a system such as this and that it survived with some modification where the environment allowed of its continuance as a general practice, and gave place to *citemene* as a more certain means of food production on the poor plateau woodland soils. On this view, the Mambwe grassland system is to be regarded as one adapted to a limited area, a special environment within the main zone of ash cultivation in which there is a relatively high proportion of land of Semi-Permanent or short-term Recurrent Cultivation types, rather than as the natural successor of *citemene* in the plateau woodland regions of long-term Recurrent Cultivation or Shifting Cultivation land.

2. THE LUAPULA VALLEY

I have used the term "special environment" to indicate a circumscribed area capable of supporting a high local density of population, in relation to the generally low figures common throughout most of Northern Rhodesia. In this category might be included the ribbon-like concentrations of population along the eastern bank of the Luapula river and around the margin of the great Barotse plain; and formerly, before the rise of Lake Kariba, along the Zambesi in the Gwembe valley.

Trapnell's phrase "a street of villages" aptly describes the concentration along the lower Luapula river from Johnston Falls to Lake Mweru. There are "277 villages strung along the 115 miles of swamp and lake edge" as described by Cunnison in 1959 (45). Here the river flows placidly through a flat valley bounded by a steep scarp. Bordering the river is a belt of swamp which widens northwards towards Lake Mweru, and between escarpment and river lies a long ribbon of fertile and productive *chipya* soils on which cassava flourishes (see Plate 3).

The population—which may be in the neighbourhood of 50,000 by now—is composed of Lunda, Chishinga, Shila, and Bwile with a considerable admixture of immigrants from other parts of Northern Rhodesia and from the Congo. Growth and accretion has been rapid: Cunnison quotes figures which indicate that the population of the east bank river strip may have increased by close on 120 per cent over the period 1914–49. Growth rates of 3 to 4 per cent per annum or even more—aided, of course, by immigration—are probably not uncommon in areas of economic opportunity. In the course of the Lamba survey I obtained indications of growth rates exceeding 4 per cent per annum in areas of Native Reserve bordering on the Copperbelt townships. The economic attraction of the Luapula valley is, of course, the long-established and developing fishing industry of the river, swamps, and lake.

Population densities, expressed in terms of Chiefs' areas, are not very remarkable. For the eight Lunda chieftaincies, the figures vary from a mere 10 (Katuta) to over 50 (Lukwesa) and average about 27 people per square mile: but, since these figures relate populations merely to administrative areas, they give little impression of the concentration along the river strip. It is an impressive experience to walk along the street of villages, an experience which is likely to give an exaggerated impression of population density and pressure on the land. Quite possibly, the general density over the river strip as a whole in relation to the area actually exploited for food production, has not yet reached or is little in excess of 100 per square mile. This, however, is an impressive figure for Northern Rhodesia.

The area is also one of large and relatively stable villages, as Cunnison noted in 1958 (45). Of 41 villages for which he obtained information, 2 had not shifted since they were first formed two or three centuries ago, 3 had shifted last sometime before 1900, and 20 others had not moved for some forty years or more. He concluded that "the size and especially the occurrence of very large villages, as well as their relative permanence, may be connected with the way in which the staple crop, cassava, is cultivated. The land may be used profitably again after a rest of about six years."

In this system, as in that of the Aisa Mambwe and the Fipa, the manurial value of rotted grass is well understood. Large mounds are made to incorporate the grass. These are generally oval in form but they tend to be larger and more rectangular where very long grass has to be turned in. The mounds may be split and re-made at intervals but they are not broken and spread, as in the preparation of a finger millet seedbed. Seven or eight cuttings of cassava are planted on each mound, together with groundnuts, ground-beans, maize, pumpkins, and other minor crops in the first year. The groundnut is an important secondary crop sometimes grown in separate mounded plots. These secondary and minor crops are harvested in the first year, but the cassava roots are not large enough to be dug until the second dry season—about eighteen months after planting—and harvesting of the roots continues until the third rains, or, sometimes, into the fourth or fifth seasons or even longer. Finger millet is grown as a beer crop but its cultivation is restricted to very small *citemene* gardens in plateau woodland under the hills beyond the *chipya* belt, though formerly it may have been more extensively cultivated in certain thicket types.

In these circumstances, if the fallow period required for the restoration of fertility to a satisfactory level is indeed something of the order of six years, as a general figure, one would expect to find forms of Semi-Permanent or even Permanent Cultivation. Furthermore, the cultivable proportion of this *chipya* belt is probably high; judging by the distribution of present and the signs of former cultivations on aerial photographs, it may be as high as 50 or 60 per cent for cassava. It seems possible, therefore—taking into consideration the large supply of fish—that the river strip may be capable of supporting population densities well over 100 per square mile. This accords with Cunnison's observation that "there is plenty of good *chipya* land," but it is probable that there are local areas of over-population, shortage of garden land and over-cultivating where the *chipya* fringe narrows. Inevitably, there is pressure on land close to the villages even where there is no general shortage and this has given rise to a certain degree of fragmentation, since cultivators prefer to have three or four plots in more favoured situations, easy of access and less liable to damage by wild pigs, rather than a single large plot on the periphery of cultivation. Probably, too, much of the land near the villages is now overcultivated and rest periods are shorter, and sometimes much shorter, than the cultivation periods. These degenerative tendencies may not yet have reached a serious stage, but they are bound to be accentuated by further population increase.

There is also a shortage of *dambo* land suitable for growing bananas and vegetables. Such land has become valuable and in high demand, particularly in the more southerly part of the valley where the town of Kasenga in Katanga across the river, a town in which there were over 200 Europeans and a considerable urban African population, offered a ready and profitable market for the produce. The trading connexion, and kinship and tribal affinities, have brought the people of the valley into close contact with the Congo tragedy.

3. The Bangweulu Islands

The largest lake basin area of Northern Rhodesia, that of Bangweulu and the lower Chambezi, contains some of the highest natural densities of population recorded in the country. Within this shallow depression, which is occupied mainly by swamp and papyrus sudd, flood-plain grassland, and open water, there are considerable areas of relatively fertile grey earths (Lake Basin soils) carrying *chipya* vegetation. These are found, typically as flat interfluvial stretches, in the lower Chambezi basin, and on some of the islands, and about the western and southern rim of the lake and swamps (176). The vegetation of these belts is open deciduous woodland containing species of *Erythrophloeum*, *Pterocarpus*, *Entandophragma*, and *Parinari*, in a high grass growth of *Andropogon gayanus* and *Hyparrhenia spp.* with much *Aframomum*, *Smilax*, and bracken; and there are local areas of dense evergreen *Syzygium* thicket which were formerly more extensive. The *chipya* soils, thought light in texture and with a basis of sand, are generally richly humic in the upper layer, deep and of good crumb-structure, free-draining, and yet retentive of moisture: but they vary to weaker types of loose structure and reduced humus content. From the point of view of traditional land-use these soils are probably to be regarded as Permanent or Semi-Permanent, except in the case of the weakest examples which may be suited only to short-term Recurrent Cultivation even for cassava culture. Like the similar soils of the Luapula valley, they are very well suited to cultivation of cassava which is the dominant crop of the region, but subsidiary cultivation of finger millet is also practised.

Where enough thicket remains it is usually cut and burned to make finger millet gardens from which one or two millet crops are taken and after that the land is mounded for cassava. The practise of burning for finger millet survives mainly among the Bisa of the islands in Lake Bangweulu whose kinsmen on the plateau are *citemene* cultivators, but the Kawendi and Ngumbu peoples of the islands and mainland probably used this method in the past and have given it up because they no longer have enough thicket. *Chipya* soils in woodland or grass and scrub are opened by making mounds on which cassava and ground-beans are planted. When the first cassava crop has been taken the mounds are broken and spread for a crop of finger millet, after the fashion of the Fipa and the Aisa Mambwe, and this cassava–millet sequence is commonly repeated and followed by an end crop of cassava before the land is rested. Duration of fallow is determined by the time required for the *Andropogon* grass cover to re-establish itself, where pressure of population does not prohibit this: but in areas of dense population the rest periods have been reduced to brief and inadequate fallows at irregular intervals.

Part of two of the Lala chiefdoms also lie within this lake-basin area, on the south-eastern margin of the swamp below the Serenje plateau. Here, where the people have access both to Lake Basin soils and to *Julbernardia-Brachystegia* woodland suitable for *citemene*, they use the former for their main gardens and their agriculture differs greatly from that of the plateau Lala. The grey, light-textured but highly humic soils to which they have access are generally cultivated to cassava and groundnuts in the first year, cassava in the second year, and sorghum in the third year, followed by a fallow period equal to or not greatly longer than the cultivation period. Small *citemene* gardens are made for finger millet as a beer crop, but so little importance attaches to the crop that an accelerated cutting cycle, with a regeneration period of only

eleven or twelve years, is commonly practised although, according
to N. W. Smyth (152) there is still plenty of woodland.

Sample measurements of main gardens in the cassava-growing
area of both chiefdoms were made by Smyth and the following
averages are taken from his data.

	GARDEN FAMILY	ACREAGE CULTIVATED	ACREAGE PER HEAD
Kafinda's area	4·81	5·30	1·10
Chisomo's area	4·22	4·55	1·08

Here again is this figure, an area of about an acre and a tenth
in cultivation at any one time per head of population, which
appears with such remarkable persistence in the hoe-cultivation
systems of south-central Africa.

I do not know whether there is still enough *chipya* land. When
I last visited this area there appeared to be more than ample, but
that was a good many years ago. Sixty years after the death of
Livingstone I camped for some weeks at the place where his last
journey ended. It was here, in 1873, "on the banks of the Luli-
mala in Ilala," that he passed his last days, suspecting yet reluctant
to believe the truth, that in this great sponge he had found the
beginnings not of the Nile but of the Congo. "I have no wish,"
he once said, "to be made into black man's pot for the sake of the
Congo." While I was there I spoke with old men, probably in
the eighth decade of their lives, who claimed to remember Livingstone. So recent is the opening up of Africa.

Within the great sponge of the swamp, agriculture takes a
more specialised form. Cultivation is, of course, restricted to the
limited areas where complete inundation is less likely, elevations
of lacustrine clays, silts, and peaty soils often so slight as to be
barely perceptible, and sandbanks. Cassava remains the staple
crop, but even in this unlikely environment finger millet continues
to be grown for beer. People travel considerable distances to
make subsidiary millet gardens in the grass and reed land of the
Lunga plain, which is above normal water level. The soil of the
selected site is hoed over, the long grass burned and the grass
roots from which the soil has been shaken out are heaped and
burned in preparation for the sowing of finger millet. When this
first crop has been taken the garden is mounded for cassava, and a
sequence of millet grown on the flat after spreading the mounds,

followed by cassava on mounds, may be continued for some years. Main gardens are made on moister sites, near to and generally below the village, on rich black organic soils carrying grass and reeds. These gardens are cultivated for some eighteen months to cassava on mounds, together with sweet potatoes, pulses, and a little maize; and at the end of this period the plants are uprooted and the garden replanted. On still lower and wetter swamp soils, banks are built to keep out the flood water and very large mounds are made for cassava: practice varies considerably with differences of environment. Within the swamp there is probably enough fertile land for those who have the hardihood and skill to master this most difficult environment, and to tolerate its disadvantages. There is an abundant supply of fish, as there is throughout the region, and the diet is supplemented by bananas, sugarcane, and some sorghum grown in kitchen gardens in the villages.

Indeed, the swamp-dwelling Unga enjoy "a waterlogged prosperity," to use Trapnell's phrase, in comparison with the people—Unga, Ngumbu, Batwa, and a few Bisa—who live on the sandbank islands of the swamp and lake. The light-brown, weakly humic sands of this third main environment are probably of relatively low potential. They have been greatly over-cultivated (possibly because the sandbanks offer less uncomfortable and arduous living conditions than the swamp) to the extent that agriculture has degenerated to the growing of stunted crops of cassava, with few or no subsidiaries, so long as the depleted soil will give any yield. In these circumstances the livelihood of the people must depend to a large extent on fishing and the exchange of fish for grain and other foods.

In 1938, in the course of the Ecological Survey, Trapnell made estimates of some of the population densities within the Bangweulu lake basin. He made no estimates of densities on the mainland, for any serious attempt to do so would have involved detailed mapping of the *chipya* regions, but he had this to say of the islands and the sandbanks, which he thought were then carrying an aggregate population of at least 22,000 out of a total population of 55 to 60 thousand in the *chipya* and swamp regions.

"The islands and sandbanks . . . clearly provide the most serious population problem in the Northern Province. Here again, more precise figures would be obtainable with more satisfactory maps. Chiluwe island, for example, may have an area of anything from

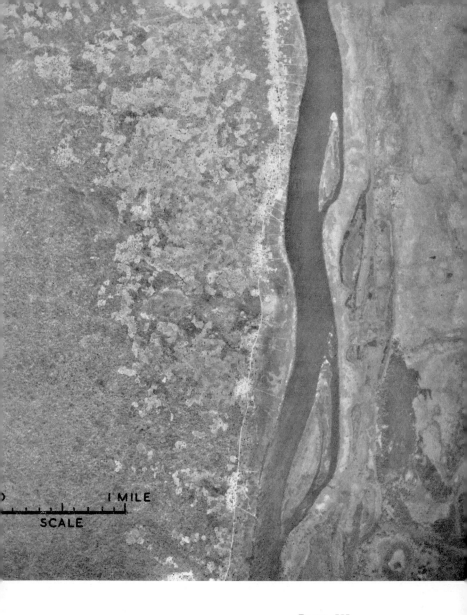

I MILE

SCALE

Plate III

Close Settlement along the Eastern Bank of the
Luapula River, Kawambwa District, Northern Rhodesia

Showing the "street of villages" by the river and the "ribbon"
of cultivated *chipya* soils.

Reproduced by permission of the Air Ministry. Crown Copyright
Reserved.   Royal Air Force Photograph.

PLATE IV

THE HAYA LAND-USE PATTERN, BUKOBA DISTRICT, TANGANYIKA

Enclosed banana groves, giving a cellular appearance, show as "islands" of fertility in poor grassland between swampy river valleys carrying tussock grass, papyrus, and evergreen swamp forest.

Aerial survey photograph. Reproduced by courtesy of the Director of Surveys, Tanganyika.

35 to 50 square miles according to such outlines as are available. Its population has been variously estimated at figures ranging from 8,000 to 8,900 and more, but would appear from the latest population records to be about 7,400. On the basis of this figure the density over the entire island must be between 148 and 211 to the square mile. . . . On the much smaller islands of Chishi and Nsumbu, some 8 and 5 square miles respectively, densities of 319 and 369 to the square mile are apparently attained. Yet these figures entail barely two acres of available land per head of population. The amount actually used for cultivation must be still less, for some bush and even thicket survives on Chiluwe and thickets are still to be seen on Nsumbu Island. If soil depletion has appeared in the cultivated areas in these circumstances it is not to be wondered at; it is indeed a tribute to the productivity of Chipya soils that they should support these populations at all. Under somewhat lesser densities the sandbanks in the swamps have been cultivated beyond recognition of their former state. Scarcely a single bush survives, even the original grass has been replaced by secondary species and the land-shortage is acute. Matongo seems to have reached this condition under a density of 220 to the square mile. Nsalushi's density lies between 177 and 195 and Ncheta, in as extreme a plight as any, has 188 to the square mile. The Kapata peninsula, where soil depletion is also marked, seems to have a density of about 112, while the sandbank island of Mbawala is comparatively sparsely populated with about 64 to the square mile" (171).

I have not been in the Lake Basin for more than twenty years, but judging by what I could see on a recent flight over the area the islands and sandbanks have continued to support such densities of population, and perhaps even greater densities, on the basis of the developing fishing industry and the great market for dried fish. The islands looked more bare than they had been and there was hardly a trace of natural vegetation.

4. THE VALLEY TONGA

The valley of the middle Zambesi, where the waters of Lake Kariba are still rising behind the great dam to their destined level, is also a special environment with peculiar potentialities and limitations. The areas habitable for African people with no more than their traditional equipment form a series of land-locked "islands." Here is a narrow trough-like valley enclosed on its northern side by a steep escarpment. Between the escarpment and the river is a dry and barren region of sandstone hills, the "barrier hills," which follow fault lines parallel to the Zambesi. The tributary rivers falling from the plateau to the valley tend first to meander over the flat country of the outer valley floor before turning at a sharp angle to break through the barrier hills and join the main river. At Kariba the hard rock of the plateau basement complex extends across the valley and through this the Zambesi has cut a narrow gorge, creating the conditions which made the technical masterpiece of the dam a practical possibility.

The main cultivable soils of the region comprise the narrow alluvial strip along the Zambesi, the riverside deposits of the tributaries and the alluvial fans at their outlets. The rich alluvials which are flooded annually by the rise and fall of the river may be cultivated continuously to two crops a year, while the soils of the older terraces about the general flood level vary considerably in fertility, though they are generally of the Permanent or Semi-Permanent categories, and they have been much over-cultivated under pressure of population. In addition, a range of soils characterised by varying thicket vegetation are cultivated under systems of short- to long-term Recurrent Cultivation; or under Permanent or Semi-Permanent systems in the case of the best examples, and where pressure of population is very great. But much of the flatter valley floor is occupied by poorly drained, clayey soils of high alkalinity dominated by *mopani* woodland. Though some of them may be capable of reclamation, the true *mopani* soils are regarded as uncultivable by the Tonga. Fortunately, there are excellent studies of the valley and its people before the flood.[1]

This pattern of very limited areas of fertility within a great extent of barren and uncultivable land determined the distribution of the valley population. Before the flooding of the lake basin the general population density of the Northern Rhodesian section of the valley—Gwembe Valley—was less than 8 people per square mile, but in the settled and exploited areas densities commonly ranged from 100 to more than 300 per square mile, in accordance

---

[1] Trapnell (175) first described the ecology and traditional systems. Thayer Scudder has recently completed a much more detailed and complete study of environment and land-use. Elizabeth Colson's parallel study, *The Social Organisation of the Valley Tonga*, has already been published.

with the extent of alluvial soils. Elsewhere the land was empty of people and full of game. Many of these settled areas were greatly over-populated, with consequent soil degeneration and fragmentation of the alluvial land. The valley as a whole, a hot, dry region of short and uncertain rainfall, had had a long history of recurrent droughts, floods, and famine. But, judging by counts made over some fifty years, populations had increased at an alarming rate in spite of chronic ill-health and periodic disasters mitigated by famine relief.

By 1957 there were some 50,000 Tonga in the Gwembe Valley, of whom about 34,000 lived in 193 villages within the basin of the future lake. It was not a great number; in fact, it was much fewer than had been moved with little difficulty and no resistance in the resettlement programme more than a decade earlier: but the problem was vastly more difficult since the Tonga could not contemplate movement beyond the valley. And in the meantime the political climate, and with it the relationship between Africans and Europeans, had changed beyond recognition.

Every effort was made to squeeze the displaced people into what would be left of their valley. For two years the soils were mapped and checked with the aid of air photographs. Cultivable land was found, including an uninhabited area at Lusitu far down the river below the dam, and another still further down by the junction of Kafue and Zambesi—but this was too far. The carrying capacity of each area was estimated in accordance with Tonga customary practice, as a basis for planned resettlement. The plan was as sound, from the land-use point of view, as could be devised in the circumstances, and the compensation for loss and disturbance was scrupulously fair: but the land within the valley was not enough and full use of what there was entailed in some cases long distance moves and in others the splitting up of villages and kin groups to fit the population pattern to the distribution of the remaining cultivable areas.

Planned redistribution of population was tried, but in the end there was little orderly settlement because of the resistance and objections of the bewildered Tonga. All that would happen had been explained again and again with painstaking care, but few could believe what they were told—any more than Noah's contemporaries could believe his prophecies of the Flood—and there was doubt, bewilderment, and suspicion of motives, a suspicion heightened by African political agents and by the chain tractor felling of woodland to clear the basin of the lake. To many of the Tonga these great clearings were confirmation of the rumour that Europeans were coming to settle there, though their real purpose had been explained to them.

Balanced settlement of a total population of about 11,000 was carried out, 6,000 in the distant Lusitu area and 5,000 at Buleya Mulema, but most other areas were greatly overpopulated from the beginning. Some did move beyond the valley to an area of the Choma plateau, but when I was there in 1959 they had given up after clearing about 60 acres of unfamiliar soil in a strange environment and were drifting back to the valley to swell the overpopulation between the edge of the escarpment and the barrier hills.

Most of the trouble that made headline news arose in connexion with the move of 6,000 people of Chipepo's chieftaincy, which had a total population of 9,000, to the distant Lusitu, a road journey of over 200 miles. It was here, at the focal point of Chisamu's village, that resistance was strongest, and here the "battle" was fought in which eight men of the Tonga died. Many more died by misfortune. Weakened by their own stubborn resistance, by the privations of the terrible flood that almost wrecked the dam, and by the emotional upset and additional labour of the move, the people were more than usually susceptible to disease. Bacillary dysentery, always mildly endemic in the valley, flared up to the proportions of an epidemic, measles broke out among the children and killed the weakest: but smallpox which so often played the part of mass killer in the past did not appear because all the people had been vaccinated. Then at Lusitu itself the strangest misfortune of all came upon the settlers. A violent epidemic, perhaps an unknown form of poisoning, broke out in some of the new villages killing only children and young women. Although it was very thoroughly investigated, the origin of this mysterious catastrophe was never discovered. The Tonga adopted their own remedy; they abandoned the stricken villages and the epidemic ended.

"Was it witchcraft?" asks David Howarth in his recent book on the movement of the valley people (84). "Is Lusitu haunted? Are the souls of dead Tonga angry about the move? Nobody who knows the Tonga would laugh at these possibilities."

The Lusitu settlers are fortunate at least in one respect; they have fertile land in a not unfamiliar environment sufficient to provide their needs for a good many years. The case in the upper valley is altogether different, but the overcrowding and threat of future land destruction was not taken too seriously because there would be land enough for immediate needs and the filling of the lake would create great new opportunities for the future. Many of the Tonga, it was thought, could leave the land and become commercial fishermen. Indeed, by 1959, as the waters rose following the closure of the dam in December of the previous year, some were already learning the techniques of nets and larger fishing craft. In addition, there is a possibility that some at least of the *mopani* soils may be made cultivable, and a prospect that in the end the people may become reconciled to the idea of movement beyond the valley.

No one can foresee the final outcome. There is another doubt, another uncertainty. When, in late 1959, I went into the valley by the new motor road that a few months earlier had led to Chisamu's village, we were stopped by the rising waters of the lake. But there was no water to be seen. Ahead of us was *mopani* woodland flushed to an unnatural green, and between the trees a a flat expanse of a different green like a gigantic lawn. Over this "lawn" the track of the road continued in a straight line through the drowning trees, its surface deceptively solid looking. The sight was so unexpected, so astonishing, that I almost plunged the car into Lake Kariba before I realised the nature of that green surface. Every square foot of water was hidden under a cover of floating aquatic plants—*Salvinia*, one of the water ferns. This strange tropical plant is rootless, but it has filamentous and greatly modified leaves that trail in the water and act as roots, and it spreads and multiplies mainly by growth and subdivision of the parent plants. Already it had made a light but complete cover over all the area we could see, a cover not dense enough to stay the passage of a large and powerful animal. Along the swathe of the road three kudu were swimming for their lives. Slowly, laboriously they came on, to scramble ashore where we were standing— a great bull with enormous spiral horns, a cow, and a well grown calf—too exhausted to know or care that were were there. They had saved themselves without the help of Operation Noah.

How much of the lake will stabilise as open water and how

much as sudd? How far does this weed, and others such as the Nile cabbage, threaten the future of the fishing industry that was to offer a new way of life to the people of the valley?

5. THE BAROTSE PLAIN

Before it plunges over the Victoria Falls and races through tortuous gorges to the floor of the drowning valley, the Zambesi flows through a region of Kalahari sands, the remnant of a wind-blown late Tertiary desert that must have been as desolate as the Sahara. Here the river and its tributaries have scooped out a great flood plain well over a hundred miles long and from fifteen to thirty miles wide. The deep mantle of the sands acts as a vast sponge, absorbing every millimetre of rain that falls on it, holding the water and feeding it out slowly through perennially moist seepage zones along the scarps which border the great plain and the smaller depressions and valleys. These moist areas extend out into the flood plains in many places as waterlogged but potentially highly fertile peats.

In this situation the Lozi of the central plain have evolved a system of land-use as complex and unique as their environment, a system remarkable for its ingenious exploitation of the environment, for the development of large-scale drainage, and for the use of cattle manure to maintain fertility. As we shall see, the use of manure is not uncommon in African agriculture but it is lacking in the other traditional systems of Northern Rhodesia, where domestic livestock are surprisingly few, and cattle, though now extending in distribution and increasing greatly in numbers, were confined to a few localities with the main concentrations in parts of the Southern Province and Central Barotseland. The Lozi herds were greatly reduced by pleuro-pneumonia over a period of twenty years, 1916–36, before the disease was finally eliminated, but in all probability cattle are now at least as numerous as they ever were in the past, though they are more concentrated.

For purposes of very brief description, a section of the plain, extending from the edge of the woodland that covers the Kalahari sands to the Zambesi river, may be regarded as consisting of four typical regions, the *litongo*, the *mataba*, the *sana*, and *bulozi*. The *litongo*, is the narrow upper belt of sandy soils between the margin of the woodland and the permanently waterlogged seepage land below. It is divided into two parts, the upper dry *litongo* where the water-table lies a few feet below the surface, and the lower moist *litongo* which is perennially moist but well-drained. Habitations are generally sited between the two, so that here again one finds the pattern of a "street of villages." The dry *litongo* is poor and it is cultivated to bulrush millet and cassava, with some maize and sorghum, either under systems of short- or medium-term recurrent cultivation or continuously with the use of manure. Where sufficient cattle are available they are penned on the land at night and the pen is moved every week or so until the whole area has been covered. By contrast, the moist *litongo* is humic and astonishingly fertile. It is used, in effect, for kitchen gardens, and the part nearest the huts receives household sweepings and the manure of small-stock. Here a wide range of food crops and useful plants is grown continuously, including a succession of winter maize crops, fruit trees, surgarcane, sorghum of saccharine types, bananas, pineapples, cucurbits, early-maturing cassava, kapok, kidney cotton, and tobacco.

The *mataba*, which lies below the *litongo* and extends up to a mile into the plain, contains a large belt of saturated peat soils carrying a vegetation of *Scleria* and other sedges and the grass *Imperata cylindrica*. The drainage of these soils, to form the fertile and almost continuously cultivated *sishanjo* gardens, is the most remarkable achievement of Lozi agriculture. A network of primary and secondary channels carries the water to natural watercourses and pools or, usually, to main canals which are often ten miles and sometimes as much as twenty-five miles in length. Such an achievement is, of course, possible only for a highly organised people.

The *sana* is a slightly elevated region between the *mataba* and the flood plain of *bulozi* in which the bulk of the soils are sandy, infertile, and generally uncultivable. Cultivation is restricted to areas of more compact sands above the usual flood level and very restricted sites on mounds of termite origin.

The fourth region, *bulozi*, the heartland of the Lozi, is a shallow depression some miles in width which flanks the Zambesi throughout its course through the plain. It is a region of lakes, lagoons, and waterways, with belts of alluvial soils and large areas of loose, infertile sand deposits. Alluvial sites are brought into cultivation, generally in June or July, as the receding flood uncovers them, and planted to crops of early-maturing maize, sorghum, cucurbits, groundnuts, sweet potatoes, and tobacco. These are clayey or silty loam soils the fertility of which is renewed annually by the floods. In addition, the better variants of the sand soils on higher parts of the flood plain are cultivated to bulrush millet and cassava for short periods under systems of short-term recurrent cultivation, or for longer periods with the use of manure. When manure is used, cattle are kept on the garden at night tied to stakes some feet apart, and the position of the stakes is altered from time to time. Ant-hill sites are of supreme importance on the flood plain. Not only are they highly prized for gardens, but they are the only practicable places for building. These sites usually carry a fertile cap of loamy soil and they are generally heavily manured by staked cattle and cultivated continuously for long periods.

For the people of *bulozi*, and many who live in the *sana*, life is dominated by the flood. They and their cattle have to carry out a regular transhumance, leaving the plains villages as the flood rises in February or March and returning in June as the waters fall. The unpredictability of the floods, added to the normal risks of this zone of uncertain climate, makes agriculture a hazardous enterprise; consequently, fishing and cattle husbandry are of higher importance in the plains economy than cultivation.

The regime of the floods superimposed upon a highly variable environment has given rise to complex systems of land-usage in central Barotseland, systems which involve the use of a very considerable range of garden types and cropping patterns determined by soil qualities and water relationships. Adequate description would require a book of respectable size. The main outlines of Lozi land-use have been described by Trapnell in 1937 (175) and much more recently David Peters set himself the formidable task of making a detailed and quantitative study. He never completed this work—it was cut short by his untimely death in 1954—but some of his notes and the data he was accumulating have been salvaged and preserved as a Communication of the Rhodes Livingstone Institute (130).

One reason for Peters' investigation was that home production of food in Central Barotseland appeared to be falling steadily. This was curious and disturbing. In the past, production from the drained land and other gardens above flood level, the mixed economy, the cattle herds, the abundance of fish, wildfowl and game, had ensured an ample and varied diet, in spite of the uncertainty of flood-plain cultivation. Livingstone had written of the central plain as a place of abundance in which hunger was not known. Gluckman, when he was working among the Lozi, noted that food was still plentiful in 1940, but when he returned only two years later he had the impression that it was in much shorter supply. In order to get enough food for his carriers and paddlers, he had to travel out into the plain and intercept Lunda and Luvale canoes bringing cassava meal from the north. In 1940 he had been able to buy local supplies at one-third of the price. When he returned again in 1947 he felt that he was entering a famine area which was kept going by even greater food imports from the north. There were, of course, no statistics by which changes in food production and local trade could be measured. Annual flood levels and special factors deriving from wartime conditions might have combined to produce an impression of declining food output: but when he had made allowance for these he was still of the opinion that there was a constant trend to greater scarcity of food, and his impression was shared by others with long experience of the area.[1]

Peters found that considerable changes had taken place in the seventeen years since Trapnell's study. He was particularly impressed by the "enormous areas of abandoned *sishanjo*"—the drained gardens of the peat lands. Within the area he surveyed in detail he found clear evidence that 25,200 acres of *sishanjo* had once been cultivated, where (in 1949) only 4,600 acres remained in use. The loss of these highly productive areas had started many years earlier, as Trapnell noted, with the abolition of customary labour service and the freeing of serfs. Without this compulsory labour the drains could not be kept open and much of the land reverted to marsh. The tribal authorities voted money for the upkeep of the drains, but this had little effect since by that time the labour migration was absorbing more than half the Lozi manpower, and the wages offered were much lower than those prevailing outside Barotseland. Peters' figures also indicate a decrease in the cultivated area of a number of other garden forms, and this decline together with the increasing loss of *sishanjo* may

[1] The evidence for increasing food shortage and its possible origins is more fully discussed by Allan and Gluckman in their preface to Peters (130).

well have accounted for the apparent decrease in home production and the growing reliance on imports of food.

The most probable explanation of this situation is to be found in the effects of labour migration on what is, for tribal Africa, a varied and complex economy. The simple economies of systems and environments which call for a high in-put of man-power only at one season of the year can withstand the withdrawal of a high proportion of the labour force for considerable periods; but the Lozi case is different. Land preparation and cultivation throughout most of the year, on a range of widely dispersed moist and dry gardens, the upkeep of drains, different methods of fishing practised also on scattered sites, the care and herding of cattle, the manuring of gardens, and the transhumance movements, call for a continuous in-put of man-power. When labour is withdrawn one or other of these multifarious activities must inevitably suffer. Gluckman's sociological and economic study, *The Economy of the Central Barotse Plain*, gives a clear picture of the complex and difficult labour problems which confronted the Lozi, even before their problems were greatly complicated by the loss of men. The rate of migration to work increased during and after the War, from 38 per cent of men in 1940 to 50 per cent in 1947, as Peters notes, and with this heavy loss the Lozi could no longer meet the labour demands of all their productive activities. The main effect, it seems, appeared as a reduction of the cultivated acreage.

By the time of Peters' study, however, a new factor had appeared—the plough. He records that ploughs were in common use by 1950. Only a few people owned them, but many others shared in their use and at that time it was unusual to find a garden hand-cultivated which could be ploughed. This was leading to changes in the garden forms. For example, large areas of the poorer sand soils traditionally cultivated briefly as mound gardens for root crops under a system of Recurrent Cultivation, and known as dry *mukomena*—were being used as plough land; they could still be identified by persistent traces of the former mounds. Other sandy soils of the plains—plains *litongo*—had also come under the plough, and fallow periods had been reduced because falling yields could be compensated by increasing the ploughed area. All the fertile ant-hill sites had long been in use, but here the cultivated area was being extended by ploughing on to the surrounding weaker soils of sandy texture—though the whole extended garden was still known by the old name, *lizulu*.

On the other hand, cultivation of the alluvium of the inner plain—the *sitapa* gardens of Bulozi—had decreased. The situation here might have been affected by unfavourable flood seasons, but Peters concluded that there had been a true and permanent decrease and he noted that the large *sitapa* gardens formerly cultivated by the richer families (recorded by Trapnell and Clothier) no longer existed. A somewhat similar garden form, the *sitapa sa matundu*, cultivated on riverside sites ranging from sandy loams to clay loams, had become practically extinct.

Another noteable change was the extension of woodland or *matema* cultivation on the sands beyond the edge of the plain. This form of Recurrent Cultivation for cassava and bulrush millet had probably been adopted from a system of neighbouring peoples, the northern Kalahari woodland system. It received some encouragement from the locust outbreak of the 1930s and the influx of the peoples from the west, but until the 1940s it was largely confined to the immediate border of the plain. Peters noted that by 1950 *matema* cultivation had been widely but not universally adopted, and the gardens extended a good many miles beyond the plain's edge. This he attributed partly to the need to compensate for loss of other garden forms and partly to the state of the land on the edge of the plain which had become exhausted by frequent re-cultivation and reduced to a short cover of *Baphia* and *Bauhinia* scrub.

It seemed, then, that ploughing and other changes such as increasing use of woodland gardens were beginning to offset the effects of labour shortage on food production, but at the same time these changes were altering the unique character of Lozi agriculture, not always for the better. On the credit side, Peters records a greater use of manure following the increase of cattle numbers, "to the benefit of the gardens of those who own or use cattle."

The degeneration of African traditional systems of land-use has been brought about most commonly by increase of population beyond the point of critical density, by the introduction of cash-cropping, by loss of land either to other tribes or for European farming areas, and, generally to a lesser extent, by loss of labour. The Lozi case is interesting as an example of a degenerative process set in train by labour loss alone and its effect on an economy of unusual complexity.

Since the time of Peters' study larger resources have been applied to the solution of the technical problems of Lozi agriculture and it is reported that the situation has improved considerably. A beginning has been made with the formidable task of bringing abandoned *sishanjo* back into cultivation, with marked success in at least one area: but large scale reclamation of these lands calls for a drainage programme on the grand scale. Ploughs are more numerous and their use has extended to the *sitapa* lands where large gardens are once more cultivated. These changes, and general improvements of techniques, are said to have altered the situation to the extent that Barotseland can now produce a surplus, or at least a sufficiency, of food in a favourable flood season such as that of 1958–9.

Part II
Environments and Systems of Land-Use

Chapter XI

BANANA CULTURES OF EAST AFRICA

1. Bananas and Plantains as Food Crops

The regions and systems we have considered so far are capable of supporting only low or, at best, very moderate densities of population, except as localised concentrations in the "special environments." All of these regions lie below 9° south latitude, within the southern Sudanian climatic regime. Further north, in the double-rainfall zone bordering the equator, between the arid zone and the equatorial rain forest, we should expect to find regions of much higher human-carrying capacity, especially where bananas are the staple food crop.

"Banana" is used here as a general term to include the cooking varieties or plantains (*Musa paradisiaca*), which are most extensively grown by the banana-eating peoples, as well as the familiar table fruit (*M. sapientum*). Many varieties of both species are used by African cultivators. The Chagga, for example, have some 40 different types and varieties, the majority of which are for cooking while others are for eating as fresh fruit and for beer-making.

On strong, rich soils under suitable conditions of temperature and moisture, the banana is a perennial crop capable of yielding fruit for many years without replanting, and without tillage or manuring of any kind. It also gives high and reliable yields. The present average yield for Buganda is, probably, rather less than four tons of green fruit per acre: but I was told by Agricultural Officers who work with the crop that 10 to 20 tons per acre can be got without much difficulty, and it is thought that standards of cultivation and yields were considerably higher in the past before cash crops absorbed so much of the cultivators' time and attention. Even at the present relatively low yield levels, one-third of an acre per head of population, or less, should suffice to provide the bulk food requirements, although a grown man eats the equivalent of seven pounds of green fruit a day. In the traditional systems, however, cultivation of bananas was supplemented by arable cropping.

These systems have changed and are changing, generally in the direction of greater reliance on bananas as a food crop, but sometimes in the opposite direction. For example, the Amba of the Ruwenzori mountains of Uganda, whose admirable environment is well suited to the permanent culture of bananas, formerly relied largely on this crop. In quite recent times banana weevil severely damaged the groves with the result that the banana, though still used largely for beer-making, has become a comparatively minor food crop. Sweet potatoes and cassava have taken its place as main staples.

2. The Chagga of Kilimanjaro

The Chagga on the moist southern slopes and magnificent vol-canic soils of Kilimanjaro have long practised an advanced form of agriculture involving the feeding of livestock, the conservation of manure, and the control and distribution of water. The German missionary Rebmann, who was the first European to go among the Chagga, wrote in 1848 of their admirably constructed irrigation works, of the great care they observed in the maintenance of these works, and of their powerfully centralised social organisation. Sir Harry Johnston, writing in 1894, echoed this praise of Chagga in-dustry and skill: "They mostly excel in their husbandry—the skill with which they irrigate their terraced hillsides with tiny runnels of water shows a considerable advancement in agriculture. Their time is constantly spent in tilling the soil, manuring it with ashes, raking it and hoeing it with wooden hoes." At this time, before coffee planting and pressure of population altered the pattern, the holding of a family consisted typically of two parts, the *kihamba* and *shamba*. The *kihamba* included the homestead and a sur-rounding permanent grove of bananas, while on the *shamba* land short-period arable cultivation alternated with brief natural grass leys which provided fodder for livestock.

Many of their cattle, the milk cows and slaughter stock, are stall-fed in small dark huts, while others graze out, where there is still some grazing to be found, or are picketed during the day. Goats, too, are commonly hand-fed. The work of supplying fod-der and bedding for these beasts is, I was told, the heaviest item in the Chagga labour budget. I found this easy to believe after I had seen the daily trek of the women from the dry lower areas where the grass is cut. They carry great bundles of fodder and bedding—some of which, I judged, must weigh 60 or 70 lb—up the steep and slippery mountain tracks, often for a good many miles. This feeding of livestock and the conservation and use of manure are traditional practices, but the transport of grass from the lower area—from which the Chagga were formerly excluded by the Masai, and which, presumably, they had little wish to colonise, since it is too dry for bananas as a staple crop—is probably a comparatively recent development, at least on its present scale. In the past all Chagga land was open to all Chagga for grazing and grass-cutting: now, with increase of population and coffee cultivation, pasturage and fodder-cutting land is very limited in the moist forest belt, and exclusive rights are asserted to the little that remains. The manure from the stall-fed beasts is now, one would think, produced at an excessive cost in women's labour, as is the meagre milk supply from the small zebu-type cow, which, as my Chagga informants put it, yields "just about enough milk to put in your tea." They have become great drinkers of tea, and they like it very sweet and milky.

In the past, the fertility of the *kihamba* was probably maintained at a fairly high level by the use of manure and surface mulching with banana litter and other crop refuse. The Chagga have retained these practices, but the form of the garden has changed with the great development of coffee cultivation. Men with ample land have separate banana groves and coffee plantations, but where land is short, and this is now the common case, a mixture of bananas and coffee is the general rule. Very often there is a more or less pure stand of bananas close to the homestead with an increasing proportion of coffee outwards towards the margin of the holding where it may be grown as a pure crop. The bananas, or the parts of the garden where bananas predominate, usually get more weeding, mulching, and manuring.

The *shamba* land of the traditional pattern has now been replaced almost entirely by bananas and coffee throughout the belt suited to these crops—a belt which lies, roughly, between the 3,500 and 5,500 contours. This is Chaggaland proper: it is only in recent times with relief from Masai raids and under pressure of population, that the Chagga have come to cultivate the dry lower area they now speak of as *shamba* land. When I enquired about the former pattern of land-use my Chagga informants took me to the eastern part of the Rombo division, a drier area which is marginal for coffee and bananas, where population pressure is less owing to generally poorer soils and shortage of water. Here they showed me a holding of rather more than four acres, supporting a homestead of seven people, which they said, was as nearly representative of the traditional pattern as could now be found. The holding consisted of a homestead banana-grove just over two acres in extent, enclosed by a hedge, with about an acre and a quarter of unenclosed land in crop and three-quarters of an acre of grass fallow adjoining the grove. The greater part of the arable land had been planted to a cash crop, pyrethrum (the altitude being about 5,000 feet), while the remainder carried a mixed crop of maize and beans. I was told that if the crop land had carried finger millet, alone or in association with sweet potatoes or other crops, in place of pyrethrum, the pattern would have approximated closely to that of a traditional subsistence holding.

The general picture I was given was of a typical homestead of 4 or 5 people cultivating an acre to an acre and a half of bananas, and, in addition, annual crop land of approximately equal extent. The main crops grown in the *shamba* were finger millet, sweet potatoes, yams, maize, and beans. Manure was reserved for the *kihamba*, and the *shamba* soils were generally rested at intervals, commonly in a ratio of about three years' cultivation to two years' fallow. On weaker soils, however, fallow periods were approximately equal to, or may have exceeded, the cultivation periods, while on the strongest and most fertile land cultivation was virtually continuous.

The remarkable water distribution system of the Chagga was formerly used for supplementary irrigation, particularly for the irrigation of finger millet. This crop seems to have been of major importance: it was used in beer making, in the payment of the customary gifts or "taxes" for the maintenance of the social hierarchy of chiefs and "nobles," and as a cereal. There is little irrigation now, as the water is required for the domestic needs of a greatly increased population and for coffee pulping, but I met a few men who said they irrigated their banana groves from time to time. The construction of the furrow system through which water is distributed to homesteads throughout the mountain, over many miles of difficult country, represents an engineering feat of no mean order, and the successful operation of the delicate machinery required to maintain the works and to administer rights and easements must be regarded as a social achievement no less remarkable. Users of a furrow formed what was, in effect, a "Water Users Association" which met to decide upon the equitable division of water and to arrange a programme of maintenance by communal effort.

Administrative rights, as Gutmann describes them (72), were based on "ownership" of canals and furrows. Some particularly large canals, constructed by communal effort, were owned by chiefs and operated by their appointed agents. Others were the property of the families of those who had made the furrow. The head of an "Association" using a furrow was normally a member and the representative of the owning family: he acquired his position by inheritance. This "owner" of the furrow had religious as well as administrative duties. He had to organise and lead the annual cleaning and repair of the furrow, and all the members were required to help in this work. If a member failed to do so without reasonable excuse, or to provide a substitute, he was liable to lose his rights to the use of water from the furrow. The "owner" also had to offer the sacrifices and prayers which would ensure the continuing flow of water, and he alone could do so.

Water sources—springs and streams from which canals and furrows were taken off—and storage basins were also owned, and these owners received nominal gifts in recognition of their rights.

Distribution of water among members of an Association was governed by rule, and doubtful cases were settled by discussion. The user at the lowest end of a furrow had first right of use, and others in their turn up the furrow; but it was a general rule that the owner could dispose of the water every third day if he wished. He was, however, expected to transfer this right to those in greatest need whose crops had reached the wilting point: these were the "days of petition," when people in urgent need petitioned the owner for the use of water. The duties of the furrow owners, apart from their ritual functions, were not unlike those of the Chairman of a regional Water Board.

The associations of water users were not exclusive. A stranger could apply for membership, but he had to be introduced by the owner and accepted by a full meeting of members. Usually he was accepted, after he had made an offering of beer.

Chiefs had an ultimate right even in furrows they did not own. If an owning family died out or migrated, or if the sole heir was found to be unfit, ownership of the furrow reverted to the Chief. He could also deprive a family and take ownership of their furrow to himself if a member of the family committed a serious crime.

Remnants of this organisation survive, but responsibility for the water system is now largely in the hands of the modern Native Authority.

The old land-use system of the Chagga, within the moist forest environment of high fertility, must have been capable of supporting populations of very considerable density. We can only guess at what the Critical Population Density for this system and environment may have been, but a figure of 400 people per square mile, as a general average, would seem to be a reasonably safe guess. The cultivable percentage of the land is undoubtedly high and may well amount to at least half the surface area, while the total requirement of cultivable land can hardly have amounted to more than 0·75 acre per head of population, allowing for the fact that rather more than a subsistence acreage was cultivated, since the cultivator had to provide a regular and reliable surplus for the maintenance of the political organisation. Old men of the Chagga told me that cultivation of finger millet, and the opening of new land for this purpose, had been encouraged in the past with the object of securing a higher surplus for the support of the Chiefs' Courts.

3. The Gishu of Mount Elgon

Such a system is readily capable of change and would, under pressure of population, have tended to change by reduction of the area of annual crops and increasing reliance on the banana grove. A sequence of change in this direction may be observed by climbing the south-eastern slopes of the Mount Elgon massif in Uganda. Here, in an environment very similar to that of the Chagga, on rich, deep volcanic loams, the Gishu have developed a closely parallel system of land-use. At lower levels, where population density is somewhere around 200 per square mile, annual crop land predominates. The typical holding, at a guess, may be something of the order of 5 acres, with one acre in bananas, 2·5 acres in annual crops, and 1·5 acres resting. Finger millet, which is usually grown in association with sorghum or maize, is a major food crop, and groundnuts, beans, and cowpeas are important subsidiaries. The finger millet association is commonly sown with the first rains, followed by cowpeas or beans with the second rains; or, where rainfall is higher, two cereal crops may. be taken in one year. Maize makes its appearance as a conspicuous crop in this area which lies between the finger millet culture to the north and the maize culture of adjoining districts in Kenya. Erosion is not un- common on steep slopes denuded for annual crop cultivation, while even in the banana groves standards of cultivation are un- impressive and mulching and manuring are often neglected. The majority of cattle are grazed at large in small herds, and much manure is lost: night droppings, which might be conserved and used, may often be seen thrown aside and left to leach and waste in rain and sun.

On the higher cultivated slopes the picture is different. Annual crop cultivation has almost disappeared though a little finger millet is retained, and the food supply comes almost entirely from the groves, which are intensively cultivated. Subsidiary food crops, including beans, cocoyams, yams, and shallots, are grown in the groves with the bananas, and now, of course, there is coffee as well. Here mulching is generally practised. A few people have sheds for their animals, but cattle and small-stock are more usually kept in a part of the dwelling hut at night and tethered out during the day. Cattle are tethered at stake on small plots reserved for the purpose where they are hand-fed with cut fodder and split banana pseudo- stems and leaves, while goats are tied up around the huts and are also hand-fed. Strict control of livestock is a necessity imposed by the intensiveness of cultivation and the contiguity of homesteads, for wandering animals can cause serious loss and create much friction in the community. Bedding is not provided for the live- stock—or at least I saw no evidence of this: the raw manure is cleared out daily and put on the grove, mostly on the upper part nearest to the homestead. Although the groves are often on steep slopes, much steeper than is generally the case in Chaggaland, there is little evidence of erosion owing to the completeness of the ground cover; and where run-off from paths or other bare ground does threaten to start the process, trenches are dug to catch the run-off and act as silt-traps. This, the Gishu maintain, is an old traditional practice.

My Gishu host gave me his explanation of these differences in land-use on the upper and lower levels. In the past, he said, the Gishu had been subjected to almost constant raiding by a number of pastoral peoples who came to steal their cattle. From one side came the Karamojong and the Teso, and from the other the Masai and a people he called the "Bazumbu." Some of the marauders might be quiescent for a time, but nearly always one or other was on the move and the Gishu could know no peace except by living on the upper slopes, which were readily defensible and difficult of access for the raiders. As population increased in this limited area the people had come to rely increasingly on bananas and to adopt more and more intensive practices. Then, when British administration had grown strong enough to stop raiding—this happened, he said, in his father's time—the Gishu colonised the lower slopes only slowly and suspiciously, but those who did found plenty of good land and they had therefore abandoned the intensive practices of the uplands. This was very sensible of them, he thought, for no African loves labour for its own sake; and, in his experience, Europeans have much the same attitude. It was a long time since he had seen an Agricultural Officer so high on the mountain, or so far from a motor road: but, he added with a twinkle, they were probably much too busy in Mbale to spare time for mountaineering.

He spoke of these things while we ate a very large and excellent meal, served by his four well-nourished and cheerful wives. There was a great dish of cooked bananas with a relish of stewed chicken, followed by fresh table bananas and a pint or two of sweet, milky tea. The Gishu, like the Chagga, have become great drinkers of tea which they take with their meals. Two meals are generally eaten in the day and all meals are much the same, except for changes of relish. Meat or chicken is eaten three or four times a week by the more prosperous Gishu, and vegetable relishes, usually beans, on other occasions.

My host did not seem to find this diet monotonous. He lived in remarkable contentment with his four wives and twenty-eight children, except for three major worries. He was worried about the increasing damage to coffee by lacewing fly, which he had heard, and believed, was due to the killing off of parasites and predators of the lacewing by repeated spraying against *Antestia*. It seemed, he said, that one could not get rid of one pest without opening the door to another. Also to be classified as a pest was a careless neighbour who would not picket his animals securely and sometimes even left them loose at night. Time and again they had come on to his land, until, in despair of getting results by any other means, he had retaliated by cutting down a number of the neighbour's coffee trees. For this he had just spent twenty-eight days in gaol, but he did not think the price too high. The gaol had been reasonably comfortable, and the nuisance had now ceased—permanently, he hoped.

In contrast with the politically conscious Chagga, he knew little of political matters and cared less—the agents of change, it seemed, were also too busy to come so far up the mountain—though he had heard vaguely and with little interest of the trouble and boycotts in Buganda, the proclamation of a state of disturbance, and the proscription of the Uganda National Movement. His biggest worry was the future of his large family, and he thought of this problem in terms of land. Although he was a considerable landowner and he was buying as much as he could, there would not be enough land for them. A small family, a man with just one wife and their children, might, he said, be able to get along on three acres of bananas and coffee: but really, what with taxes, schooling, clothing, and all the other commitments one had to meet nowadays, this was not enough for decent living. The Chagga, too, repeatedly mentioned a figure of 3 acres as the bare minimum needed to provide a family of four or five with what they considered a reasonable standard of living.

The land requirement of a subsistence economy based largely on the banana grove may well have been somewhat lower than this. I have already suggested (page 61) that the Cultivation Factor for such a system may not have exceeded half an acre. Perhaps it was even lower than this where dependence on the grove was almost complete, for it is said in Buganda that two acres of bananas will provide ample food for a family of eight. If, however, we assume a Cultivation Factor of 0·5 and a general cultivable percentage of 50, a not improbable figure even for the higher cultivated slopes of Mount Elgon, there seems no reason why such systems should not have supported populations of about 600 per square mile in environments suited to permanent, intensive cultivation of bananas. It is not inconceivable that the best environments may have been capable of supporting even higher densities, of the order of 800 or even 1,000 per square mile, without damage to the land or disruption of the system. The present general population density of the higher areas of Mount Elgon is probably of the order of 600 per square mile or more, while that of the Chagga homeland is almost certainly between 800 and 900 per square mile.

4. BUGANDA

The "low" population density of Buganda is in striking contrast with these figures. Here is a region of fertility and potential productivity almost without parallel in Africa. The system of food production is based largely on the banana grove with only very limited subsidiary cultivation, mainly of beans, sweet potatoes, maize, groundnuts, and cassava. Yet the general population density for the province is well below 100 to the square mile, and it is little above this figure in Mengo which is the most populous of the three districts and which includes the town of Kampala. On the basis of the 1948 census figures, the general population density for the province was 78, with 90, 80, and a mere 33 per square mile in Mengo, Masaka, and Mubande respectively. Even now, despite the great area planted to coffee and cotton, rather less than 16 per cent of the total available land surface is cultivated— according to the 1958 crop estimates (20). This situation appears to be due to the impact of forces making for depopulation upon a people of peculiarly low fertility. The later years of the last century were marked by social and economic disruption on a large scale, and the first two decades of the present century by devastating epidemics of disease. From 1900 to 1905 a terrible outbreak of sleeping sickness decimated the population of Buganda and this was followed by plague, which has been brought under control only comparatively recently, and by smallpox, cerebro-spinal fever, dysentery, and the great influenza epidemic of 1918–19. Sir Albert Cook, writing in 1918, doubted if even "the dreadful ravages of the slave trade" had accomplished greater destruction than "the epidemics of recent years." It seems that the Ganda are, biologically, ill-equipped to sustain such an extraordinary succession of catastrophes. The low fertility of this people has been remarked by a number of observers, starting with Sir Harry Johnson who noted that Buganda women were "very poor breeders" and added the curious and obviously mistaken observation that a second child "is a very unusual occurrence." The reasons for this unusual infertility are not yet clear, though they are being investigated. Whatever the reasons, there is little doubt that the

Buganda population was decreasing during the period 1892–1920 (99).

5. THE HAYA OF BUKOBA

The banana cultures we have noted are practised on soils which are, for sub-Saharan Africa, of extraordinarily high fertility. Within the regions of continuous moisture and warmth suited to its growth, the duration of survival and fruiting of the banana plant is a very good indicator of soil quality. Only on soils of the highest strength and fertility will it go on yielding almost indefinitely with little care and attention. On what are regarded as "good" soils in the forest belt of Ghana three, or at best four, crops can be taken before the plants die, while on the leached lands of the Congo basin no more than two harvests are expected, and on still weaker soils the plants may yield one poor crop or none at all. It is, of course, possible, with the resources available to a people of advanced technology, to upgrade a number of soil types to the level required for banana culture, and this is not uncommonly done in commercial production of the crop where high capital expenditure is practicable and justifiable: but it would be very surprising to find an indigenous banana culture—that is, a system of food production based almost entirely on this fruit—developed by an African people in a region of low fertility. Yet, at first sight, this is what the Haya people of the Bukoba district in Tanganyika seem to have done.

The Haya practise their system of banana culture within a relatively narrow coastal belt on the south-western side of Lake Victoria, extending some 12 to 16 miles inland from the lake. This coastal region receives an abundant, well-distributed rainfall, with a mean annual precipitation exceeding 80 inches at Bukoba; and, although there are two well-defined peaks, of which the first, in March–April, is the higher, there is no really dry month of less than 1·5 inches. The second peak comes, usually, in November–December, and July is the driest month. Under such conditions of rainfall and equable temperatures one might well expect to find high forest vegetation: but in fact much of the country is grassland on soils which have been described as "leached, light, non-retentive and empty of nutrients." So poor are these grassland soils that, under arable cultivation without manure, they are commonly used for only one crop of groundbeans followed by a fallow of from seven to ten years duration. Yet, in this unlikely environment, the main food supply is derived from flourishing banana groves often of luxuriant growth. The pattern of land-use is strange and possibly unique. "Villages" or groups of homesteads, with their groves of bananas—and now, of course, robusta coffee on a considerable scale—form compact islands of fertility in the sea of grassland (see Plate 4). Within these "islands," land-use practice is very similar to that of the typical banana cultures. The main grove, generally very close to the homestead, is well tended. The stools are uniformly spaced at intervals of about six and a half feet, and cattle manure is applied to the grove where any is available, while banana peelings and any other suitable household refuse is placed around the stools. Beans and other minor annual and perennial crops are planted between the stools. Mulching is generally practised, with banana leaves and split pseudo-stems as the main material, in the groves. Cut and transported grass is more commonly used as a mulch for coffee. As usual, manure is applied unevenly, generally on the upper side of sloping land near the dwellings; consequently, the state of the groves becomes progressively poorer with distance from the homestead. The care given to the main groves is rarely extended to the coffee which has been described as being "in various stages of neglect."

Cattle are now few and many people are no longer interested in keeping them, probably because of the disasters of the past and the continuing danger of loss from disease, especially east coast fever. They are kept in the dwelling huts or kitchens at night and taken out to graze in the tick-infested grassland for a few hours each day. Milk yields are negligible and those who keep cattle value them mainly as producers of manure.

I have heard it argued by agriculturalists that the fertility of the cultivated "islands" was artificially created and built up in the past by the addition of great quantities of manure from vanished herds; that is, in effect, by denuding the grassland and transferring its fertility. But, allowing the existence of the herds, it is difficult to understand how a people with no means of making, handling, and transporting manure in bulk could have achieved so dramatic a result over such an area, even though the soils "react magnificently to dung" as I was told they do. Undoubtedly, the Bukoba district carried very large numbers of cattle in the past: the explorers of last century, Speke, Grant, and Stanley, all bear witness to this. But the great herds were owned by pastoral people who had established the Hamitic kingdom of Karagwe in the now sparsely-populated and tsetse-infested western part of the district.

McMaster (107) points out that, although the eastern area bordering the lake was vaguely tributary to Karagwe, it is far from ideal for cattle and it is separated from high Karagwe by the poor country of the central depression. One cannot, therefore, postulate with any certainty that there were very large numbers of cattle in the country of the coastal ridges where the Haya cultivate their banana groves.

Before the end of the century the power of Karagwe, which seems so stable in Speke's descriptions, had collapsed utterly and dramatically, almost overnight. Rinderpest killed the cattle. In the terrible epidemic of the early 1890s, nine-tenths of the animals may have died, according to Mettam's estimate (112), "and in some areas not a beast survived." This would have been enough to bring about the collapse of any structure based on pastoralism without the addition of dynastic disturbances, which were rife at the time, and a killing epidemic of smallpox among the people which followed the rinderpest. Bush invaded the ungrazed and depopulated grasslands, and with it the tsetse advanced from the central depression and the Kagera river valley, reducing the western area to a condition of desolation.

The great bulk of the population now occupies the lakeside strip of humid ridge-and-valley country, an area of approximately 1,000 square miles, or one-sixth of the district. Here, the general density exceeds 250 per square mile. The highest concentration of population in Tanganyika—1,235 to the square mile!—is reached in one of the sub-chiefdoms (62), while in five other sub-chiefdoms densities of well over 400 per square mile have been recorded.

The concentration of population is explained by the nature of the environment, which allows of permanent banana culture, and the peculiar pattern of land-use reflects the distribution of soils of naturally high and low fertility. As long ago as 1938 Milne offered an explanation of the existence of the fertile "islands" (113). The main underlying rock of the coastal ridges is a sandstone containing only quartz grains and cementing silica, incapable of providing parent material for a fertile soil: but there are also interbedded shales containing mica in the form of sericite and thick sills of intrusive dolerite which yield excellent clay-forming and soil-

making materials. The weak, empty soils derive from the coarse
sandstones, while deeper and more fertile soils have been built up of
transported and mixed material from the shales and dolerite, in
a pattern determined by the processes of land elevation and surface
sculpturing. Consequently, the distribution of the fertile sites appears to be haphazard; they occur on the tops of the planated
ridges and also on the flanks of the valleys and along the coastal
fringe.

These sites form what Milne described as "relatively small en-
claves of fertile land," and McMaster estimated that they are to
be found over only about one-fifth of the region. The remainder
consists of the poor grassland, and of bare rock out-crops, skeletal
soils, and rubbles where the ridges end in sandstone bluffs and
scree slopes, and valley swamps carrying tussock grassland or
papyrus or dense evergreen swamp forest. Even if the proportion
of cultivable land, in the sense of land suitable for permanent
banana culture, is as low as 20 per cent, this is not inconsistent
with a general Critical Population Density of 250 per square mile,
or with regional densities of a considerably higher order, since less
than half an acre of permanent grove will suffice for the support of
an individual.

The critical point has, however, been exceeded over most if not
all of the region, as a result of population increase and development
of coffee as a cash crop. Even at the time of Milne's survey land
shortage was general, although as he puts it, "there are wide areas
of little-used land almost everywhere, and on much of this the soil
is sufficiently well-drained and deep to be eminently cultivable"—
"cultivable," that is, in a physical sense, but too poor to allow of
the establishment of banana groves, or of more than long-term
Recurrent or Shifting Cultivation. This situation was misunder-
stood by the administrators of the time. Their reports refer repeatedly to a "grave social problem" created by a new generation
of young men lacking in initiative, who, "while awaiting their inheritance of the family holdings, are disinclined to develop new
ground for themselves." It was left to Milne to point out that such
statements laid blame unfairly on the "unambitious" young men,
who were faced with technical problems of regionally poor soils
"beyond resolution by themselves unaided."

The accessible fertile sites have all been used up and divided
and subdivided into permanent heritable holdings. These sites

once carried high forest, small remnants of which remain on some of the steeper ridge slopes; but whether the whole region was forested, as both Milne and McMaster have postulated, is more debatable. They suggest that the forest was destroyed and the poor grasslands created by haphazard exploratory cultivation. More probably, the Haya system was one of selection, rather than creation and destruction, of soils; but their practices have preserved, and probably in some degree enhanced, the fertility of the banana lands, and it may be that they have still further impoverished the intrinsically poor grassland—thereby accentuating the initial contrasts in fertility.

Populations continue to increase and McMaster says that pressure on the land is now "a formidable problem," while the balance has been further threatened "by rapid growth of coffee production and development of a cash economy."

CHAPTER XII

OTHER REGIONS OF HIGH POPULATION DENSITY IN EAST AFRICA

1. KIKUYULAND

Exceedingly high concentrations of population, possibly among the highest in sub-Saharan Africa, are reached in the three Kikuyu areas of Kenya's Central Province, the Nyeri, Fort Hall, and Kiambu districts. It is difficult to say with any certainty just what the population densities are in these districts, for the available data vary very considerably. Populations change in numbers and distribution, estimates vary, and the pattern of land categories is complex. There are Administrative Districts, Crown lands, Alienated lands, African Land Units—a euphemism for what were formerly called Native Reserves—which sometimes overlap two or more administrative districts; and there are Forest Reserves and other smaller categories such as Native Leasehold Areas, Native Settlement Areas, Communal Reserves, and lands devoted to special schemes. Estimates vary greatly, according to the figures for population and area one chooses to use, and in some places the results can be varied quite a bit by including or excluding open water. *See table on p. 177, at foot.

One may conjecture from these figures that general African population densities per square mile, in relation to accessible land —excluding alienated land and unavailable Crown land, forest reserve, and open water—are now something of the order of 600 in Fort Hall, 700 in Nyeri, and 900 in Kiambu, and it is possible that the figures may be higher. Such densities are comparable with those of the teeming Shan-Tung and Central provinces of China.

The breakdown of the Kikuyu traditional systems of land-use and land-holding probably began at least fifty years ago, under pressure of what must have been much smaller populations. Humphrey, in his essay on the Kikuyu lands (85), gives the population density of South Nyeri as 463 per square mile in 1936 and 542 in 1944, and he made the interesting prediction that the figure would reach 674 per square mile by 1955. Kuczynski was sceptical of such high increase rates, but they have not been disproved by events and it is now conceded (68) that "there seems good reason to confirm Sir Philip Mitchell's statement that the annual increase of population in Kenya may amount to 2 per cent in the most favourable areas" (117). Under this dynamic upsurge of population, within a limited and diminished land area, the Kikuyu system broke down rapidly in a chaos of subdivision and fragmentation

*

	AREA (Sq. miles)	AFRICAN POPULATION	SOURCE*
Nyeri	673[1]	183,057[2]	A (220), B (474)
	307[3]	253,328[4]	A (84, 222)
	322[5]	217,076[6]	C
	689[7]	229,000[8]	D
Fort Hall	739[1]	303,646[2]	A (220), B (474)
	585[3]	384,851[4]	A (91)
	568[5]	322,757[6]	C
	724[7]	380,000[8]	D
Kiambu	615[1]	258,085[2]	A (220), B (474)
	615[1]	388,162[4]	A (91)
	615[1]	303,573[6]	C
	315[9]	—	C
	733[7]	323,000[8]	D

* A = *African Land Development in Kenya;* B = *East African Royal Commission Report;* C = Working Data of the Agricultural Department (personal communication, unpublished); D = Elspeth Huxley, *A New Earth.* In these refs. to sources, the figures in brackets are page numbers.

Notes

1. Incl. Crown Land (alienated and un-alienated), as well as African Land Units, but excl. open water.
2. *Quarterley Economic and Statistical Bulletin* of the East African Statistical Dept., quoted in B.
3. "District Betterment" E figures.
4. East African Population Census, 1948.
5. Presumably African Land Units, in whole or in part.
6. Village census figures, 1955–6.
7. Administrative districts.
8. Estimates based on the last (1948) census of population, and "an arbitrary, bu possibly conservative, increase of 25 per cent" in the 12 years 1948–60: D (275).
9. Kiambu District Statistics, which give the total area of the 5 African Divisions of the district as "236,001 acres less the 34,600 acres of the Nydeiya Grazing Scheme," or approx. 315 sq. miles.

and degenerated into virtually continuous cultivation of a mixture of basic food crops.

This is a region of deep volcanic soils, the Kikuyu red loams, and of high fertility: but the climate lacks the equable, "hot house" quality associated with the regions of permanent banana culture. There is a dry and rather hot period at the beginning of the year, then the "long rains" come in the period March–June, followed by three cool, dry months and the "short rains" of October–December: but the "dry" seasons are only comparatively dry and there is no month without rain. Early travellers from Europe were much impressed and permanent settlers were attracted by this healthy and, in the cool months, tonic and invigorating climate. I myself can think of no more pleasant place than Nyeri in June.

The changes of the last half-century have been so profound that little remains to tell us how the Kikuyu exploited this admirable environment in the past. They had a complex system of land tenure and administration based on what has been described as "groups of committees composed of clan elders each with its jurisdiction over a defined locality, which normally lay between ridge and valley, as typified by the topography of Fort Hall and Nyeri districts" (98). In Kiambu, however, into which the Kikuyu infiltrated by "buying" land from Dorobo hunters and craftsmen in exchange for goats, "every individual claimed outright ownership to the land he bought." The pattern of land-use may also have been determined by topography and the "catenary" sequence of soil types from ridge to valley. The flat or gently sloping ridge tops, commonly varying from less than a mile to about two miles in width, carry a deep cover of highly fertile volcanic loams over the porous tuffs and phonolitic lavas in which the streams have carved the complex pattern of valleys. Downwards along the slope to the valley, soils become shallower, lighter in colour, and lower in fertility; and towards the base of the slope there is generally a "step" of outcropping ironstone above the moist or seasonably waterlogged dark brown loams or clay loams of the valley bottom.

I have come across only one attempt to reconstruct the traditional land-use pattern of the Kikuyu. This was made by James Mburu, himself a Kikuyu, as part of a study of agriculture in the Kiambu Native Reserves which he undertook when he was an agricultural student at the University College of East Africa. According to this account, the deep rich soils of the ridge tops were normally opened to a mixed crop of maize and dolichos beans grown with the first rains, which the Kikuyu still call *Mburu ya Njahi*, "the rains for dolichos beans." Sometimes but much less frequently, a pure crop of maize or beans was sown. In the short rains of the same year, "the rains for bulrush millet," a second crop was taken, this time of bulrush or finger millet. A similar sequence of cropping was followed in the second and third years, with the difference that sorghum was often mixed with or substituted for maize in the long rains, and after not more than three years cropping, or six successive crops, the land was rested. The main slope from ridge to valley was used in a different way: here, pigeon pea was planted together with sweet potatoes of varieties which produce vegetative growth throughout the year and yield vines rather than tubers. These vines were cut at intervals to provide fodder for stall-fed sheep and goats, and when all had been reaped and the pigeon pea harvested the land was rested. The valley slopes and bottoms were used mainly for perennial crops, sugar cane for brewing and bananas mostly of sweet varieties consumed as fruit, as well as sweet potatoes and a biennial variety of cocoyam which was grown in wet soil near the stream. These valley lands were maintained in production for up to five years, or as long as the bananas continued to bear.

Nothing, it seems, is known regarding the rest periods observed in traditional Kikuyu practice. Recent writers content themselves with the usual references to "shifting cultivation" and statements that the land was allowed to revert to grass or bush after two or three years cropping, or "when fertility fell below a certain level," or even "when the land became exhausted." Yet we must suppose, at least in the case of the highly productive Kikuyu grass and Star grass zones, that this is Permanent Cultivation land, in the sense that the fertility of the main arable soils can be maintained at a satisfactory level under relatively short periods of cultivation, such as seem to have been customary, alternating with fallow periods of equal or shorter duration. There is little reason to suppose that traditional Kikuyu agriculture was not "permanent" in this sense. Early travellers remarked on the extent of cultivation in the lands occupied by the Kikuyu. Thus, C. W. Hobley, in his diary for 1890, says of Kiambu that "there is very little waste land as nearly every acre is cultivated and occupied."

This suggests a "permanent" system of land-use and a high

proportion of cultivable land. The Cultivable Percentage is certainly high, possibly as high as 50 taken over all, though Humphrey (86) concluded from his assessment of Nyeri that "it is probably a generous estimate to say that half the district is suitable for arable purposes." If we assume a general Land-Use Factor of 2, a Cultivation Factor of about half an acre and a Cultivable Percentage of 40, we may suppose that the Kikuyu country was capable of supporting population densities of the order of 250 people per square mile without damage to the land or disruption of the traditional system. Again, this is no more than a guess, with little to support it other than the complaints of land shortage that followed when population exceeded such a density. Leakey, in the portrait of Kenya he painted a quarter of a century ago, has this to say of the Kikuyu lands at that time: "The lands of a certain section of the Kikuyu tribe are today populated to a density of 500 to the square mile, but in a few parts the figure is much lower. Where density is over 250 per square mile there is a continual complaint that there is no room to expand, no room to grow more than the bare necessities of life and to graze stock" (102).

Yet, to one who is more familiar with conditions in southern Africa, the Kikuyu lands do not look like a mortally stricken, eroded, and depleted area. The marks of erosion are to be seen on the steeper slopes, but the land still gives an impression of green fertility and soil strength and a latent capacity for rapid recovery even after prolonged and punishing misuse. The picture is quite different from that of the "Ngoni devastated area" and some others of the Native Reserves in the south, where the grip of vegetation is weaker and land has been degraded to a lower level by much smaller populations. In these fertile lands of double rainfall, nature is an ally rather than an enemy of the agricultural improver. The problems are, in some ways, simpler, but the fundamental question remains: can one put a quart into a pint pot, however strong and excellent the pot may be?

2. THE NYANZA PROVINCE OF KENYA

The three little Kikuyu districts together with three others, the old Northern district and the Central and Southern districts of Nyanza Province, support nearly half the population of Kenya although they comprise only about 4 per cent of the country's area. This other region of high population density, the Nyanza

Province, lies between the highlands and Lake Victoria, along Kenya's south-western border. There is a fourth district, Kericho, on the western slopes of the Mau Massif, occupied by the Nilo-Hamitic Kipsigis at a general population density of about 100 per square mile. Central and Southern Nyanza embraced the Kavirondo gulf and extend along the whole eastern shore of Lake Victoria within the Kenya border, while the Northern district reaches up the slopes of Mount Elgon to the country of the Gishu.

This also is a fertile and well-watered region, except for the dry lake shore savannah, with rainfall of 40 to 70 inches or more in the year and two seasons of heaviest precipitation, the "long" and "short" rains of March–June and October–December. There are large areas of high agricultural potential with volcanic soils, red earths, and deep alluvial soils of ancient lake beds such as the Kano plains: but there is also a good deal of poor or useless land, including undulating country with lateritic soils of low fertility at higher altitudes within the lake basin, and swamps and barren escarpment hills. The Nilotic Luo have, on the whole, the worst of the land, the poorer and drier parts, while the Kavirondo, Maragoli, and other Bantu peoples occupy the larger and more fertile areas.

Here, too, the old systems of land-use have long since broken down as a result of population growth and the cultivation of cotton. It is by no means improbable that these systems of the past could support a general population density of 100 or 120 per square mile on a subsistence basis: but present densities are much above this level, while the introduction of cotton has increased the land requirement and produced an effect similar to that of a further growth of population. The African Land Unit which includes the Elgon Nyanza and North Nyanza districts (the old North Nyanza district was split into two in 1956) and Central and Southern Nyanza, is some 7,190 square miles in extent. Population is now, very probably, close to the two million mark, perhaps a little more or a little less, and the general density must be about 280 per square mile with local variations from 100 or less to more than 1,000 per square mile. In addition, the province has to support over two million cattle, mainly stunted and half-starved scrub stock, a number vastly in excess of the carrying capacity of the grazing. Nevertheless, by far the greater proportion of Kenya's cotton production and "surplus" maize and rice from the African areas comes from Nyanza: but for such an area and so great a rural population—a third of the African population of Kenya—the production is poor and the surplus sadly small.[1] Even this little has been getting less, it seems. "During the last three years, the output of crops in the province has halved," says Elspeth Huxley (91), "because yields have dropped so sharply."

3. KIGEZI AND RUANDA-URUNDI

The Nyanza province forms the eastern segment of a crescent-shaped region of high population density about the northern end of Lake Victoria. West of the crescent a break in distribution occurs before one reaches the concentration that lies in the south-west corner of Uganda, the Kigezi district. This, too, is a region of high fertility: "the soils are well supplied with bases, the percentage of crumbs greater than half a millimetre is very high even in plots that have been cultivated for many years, and this is the probable explanation of the extreme permeability and resistance to erosion of the Kabale soils" (133). This fertility is matched by an admirable climate for the growth of annual crops: the rainfall of about 40 inches in the year is very well distributed, and there are only two relatively dry months, June and July, separating the two rainy seasons which have their peaks in March–April and October–November. Morning mists are common and the mean temperature for Kabale is 61·3°F, with an absolute minimum of 41·0°F and an absolute maximum of only 87·5°F. This relatively cool and humid climate allows not only of double cropping but of a succession of harvests throughout the year, as is illustrated by Purseglove's table of planting and harvesting months for the main crops.

	Planting	Harvest
Sorghum	Dec.–Jan.	Jun.–Jul.
Finger Millet	Sep.–Oct.	Feb.–Mar.
Peas	Sep.–Apr.	Jan.–Aug.
Beans	May–Sep.	Aug.–Dec.
Maize	Aug.–Sep.	Jan.–Feb.
Sweet Potatoes	All the year	After six months

This is an environment which might well be capable of sup-

[1] Cotton, 9,207 bales (of 400 lb lint), 1957; Maize, 579,800 bags (of 200 lb) 1958; Rice (paddy), 57,200 bags (of 180 lb), 1958; *Ann. Rept. Dept. Agric.*, Kenya 1958.

porting a general population density of 100 to 200 per square mile without damage to the land, if we suppose that there is a pre-dominance of Semi-Permanent Cultivation land, an assumption which appears to be justified by survey data (169) and by existing densities, and if we also assume that the Cultivable Percentage for the district as a whole is not less than 25 or more than 50. Purse-glove's estimate of the Cultivable Percentage for a sample area of Kabale is much higher than this. His assessment was based on 32·8 miles of line traverses a mile and a half apart and two to four miles long, and from the total area he deducted as "uncultivable" all land with slopes over 20°, swamps, and an allowance for house compounds and paths. In this way he arrived at the conclusion that "71·4 per cent of the land surface can be cultivated." The figure is almost certainly too high for general application to a dis-trict a good deal of which is mountainous and it may be over-generous even for the best areas, since the land categories included as wholly cultivable are likely to contain outcrops, poor variants, stream courses, seasonally and permanently waterlogged areas, and some marginal land such as "shallow soils on hill tops," which, Purseglove says, were "formerly used only for grazing but are cultivated under pressure of population." (See Plate 5.)

On the basis of the 1948 census figures, the general population density of Kigezi, in relation to available land, was about 225 per square mile[1] and it may now exceed 250. The extent to which these figures represent overpopulation is debatable, but it is cer-tain that by 1941 very serious congestion had arisen in the southern part, Kabale, where population densities had reached 360 per square mile overall and 717·9 in the problem area of highest population (133). All the usual symptoms of over-population in such an environment were then very evident: almost continuous cultivation and consequent soil degeneration, subdivision and ex-cessive fragmentation of land, with fragments often far distant from the homesteads, intense competition for land and the buying and selling of holdings. The situation was, however, one which could be, and which has been, alleviated to some extent by planned resettlement of populations.

In this area livestock are not very numerous and the cultivation of cash crops throughout Kigezi is on too small a scale to have had any significant effect on the population-land balance. The intense

[1] *Ann. Rept. Dept. Agric.*, Uganda 1957.

congestion in the south came about, it seems, over a space of some two decades, as a result of immigration, mainly from Ruanda, combined with a high rate of natural increase.

The Belgian-administered Trusteeship Territory of Ruanda-Urundi sends out a plethora of population, not only to the mines of Katanga but also into Uganda where the coffee industry depends to a large extent on this supply of immigrant labour. In this little country of about 19,500 square miles there are four million people or more (1954 estimate 3,957,794), including the pygmoid Twa, the giant Tutsi pastoralists and overlords, and the far more numerous Hutu cultivators. This human density of 200 per square mile or more, and a cattle population little short of a million, is more than the land can carry, even though there are large areas of strong and fertile volcanic soils with a double rainfall and two sowing seasons in the year, and even though the Hutu "grow their crops right up to the very tips of the volcanoes." The quotation is from Negley Farson. Writing of Ruanda-Urundi as he saw it in the late 1930s, when there were, he says "3,000,000 natives in this tiny Mandate . . . they have cultivated their towering mountains until they are practically devoid of trees, so that the Belgians now make them plant eucalyptus and wattle. And now, under the strict Belgian administration, every adult male in Ruanda-Urundi has one and a quarter acres a year under cultivation *all the time*, and at least a third of this must be under tapioca (cassava) and sweet potatoes. They must sow twice a year. They must irrigate and cultivate the swamps during the rainy season. In this reforestation campaign every tax-payer must plant at least a fifth of an acre in trees. And some of these trees must belong to a communal plot. . . . Yet, in spite of all this regulated, swift progress, and the recent opening of gold and other mines in the Mandate, anywhere from 50,000 to 70,000 natives have to migrate every year to work from two to six months in the rich Uganda natives' coffee plantations and cotton fields." (56)

This applies mainly to the coffee areas. In the next region we shall consider, Teso, one of the main cotton-growing districts of Uganda, practically the only full-time labour employed is that of Hima herdsmen from Ankole, who look after the Teso cattle in return for milk and an occasional calf. They do so with one object: to return eventually to their pastoral life with the nucleus of a herd. Agricultural labour is mainly provided by reciprocal help and exchange of labour through the medium of the "beer party," but some is hired at peak periods.

4. TESO

We have already noted (pp. 50–51) that north of the eastern equatorial zone of double rainfall the two rainy seasons tend to converge and a marked dry season develops at the end and the beginning of the year. Such conditions become evident in the Teso district of Uganda (see Plate 6), where, though rainfall is still binodal, with the mid-season dry spell becoming less pronounced in the north, there is a major dry season in the period December to March. During this period occasional showers occur but maximum temperatures exceed 90°F, a dry dessicating wind blows across the country from the Karamoja plain, and conditions are generally hot and parched to the extent that the vegetation burns. The main rains of March–June are reliable but the later rains of August–October, following the cool mid-season dry spell, are uncertain and crops grown on them are chancy and generally yield poorly. Bananas are a very minor crop and often consist of no more than a few scattered and neglected stools around the compound. The system of food production therefore depends mainly on the first rains and on the cultivation of annual crops, with finger millet and sorghum as staples.

It is now very difficult to say what that system was in the past, since cultivation of cotton, the general use of the plough, and acute land shortage in some areas, have all affected the pattern of land-use. Perhaps there never was any very fixed system or sequence of cropping, for the Nilo-Hamitic Teso are former pastoralists whose conversion to agriculture probably dates back little more than a century, and they still have great flocks and herds amounting to more than 700,000 cattle and 300,000 sheep and goats. Very probably, land was commonly opened to groundnuts in the first year, followed in the second year by the main food crop association of a mixture of finger millet and sorghum grown with the first rains and cowpeas with the second rains. Quite often the land was then left to rest, but it was frequently cropped again in the third year, to sesame or a root crop, or to sorghum followed by cowpeas in the second rains; or the field might be split up in the third year into smaller areas planted with different crops such as sesame, sweet potatoes, and cassava. A parallel sequence of minor crops, which might include millet, was sometimes maintained side by side with the main sequence but in a different garden, a practice probably associated with the cropping of the main garden for two years only. Thus, in traditional practice, the arable land was cultivated for two years during which three crops were taken, or, perhaps more commonly, for three years of four or five crops, and rarely for a longer period.

This short-period cultivation was, no doubt, a concession to the character of the soils of the region. These are clay loams and loams, interspersed with sandy and silty loams and sands, all derived from granites and gneisses of the basement complex. They have been described as "not high in fertility on Uganda standards"; yet most of the soils in use for cultivation appear to fall within the Permanent and Semi-Permanent Cultivation categories. In many variants, however, the structure breaks down readily to a fine tilth which consolidates to form an erosive surface pan after violent rain followed by a baking sun. This tendency to erosion was dramatically demonstrated when the first experimental farm at Serere was opened, on moderately sloping land, some forty years ago. Worked on European farming principles, with continuous rotational cropping—designed to replace "shifting cultivation"—the land eroded away and had to be abandoned within ten years. Yet, on the long-term fertility experiment laid down at Serere in 1936 and continued since then, the drop in soil productivity after twenty years of continuous cropping has been relatively small, even under the most heavily cropped rotations without manurial treatment of any sort, a result almost certainly due to the lay-out of the experiment which has protected the land very effectively against erosion. Results from this remarkable and long-continued experiment indicate that only two years of natural fallow after three years cropping can maintain fertility on the soils, which are of the better class, and under the conditions of the experiment—provided, of course, that the land has not previously been impoverished and the soil structure has not been destroyed by excessive cultivation.

A natural fallow break of two years is thought to be the minimum required to maintain fertility in the environment of Teso, but there is evidence to indicate that equal periods of cultivation and rest will do so on many soils, if the cultivation break is not over-prolonged. This evidence includes detailed surveys of two "village areas" conducted by staff and students of Makerere (now the University College of East Africa): Moruita Erony,[1] a heavily over-populated area, and Kasilang Erony, a "medium density" village. The 1955 survey at Moruita showed the average crop/rest ratio to be 4·4:1, "a ratio which must definitely be regarded as insufficient to maintain soil fertility" (188), while the ratio at Kasilang was 1:1·5 in 1937 and 1:1·2 in 1953 and it was concluded that "there could be a slight expansion of the population in this area without prejudicing soil fertility (189). African cultivators, not only in Teso but in Busoga and Lango also, repeatedly assured me that fertility could be maintained under a system of three years' cropping and three years' rest, but I had no means of judging whether these statements were based on experience, or traditional knowledge, or the teaching of the Agricultural Department. This ratio has been adopted as a departmental standard, on experimental evidence, for use in conjunction with improved systems of farming, incorporating rotations and limited grazing of resting land: but some of the lighter cultivated soils of Teso, the sandy loams and loamy sands which overlie ironstone *murram* at no great depth, do not give the impression of being able to stand up to such a regime under customary practice, particularly if the resting land is ungrazed or over-grazed.

It is possible that here, as elsewhere, the cultivation/rest ratio varied with the fertility and regenerative power of the soils, and that Semi-Permanent Cultivation was the rule on the lighter and weaker variants, or, perhaps, even short-term "recurrent" cultivation in the case of the weakest of the "cultivable" soils. This possibility is suggested by early village survey data which indicate that cultivation periods in the past were usually of two to three years duration while rest periods varied from two-and-a-half to seven years, and by Tothill's report (169) that "the indigenous farming system" practised in many parts of Uganda was to crop land for three to four years and then to rest, by abandoning to bush, for about eight years. Watson (180) noted in the late 1930s that throughout Teso wherever population was not dense, fallow periods were generally of three to six years duration.

If we accept this interpretation of soil capability and customary

---

[1] An Erony is the smallest administrative area, administered by a 4th-grade chief. It consists, generally, of a group of hamlets and their associated lands.

practice, we must still regard the Teso district and the Lake Kioga basin in general as an area of relatively high human-carrying capacity for subsistence agriculture on a traditional basis. There is undoubtedly a considerable proportion of Permanent Cultivation land: in addition, less than an acre of land in cultivation at one time would probably suffice to ensure the food supply of an individual, and the Cultivable Percentage is relatively high. In traditional practice, before the introduction of cotton and the general adoption of the plough, the Land-Use Factor may have been about three-quarters of an acre—equivalent, with double cropping, to about an acre of land under crop each year per head of population. This, however, is no more than a guess based on my own enquiries, the data obtained in the pre-war surveys, and probable crop yields on soils of unimpaired fertility.

Any guess at the proportion of land within the district which is capable of being used for cultivation by subsistence producers is liable to even greater error. The village surveys give very high estimates of cultivability: 75 per cent for Moruita (188), and 64 per cent (180), and 67 per cent (189) for Kasilang, while Courcy-Ireland (43) estimated that nearly 99 per cent of Opami Erony in Amuria county could be cultivated. These were, very largely, surveys of cultivated lands, which did not take into account the extensive swamp regions lying beyond, or even within, the boundaries of the village areas. Courcy-Ireland points out that his figure does not include a considerable extent of swamp lying within the boundary of the area he studied, "because there was too much water in the swamp to be able to measure these areas." Throughout the district there are extensive regions of aquatic grassland, carrying such grasses as *Echinochloa pyramidalis*, *Oryza barthii*, and *Leersia hexandra* on grey or black alluvial soils, and swamp fringes of silty clay loams that become waterlogged during the rains and set as hard as cement when they are dry. This swamp system forms a complicated network which drains eventually into Lakes Kyoga, Salisbury, and Gedge. The lake levels recede during the dry months, exposing large areas of excellent grazing land in which *Panicum ripens*, regarded as one of the most valuable feed grasses, is often dominant. Swamps and swamp fringes, together with resting and unused arable land, provide the grazing for the livestock.

Some indication of general cultivability may, perhaps, be obtained from the proportion of land actually cultivated at one time. Uganda is one of the few countries which attempt to make an annual estimate of the amount of land under cultivation by Africans, though any such estimate must, of course, be subject to very considerable error. Excluding large open water areas and reserved forest, but including aquatic grassland, the extent of Teso district is some 4,500 square miles and the cultivated area (1959 estimate) may be about 1,150 square miles, or approximately 25 per cent. Allowing for resting land, and for the fact that in some places there is tillable land still unused, it seems probable that the general Cultivable Percentage may approximate to 50 or may even exceed this figure.

Here again, it seems, we have an area of high carrying capacity for subsistence agriculture, capable of supporting a general human population density of 100, or even 150 to the square mile, and a considerable livestock population as well, without damage to the land. The higher figure is supported by an observation at Moruita (188). "By an *ad hoc* comparison of farms where soil fertility was being maintained with farms where soil fertility was declining it was estimated that a total of 2·7 acres of cultivable land per head of population was the minimum required on the existing systems of peasant farming." This figure, related to a Cultivable Percentage of 50, indicates a general Critical Population Density of about 120 per square mile *for present land-use practice*; or 150 per square mile when related to the surveyed area of the erony, assuming it to be 65 per cent cultivable. The actual population density of 230 per square mile at the time of the survey "was exercising a markedly deleterious effect on the agricultural land of the area." On the other hand, the population density of 150 per square mile at Kasilang could, it was thought, "easily be supported by the available natural resources" (189, 188). The higher figure for Critical Population Density is also suggested by the fact that it is in the southern counties of Teso, where general population densities exceed 150 to the square mile, that the deleterious effects of over-population are very evident. The *saza*, or county, in Uganda is the largest administrative division of a District. There are usually some half dozen such counties in a District but Teso has eight, varying in extent from 185 square miles (Ngora) to 980 square miles (Amuria), and their overall population densities per square mile (1959 population estimates) are probably as follows:

Ngora	242	Seroti	120
Kumi	177	Kaberamaido	101
Bukedea	166	Amuria	66
Serere	127	Usuku	56

The "southern counties region" of Ngora, Kumi, and North Bukedea is recognised as a problem area in which over-population, over-cultivation, and over-stocking have led to deterioration of fertility, decreasing yields, and the onset of soil erosion. Elsewhere, it is thought—and this is the impression I formed when travelling through the district—there has as yet been no serious decline in basic fertility. Where cultivation and rest periods are both short, a thick and even stand of *Imperata cylindrica* takes possession of the land, replacing the *Hyparrhenia filipendula*, *Eragrostis superba*, *Pennisetum polystachyum*, and other species dominant in the natural grass communities, and this rapid establishment of a ground cover is doubtless a major factor in restoration of soil structure, protection from erosion, and regeneration of fertility: but where the land is greatly over-cultivated, as it is over large areas of this southern region, the grass cover fails and the resting plots carry no more than a sparse growth of *Rhynchelytrum roseum* and annual weeds, while the surface soil shows obvious signs of panning and sheet erosion. Here, too, sorghum tends to become the dominant grain crop as the land loses the fertility required for finger millet.

It may be, however, that the staying powers of the lighter and weaker soils have been somewhat over-rated and that they are to be classified in the Semi-Permanent and short-term Recurrent Cultivation categories; or, in some cases, as marginal soils cultivated only under extreme pressure. Land degeneration to the degree which has been reached in parts of this southern region is usually associated with population densities two or three times greater than the critical level.

It seems very likely that the old, purely subsistence agriculture could support in perpetuity population densities of 100 to 150 per square mile, but the critical point for present-day "peasant farming," with its greater land requirement, is probably under 100, except, perhaps, in Kaberamaido and Serere which have a high proportion of the best agricultural soils. Indications that the soils are being worked out can be seen in places where population densities are around 90 to the square mile, though the process is slow and the effects are not yet spectacular.

5. SUKUMALAND

The area known as Sukumaland, the country of the Sukuma people, borders the south-eastern shore of Lake Victoria in the Lake Province of Tanganyika. This is a country of Acacia savannah in the lowlands, with *Brachystegia* and combretaceous scrub on hillsides and hill tops; and of great plains where the soils are black clays, and treeless plateaux broken by rocky kopjes and divided by wide valleys. Much of the occupied land is so largely cultivated and treeless that it is known as the "cultivation steppe," a term also applied to a greater area of over-populated land extending into the Western and Central Provinces. The cultivated soils of Sukumaland are, on the whole, deep and fertile, though they range to lighter variants of no more than moderate fertility: but the climate is such as to limit double cropping even more strictly than the conditions of Teso. The rather unreliable rainfall comes in the period November–May, with a gap in February, and the average annual fall varies from 45 to 30 inches, decreasing eastward and southward.

Here, within an area of about 9,000 square miles, surrounded and restricted by tsetse-infested land, live more than a million people with two million "livestock units"—cattle, sheep, and goats.[1] The human population density appears to average something of the order of 130 to 150 per square mile, but there is very considerable variation. Rounce (144) found that of 470 village areas, in a sample drawn from three districts, 62 per cent were populated at densities exceeding 100 to the square mile, while in a small proportion of cases—about 2·5 per cent—densities exceeded 400 to the square mile, with a maximum of 704. He observed that three years of cultivation alternating with three years of fallow was a general rule closely followed in the least congested parts of Sukumaland, while elsewhere population pressure was such that rest periods were shorter than cultivation periods; and his sample figures show a cultivated area exceeding one acre per head of population. Thus, in Kwimba district, the average acreage of land cropped at one time by a household was:

[1] Five sheep or goats = one bovine = one livestock unit.

Grain and interplanted crops	4·95
Cassava and sweet potatoes	1·18
Other food crops	0·86
Cotton	0·79
	7·78

The average household, or "garden family" in the Kwimba district was assessed by Rounce, on the basis of a one per cent random sample, as 7·11 persons and it would therefore seem that about an acre of land per head was cultivated to food crops, and little more than a tenth of an acre to cotton—though the figure is higher for some other districts and may average 1·3 acres or more when cotton is included. Rounce showed that the ratio of food to cash crops, in terms of area, varied from 3 : 1 to 11 : 1 in accordance with the availability and productivity of land. Where, as in this region, the plough is not in general use, production of cotton tends to fall off as land becomes scarce and fertility declines, because the available labour has to be devoted increasingly to ensuring the food supply.

The high degree of overstocking throughout Sukumaland— the need to reserve grazing for a great number of animals, and pressure of livestock on the fallow lands—has been cited as the main cause of land degeneration and loss of fertility. Rounce notes that longer fallow periods seem to be no more effective than short breaks of two or three years, probably because the benefits of the longer rest and the added manure are offset by continuous overgrazing and consequent denudation, trampling, and erosion of the resting land. No doubt, this great concentration of livestock is to be regarded as a major factor of degeneration, but population increase and cash crop production may have played their parts. Sukumaland, it would seem, is also a region in which there is a high proportion of Permanent and Semi-Permanent Cultivation land; and—although the land requirement of subsistence agriculture is probably greater than in the other high-population regions we have considered, and may approximate to an acre of food crops per head of population—it is not unlikely that the purely subsistence systems were capable of supporting a Critical Population Density somewhere in the region of 80 to 100 per square mile. The critical point has probably been exceeded over most of the region, while in the least congested areas the lower population density has been offset by larger cultivated acreages for the production of cotton.

6. Upland and Coastal Regions of Tanganyika

If we now look very briefly at other highly populated areas of Tanganyika we will find a fairly definite association of high population densities with highland and mountain regions of fertile soils, commonly of volcanic origin, and excellent rainfall. The Ngara district in the west of the Lake Province appears to form part of the Ruanda-Urundi-Kigezi highland complex; here one finds banana cultures, to which arabica coffee has recently been added, and population densities well in excess of 100 per square mile. The remaining regions of comparable population density are mainly in the two foci of recent vulcanism: the northern focus of Kilimanjaro and Meru and the southern focus at the head of Lake Nyasa; and on the great arc of mountains that extends south-eastward from Kilimanjaro and Meru towards Tanga and then trends south-westward to end in the Poroto mountain region of the southern volcanic zone.

On the moist slopes of Mount Meru, a volcanic giant to the west of Kilimanjaro, the Rusha and Meru peoples, who combine banana culture with annual cultivation of beans and maize, are hardly less congested than the neighbouring Chagga; and in high rainfall regions of the mountain arc population densities of several hundreds to the square mile are reached. Where it is not too far inland, the outer face of this high land-block acts as a condenser for moisture-laden air from the Indian Ocean, with the consequence that the natural vegetation of the higher altitudes on the seaward face consists of evergreen montane forest. In the Usambaras, the annual rainfall on the eastern side of the mountain mass is about 80 inches: on the west it falls to less than 25 inches.

The situation in the Usambaras is typical of the population congestion that has arisen in several of these mountainous regions. A survey of the Mlalo basin, a comparatively dry part of the mountain selected as representative of the land-use problems of the whole, showed the population density in the surveyed areas of 41 square miles to be 460 per square mile. This survey was made in 1949 and the rate of population increase was then estimated at the very high figure of 2·5 per cent per annum. It is hardly surprising that the area cultivated by the average family is no more than three acres, that cultivation has been forced on to exceedingly steep slopes, and that there are acute problems of land shortage and soil erosion. In the Uluguru mountains near Morogoro there is a similar problem area. Here, it seems, a new form of land-use is developing, with concentration on the production of pulses and vegetables which are sold or bartered to obtain the bulk of the cereal requirement from the plains.

The Poroto mountains of the southern volcanic zone is another densely populated and heavily cultivated region. In the Rungwe district, within this mountain zone at the head of Lake Nyasa, the Nyakyusa occupy an area with a rainfall of nearly 100 inches in the year. This precipitation may be accounted for by local condensation of moisture evaporated from the lake. The Nyakyusa were skilled cultivators and it seems probable that they included the terracing of sloping lands in their traditional practice. Frederick Elton, who visited their country in 1877 and was the first to leave a record of his visit, says that he found "terraced cultivation everywhere." They combined permanent cultivation of bananas with annual cultivation of millet, legumes, and other crops in a system similar to that of the Chagga and Gishu. Cattle were stalled at night and the manure was cleared out daily and used to maintain the fertility of the homestead banana groves. But the Nyakyusa were also cattlemen in a more extensive sense, counting wealth in terms of beasts and attaching a high prestige value to them. These attitudes are still evident today.

Even with large numbers of cattle, the system may have been capable of supporting relatively high human population densities: but there is serious land shortage at the present general density of about 250 to the square mile. It would seem however, that shortage is due in a large degree to the cultivation of greater acreages, as a result of cash cropping and use of the plough, and to acquisition of relatively large holdings by the more progressive elements among the Nyakyusa. If, as is said, land shortage has become apparent only within the last decade, and if, as population counts indicate, the rate of increase has been of the order of 1·4 per cent per annum over the last two or three decades, one may hazard a guess that the traditional system in this environment may have been capable of supporting a general density approaching or perhaps even exceeding 200 per square mile.

In addition to these concentrations of population about Lake Victoria and in highland and mountain regions of high rainfall, there are some considerable settlements on the narrow coastal plains of the East African littoral which occasionally extend inland along the alluvial reaches of the few large rivers and on to the more fertile parts of the low coastal hinterland. Thus, on the basis of 1948 population figures, general densities of population in the Mombasa and Tanga districts were 523 and 93 respectively (138) while on the islands of Zanzibar and Pemba, with their production of cloves and copra, the present density figures are probably between 250 and 300 per square mile. These concentrations are, however, associated with urban and peri-urban settlement and have developed under long-continued contact with Arab and Portuguese influence.

The agriculture of this eastern coastal belt is characterised by extensive plantations of coconut palm, a plant which probably originated in the Malayan archipelago and has been spread by human agency to many tropical and sub-tropical coastal regions of the world. The main soil group of these regions of coconut culture and subsidiary arable cultivation is a complex of light-coloured loose sands forming ridges between moist bottom lands of dark-grey clays intermixed with sand. In spite of their texture, the sands appear to be fairly fertile and they are commonly cultivated for about three years to associations or sequences of crops, including maize, cassava, and vegetables such as okra. Coconut-palms may be established during this period of annual cropping. Rice, grown on a fairly large scale in the moist bottom lands, is also an important annual crop. The sands are said to require, on the average, ten years rest after three years of cultivation to annual crops and this "land rotation" is still in use where land is ample. Cultivators in the Dar-es-Salaam neighbourhood, with whom I spoke, were emphatic that this is the minimum rest period which will restore full fertility, although lack of land in this peri-urban neighbourhood compelled them to employ much shorter fallows.

In spite of the slow regeneration of the sands, it is not improbable that this coastal form of land-use, with its permanent arboreal culture and use of seasonally waterlogged land for high-yielding rice crops, is capable of sustaining rural population densities approaching or even exceeding 100 to the square mile, at least in the best environments. The cultivability of these regions, in

relation to the range of crops, appears to be very high—if one ex-
cludes the tidal muds and mangrove swamps of the littoral fringe.

7. THE MATENGO HIGHLANDS

Concentration of population, particularly in mountain regions, is
not altogether a new phenomenon. It happened also in the past,
but the response of the cultivators to the challenge of land shortage
and erosion was then more positive than is now the case. There is
ample evidence of ancient land terracing in many parts of eastern
Africa; and, as we have seen in the example of the Nyakyusa,
some modern peoples continue to practise terrace cultivation,
though it may often be argued that they took over and maintained
old or ancient works created by peoples of the past. No such
argument can be sustained in the case of the system practised by
the Matengo people in southern Tanganyika, for their excellent
and highly conservative methods of land-use are almost certainly
of recent origin.

East of Lake Nyasa, a southward offshoot of the great highland
arc comprises the Livingstone mountain range and its continuation, Songea-Matengo, in the extreme south-west of Tanganyika
near the Portuguese border. Here, between Songea and the lake,
the Matengo people cultivate a small highland area ranging from
4,000 to 7,000 feet, a mountain grassland region of steep slopes
and narrow valleys with surviving remnants of former rain forest
on the higher mountains. Rainfall is good, averaging about 45
inches with greater totals at the upper altitudes, and temperatures
are relatively low.

According to all accounts, raiding Ngoni and slave traders
drove the small, weak Matengo tribe into this upland country,
where they made their settlements near large natural caves offering a readily defensible refuge, or on the more inaccessible mountain tops. Hemmed in and condemned to increasing land shortage,
with no option but to cultivate the steepest slopes or starve, and
with no cattle to provide manure, they evolved an admirable system
of agriculture which includes crop rotation, maintenance of fertility by composting grass, weeds, and crop refuse, systematic use
of grass fallows, and a highly effective device for protection of the
land against erosion. About 1890, when the Germans first reached
Matengo country they found a large concentration of the tribe in

the fertile Litembo area, all practising this system. The system has been described in some detail by Stenhouse (156).

When land is broken from grassland or fallow, the grass is first cut by the men, who use billhooks for the purpose. They lay the long grass in rows forming a grid over the whole area, with one set of rows across the slope, roughly following the contour, and the other set running up and down the slope at right angles to the first. The rows are from 7 to 10 feet apart in each direction, the distance varying with the quantity of grass to be covered in the following operation and the depth of fertile topsoil available to cover it. This work is co-operative, all the men of the village working together, stimulated by the prospect of the traditional beer party.

The remaining work is done mainly by women, for it was the duty of the men to stand guard against invaders once the grass had been cut. The topsoil in the squares enclosed by the grass rows is dug out with the hoe and pulled on top of the cut grass. The cultivator works round each square in turn, first facing downhill to pull the soil up over the row of grass forming the top of the square, then standing astride the slope to cover the vertical row, and then facing uphill to pull the soil over the lower row. In this way the cut grass and all the original vegetation on the site is buried under large banks of topsoil some four to five feet wide, leaving a pit of similar diameter in the centre of each square with the subsoil exposed over an area of about a square yard at the bottom of the pit.

These banks with their content of composted grass are planted to maize and pulses as separate crops, half the land being sown with maize and the other half with beans and peas. At the next planting the cropping is reversed, and this sequence is repeated to give a simple but strict rotation of cereal and leguminous crops over the whole period of cultivation. Maize is planted in short lines radiating from the pits, probably to facilitate clean weeding, the rows being about three feet apart and the plants at intervals of one foot in the rows, while pulses are generally planted some four to six inches apart. The Matengo, it seems, are well aware of the importance of plant spacing and the value of clean weeding. Weeds are pulled out and thrown into the pits, to be preserved for compost, and all crop residues also go into the pits for the same purpose.

Two crops may be taken in one year. At the end of the year, when the last crop has been reaped, the earth banks are split and the soil is turned over to make new banks in which all the collected and crop residues are incorporated. The new banks are built over the old pits and the new pits are formed where the old banks intersected. By repetition of this highly laborious process the land is maintained in production for eight or even ten years, after which it is allowed to revert to natural grass fallow. The banks and pits remain during the fallow period, preventing erosion and aiding the establishment of a grass cover after the long cultivation period. All the water that falls on the cultivated land is conserved, and the pitted surface can hold the heaviest downpour. After prolonged rain, water may stand in the pits for some time before it soaks into the ground and this, of course, limits cropping to some extent. Root crops, especially cassava, suffer from excess of moisture and finger millet is said to be unsuccessful because it lacks flavour when grown under these conditions (131).

There appears to be no information on the normal or necessary length of the fallow period and it is impossible even to guess at the probable carrying capacity of this system, which has attracted attention mainly as an example of erosion control in indigenous practice. Even storm drains are employed. When the grid of cultivation does not reach to the top of a hill a special storm drain is constructed above the highest plot as a protection against run-off from the upper slopes. The technique is similar to the well-known "box-ridging" method of soil conservation, and it is highly effective. No deterioration has been observed even where the system has been in use for more than sixty years.

Indeed, the Matengo pit system may be a more effective device than most of the introduced methods of erosion and water control, at least in some circumstances. This is suggested by results, over the six-year period 1950–5, from an experiment conducted at the Regional Research Centre in the Northern Province of Tanganyika, far from the home of the system. In this experiment, which was sited on a rich and stable volcanic loam of moderate slope, under a double-rainfall regime with an average total of about 37 inches, the Matengo pit system was compared with normal ridging, constructed and formed bench terraces, narrow-based contour banks, and unprotected cultivation on the "flat." The Matengo system gave the best results, as judged by maize yields, over the period of the experiment, but its superiority over normal ridging and "flat" cultivation was not great except in the very wet year 1951. In that year yield differences were spectacular.

MAIZE YIELDS AS PERCENTAGES OF HIGHEST YIELD
1951

Matengo system	100
"Flat" cultivation	49
Constructed bench terraces	44
Ridges	43
Narrow-based contour banks	27
Formed bench terraces	22

There is evidence in the Matengo highlands of past erosion associated with a former more extensive agriculture, more especially on the poorer land about Langiro, and there can be little doubt that the pit system was evolved comparatively recently, probably within the last century, and that "the dominating cause was lack of land for cultivation" (156). This lack of land was accentuated by the need to provide tribute in the form of food crops for their Ngoni persecutors, an imposition which compelled the Matengo to cultivate approximately twice the area of crops required for their own use.

The older people still maintain the admirably conservative pit system for the production of traditional food crops, but since the advent of British rule many groups have migrated to other fertile parts of the highlands and, according to Pike (131) "the further they go from Litembo, the less inclined are they to follow the system which the tribe evolved for its safety in the past." Stenhouse (156) says that the younger Matengo "are adopting lazier methods of cultivation, while the introduction of cash crops is accelerating this deplorable breakdown," and a more recent district report adds that "the younger generation are engaged in exploitation of land by wholesale cultivation of cash crops."

8. UKARA ISLAND

Surviving examples of intensive land-use developed in mountain refuge areas are not uncommon—among them is "the truly glorious Jebel Mara region" in the Sudan, as an enthusiastic Agricultural Officer describes it (170), with its splendid terraces and ingenious irrigation—but what might be regarded as the ideal of agricultural perfection, the highest attainment of the indigenous systems, is to be found on a little island in the south-eastern sector of Lake Victoria (see Plate 7). Ukara Island is 29 square miles in area, about the same size as Guernsey. The people of the island, the Kara, are unremarkable except for their agriculture. They have no implement of cultivation save the hoe, no wheeled vehicles, and no pack animals. What they have done, any African people could do, given similar conditions and circumstances.

What they have done is to evolve for themselves a highly intensive system of mixed farming, with integration of livestock and crop husbandry, in which use is made of devices commonly associated only with the most advanced farming practice. The environment has some advantages, principally as regards climate and the possibility of lake-side irrigation. Rainfall, which averages some 55 inches, is so distributed as to give two reliable crops a year, with a relatively dry period in June–August and the heaviest falls in November–May. But the cultivable soils of the island appear to be, on the whole, weak and of no great intrinsic fertility. They range from medium loams and stronger reddish loams to sandy granite soils and almost pure sands.

Faced with the problem of maintaining permanent cultivation on soils which may fall within the Semi-Permanent or Recurrent Cultivation land categories of normal traditional practice, the Kara adopted the expedient of manuring. There is nothing remarkable in this; it is a mistake to suppose that African people are ignorant of the use of manure or that its value as a soil fertiliser is beyond their understanding. As we have seen, the use of manure is customary in a number of traditional systems, where it can be conveniently applied without great labour, and its value must be obvious to any stock-owning people. The remarkable thing is the way in which the Kara tackled the problem of livestock maintenance. They resorted to the cultivation of grasses as fodder crops, making use of such species as *Vossia cuspidata*, *Echinochloa spp.*, *Pennisetum purpureum*, and *Phragmites mauritianus*. These grasses are grown in pits some three or four feet deep, dug by the shore, so that the lake water may be admitted for initial irrigation; later, the grass roots penetrate below the water table and, as the equable climate allows of continuous growth, numerous cuts may be made each year. In addition, trees are lopped and the leaves of palatable species—such as *Markhamia platycalyx*, *Maesopsis eminii*, and a number of figs—are fed to the livestock. Practically all the trees on the island have been planted or conserved for lopping to provide fodder and, in the case of unpalatable species, bedding for the animals. These fodder grasses and leaves, together with crop residues which provide the bulk of the feed, cut grass, and the little grazing the island affords, serve to maintain considerable numbers of cattle and small-stock.

The Kara have lost the pastoralists' attitude to cattle. They look on them not as a symbol of wealth and prestige, though they are used as bride-wealth and in certain ritual observances, but as an integral and essential part of their farming system. The animals are kept in part of the dwelling hut where they are hand fed and bedded down, and a pit is dug in the floor to collect the dung and urine. From time to time the partly-rotted bedding is turned out and left for further decomposition before being laboriously transported to the fields in small head loads.

By this means three tons of manure can be obtained from an adult beast in the year, but even this production it seems was not enough. Another method of maintaining fertility was devised by this isolated people on their little island, the device of green manuring. As green manure crops they use *Crotalaria striata*, an indigenous legume of the same genus as the sunn-hemp used in European farming practice, and *Tephrosia erecta*, usually the former.

These practices are applied in the course of a regular three-years rotation of bulrush millet, groundbeans, and sorghum, during which two dressings of farmyard manure are given, while in the intervening year a green manure crop is dug in. The main crop, bulrush millet, is sown at the beginning of the season, invariably after a dressing of manure or a green manure crop, and the following sequence is commonly used.

The first crop of bulrush millet is sown on manured land and, when the millet has grown to about a foot in height, the green manure crop is interplanted. This *Crotalaria* is slow-growing; it takes possession of the land after the millet has been harvested and is ready for digging in some nine months after planting, by which time it has reached a height of four or five feet. In the following season, after the digging in of the green manure crop, bulrush millet is planted again: but in this second year a crop of groundbeans is interplanted when the millet is well grown and about to set seed. After the millet harvest, the stalks are removed to allow the groundbeans to develop fully, and when the crop has been taken the land is manured again with farmyard dung. In the third year another crop of bulrush millet is taken and this is followed, very often, by a crop of sorghum in the same year. This succession of interplanted crops ensures, incidentally, an effective cover protecting the soil to some extent against erosion.

Cassava also is generally grown, but not as a pure crop; it is usually planted at a very wide spacing in the growing bulrush millet, to mature after the millet has been reaped. Sweet potatoes, too, are of some importance, but this crop is grown separately on large ridges near the lake shore, where the soils are wet and sandy, or as a catch crop on the rice lands after the paddy has been reaped. Rice is grown on the restricted areas of intrinsically fertile soil in the main valleys and on the lake shore, the "delta regions" of the island. Manure is not used on the rice lands, possibly because of labour limitations or because there is not enough: but *Crotalaria* may be cut and carried and dug into the soil, together with wood ash from the household fires. Seedlings are raised in seed-beds, which are fertilised with ash, and transplanted in the field. But, though they take much care over its cultivation, rice is little eaten by the Kara; it is their main cash crop, the crop that pays the taxes.

Laborious and skilful soil conservation is also a part of this remarkable system of land-use, by such means as tie-ridging, with the incorporation of weeds as organic manure, terracing with and without stone walls, the use of banks and ridges and live wash-stops of *Phragmites*, and control of drainage by stream-side banking. An intricate pattern of tiny terraced grass fields supported by drystone walls covers the rocky hill slopes. Though they may be no more than a few square yards in area, these grass-planted terraces are highly valued for the feeding of livestock and they are both cut and grazed.

Equally remarkable is the Kara system of land tenure, which amounts to virtual ownership of land by the male heads of families, ownership not only of arable land but also of grazing land and trees and thatching grass. Every tree is owned and looked upon as a valuable possession for its yield of fodder or animal bedding or building timber. Areas of *Trichopteryx uagerensis* reserved for thatching grass are also privately owned and the grass is sold in bundles to those who have need of it. Land is heritable: it may also be bought and sold, and cash transactions in land are now common.

Here, then, is an example of excellent land-use, seemingly evolved by an African people without outside aid or influence. They have not merely adapted their system to the environment; they have adapted the environment to meet their needs. Throughout the island no natural vegetation remains but the grass cover of some hills and a few bushes, and the only trees are those planted and conserved by the people. Their arable lands are permanently cropped and in addition to the land, they have the lake with its harvest of food fishes.

If a high standard of land-use alone were the key to the happiness and progress of the African, then the Kara should be singularly happy and progressive. They are nothing of the sort. A bare subsistence is their reward for unremitting labour, an almost continuous burden of toil which is lightened only by their robust enjoyment of beer-drinking and the tribal sport of bull-fighting. Bull is matched against bull, with care to ensure that neither can do the other much damage, for bulls are valuable.

Rounce and Thornton, who first described the agriculture of the Kara (144, 165) estimated that 13·5 of the island's 29 square miles are suitable for cultivation. These two investigators also found that the extent of land in cultivation approximates very closely to half an acre per head of population, as one would expect of a subsistence system in a region with two reliable growing seasons in the year. We therefore have the following values for the three main factors involved in the estimation of Critical Population Density: Cultivable Percentage 46·5; Cultivation Factor 0·5; Land-Use Factor 1, since cultivation is continuous.

The cultivated area is not entirely in food crops for consumption by the cultivators—since rice, which is produced mainly for sale, occupies about 0·06 of an acre per head: but, when allowance is made for this small departure from a wholly subsistence level of production, the data indicate that the Kara system of land-use in the island environment may be capable of supporting a general human population density exceeding 500 to the square mile. If, however, we make this assumption, and accept a figure of this order as the Critical Population Density, we imply that the system is capable of maintaining fertility indefinitely under continuous cropping on the weaker arable soils. There is evidence that this may not be the case.

Lunan and Brewin (105), who reported on the condition of the island in 1956, found ominous evidence of falling fertility. They judged that yields of crops, with the exception of rice and sweet potatoes, were lower than when Rounce described these, and that the soils "were being depleted by almost continuous cropping faster than they can be replaced by the rotting of parent material and subsoil." "It is evident," they conclude, "that the soil conservation and other practices of the Wakara merely slow down the gradual deterioration in fertility of soil and yield of crops."

Rounce had described these laborious soil conservation methods as protecting the arable land very successfully against erosion, but this was no longer wholly true in 1956, for there was "evidence of neglect of these measures necessary to keep soil stable under continuous, or almost continuous, cultivation on steep slopes." The grass terraces and grazing lands, too, had changed since Rounce wrote of them. Drystone retaining walls were not always in good repair, the grass was weedy and infested with periwinkle (*Lochnera rosea*) in places, while hillside grazing had become badly eroded on the steeper slopes. Lunan and Brewin speak of "gullies 25 feet deep and half a mile long" scoring some of the hillsides, and in 1959 the Western Region Land Planning Unit carried out a survey of 2,000 acres of badly eroded land on Ukara Island (18). Considerable areas of eroded and gulleying slopes are visible on recent aerial photographs I have seen.

The conclusion of the two later investigators is that "the Wakara are fighting a valiant rearguard action with all the weapons at their disposal, to conserve the productivity of the land, but sooner or later they must bring in fertilizer and reduce the human population if they are to improve or even retain their present standard of living."

What causes lie behind the breakdown of this remarkably advanced system of African land-use? Are we to look to population pressure? Rounce gives the total island population as 16,584, or 572 per square mile, at the time of his survey, while Lunan and Brewin speak of a population density of 1,220 per square mile of *arable* land, which indicates virtually no change. There is a constant draining off of population as families emigrate, attracted by the easier life and the comparative wealth to be gained by cotton growing on the mainland, and the young men leave the island for long periods on fishing expeditions and to seek employment.

Has the system failed to maintain the fertility of the arable lands? Their fertility depends on the heavy dressings of manure, without which, as Lunan and Brewin point out, "yields of crops, apart from rice, would be reduced to virtually nothing and the people would starve." One weakness of the system may lie in the failure of the methods of livestock management to support the necessary numbers of animals. Rounce found 9,892 cattle and 4,833 sheep and goats—11,000 livestock units, or 3 units per household, sufficient, with Kara methods of manure-making, to allow of an annual dressing of 4 tons per acre on all the arable land. Lunan and Brewin give no figures, but they found that cattle and goats were fewer than when Rounce wrote, and very few sheep remained; yet the cutting and carrying of the now sparse grass still entailed a vast amount of labour. One must suppose that manure production had declined, as a result of the smaller numbers of stock, combined, very probably, with a decrease in the amount of material available as bedding, and over-cutting of the trees. This situation may have come about through degeneration of the grassland by constant and long-continued drainage of its fertility to feed the arable land. Lunan and Brewin also point to a drainage of fertility from the island, in the form of 400 tons of produce a year, mainly rice, with no compensating import of fertilisers: but this may be less significant than it seems at first sight, since the loss fell chiefly on the naturally strongest and most durable soils, which, it seems, have not declined greatly in fertility. Degeneration of the grassland would set up a vicious circle: less manure, declining yields, smaller quantities of crop residues, and still less food for the animals.

Here is one possible clue: but it is evident that other factors have also been at work, including loss of labour power and fragmentation of the land to a fantastic degree. Recent reports refer frequently to "neglect" and to "the noticeable deterioration of the high standard of farming described by Rounce." Change in the composition of the labour force, by increasing withdrawal of young men who now go on long fishing expeditions or leave the island to seek work, might well account for this. Indeed, it is inconceivable that this high standard, with its vast labour requirement, could have been maintained despite the loss of the most effective part of the labour force.

While the labour strength declined in this way, the efficiency of the remainder was reduced by increasing fragmentation of the land. At the time of Rounce's survey fragmentation was already far advanced, as a result of division of land among heritors. He describes holdings composed of a large number of small plots, rarely exceeding a tenth and averaging about a twentieth of an acre (242 square yards) scattered over a wide area. Lunan and Brewin found the land even more fragmented than when Rounce had described it. They speak of tiny plots, about 25 square yards in area, as common; and they say that "the plots owned by one man may be scattered all over the island." Fragmentation has been increased by purchase of land, wherever plots can be bought: in 1956, small plots were changing hands at £50 per acre—"for land," say Lunan and Brewin, "which almost any other African would deem as useless." This continuing sale and purchase leads to increasing fragmentation, even when there is no increase of population. A man may sell a piece of his holding to meet exceptional financial commitments with which he is faced, and later, when he is in a position to do so, buy another piece far away from his homestead. He cannot pick and choose, but must take what land is offered.

CHAPTER XIII

REGIONS OF LOW POPULATION DENSITY IN EAST AFRICA

1. High and Low Population Densities and Water Supplies

The highly populated regions of Tanganyika, with densities approximating to or exceeding 100 per square mile, represent, perhaps, 5 per cent of the territory's area and support well over a third of the total population. The remainder of the country is relatively sparsely populated, at a general density of about 16 per square mile, with variations ranging, on a district basis, from 2 or 3 to as much as 40 to the square mile. The inequalities of population distribution are very great, but perhaps not quite as extreme as Gillman suggested when he wrote, "two-thirds of the people live on one-tenth of the land, one-third occupy a fifth of the land, and nearly two-thirds of the whole territory is uninhabited" (62). He attributed these inequalities of population distribution largely to variations in the distribution of permanently available domestic water supplies, but he later altered this view in regard to large sparsely inhabited areas in the south of the territory. An explanatory note on his last paper (63), which was published after his death, reads as follows: "The large areas in the western part of the Southern Province shown as 'uninhabited' or occupied by a 'widely scattered population' [in a previous paper, *Geogr. Rev.*, Vol. 26, 1936, p. 356] were attributed to the absence or only sporadic occurrence of permanent domestic water. At the time of writing, the author, having no personal knowledge of these regions, was forced to rely on the scant available older literature. He later had the opportunity for extensive exploration of the Rovuma basin, which revealed comparatively ample permanent streams and compelled him to account for the sparsity of population on historical grounds."

Regions where domestic water supply is a problem, at least during the long months of the dry season, often support considerable populations while well-watered regions are sometimes sparsely inhabited.

2. GOGOLAND

Gogoland, in the semi-arid centre of Tanganyika, covers roughly 18,000 square miles and carries a human population of about 320,000, or 18 to the square mile, in addition to large numbers of cattle. The rainfall of this region, which averages only some 20 to 24 inches, comes mainly in the short period December–March, and there is a long and severe dry season in the remainder of the year. Vegetation is typically low scrub, forming thicket in places, of *Commiphora spp.*, *Dichrostachys glomerata* and *Dalbergia melanoxylon*, with *Combretum spp.*, *Cordyla Africana*, *Albizzia brachycalyx*, *Acacia mellifera* and other species of trees and shrubs, often dominated by the large and grotesque baobab (*Adansonia digitata*).

It was in this environment that the Groundnut Scheme was started, at Kongwa on the southern extremity of the Masai steppe. In this country of ridges and valleys, *Commiphora* thicket, some 15 feet high and quite impenetrable, covers nearly all the higher ground, presenting an extraordinary problem not only in preliminary clearing but also in dealing with the chaotic tangle of roots and plant debris.

Much soil work was, of course, carried out in connexion with the scheme, and three main groups were recognised. The soils of the Pauling and Chamaye series range from shallow, non-laterised red earths on ridge crests to deep red earths on the lower slopes. Although structure is poor and the surface becomes compacted on drying after heavy rain—a phenomenon which may greatly reduce plant populations when it occurs at the time of germination—and although the soils set so hard that dry season working is impracticable, they are regarded in general as useful agricultural soils capable of producing good crops without fertiliser, at least for a few years after clearing, provided rainfall is adequate in quantity and satisfactory in distribution. But over a recorded period of six years at Kongwa, rainfall averaged only 17·90 inches and distribution was often far from satisfactory (124).

The Mtanana series comprises pallid upland soils, usually of sandy loam texture, with a concretionary ironstone horizon, and similar soils of drainage channels. They are leached and acid, and are graded generally as of little or no agricultural value. The difference between these two groups (the one of relatively strong and fertile, and the other of weak and sterile soils) is thought to be due to difference in the rate of natural erosion—nature's method of making and regrading soils, which is not to be confused with the destructive processes of accelerated, or man-made, erosion. Where natural erosion is fairly rapid, the minerals of the soil profile are renewed before any great degree of leaching has taken place, but where the process is slow the complex clay minerals are severely leached and, eventually, they break down. The silica and alumina of the clay minerals are lost in the drainage while the iron is deposited as a concretionary ironstone horizon. Similar changes may occur in the soils of drainage channels where the passage of large volumes of water through the soil profile causes very rapid leaching.

Commiphora thicket covers the red earths and the pallid upland soils alike, but giant baobabs are common on the former and rare on the latter.

A third group, the Mankhunzi and Lubiri series, includes soils of the wider valleys and the low-lying grassland areas of poor drainage, known in East Africa as *mbugas*, into which streams from the ridges discharge in the wet season and disappear. Among the Mankhunzi soils are brown loams of good structure well supplied with plant nutrients and moister than the upland soils. These are, probably, the most valuable agricultural soils of the region, but their extent is very limited.

This range, no doubt, includes soils which, for the traditional subsistence cultivator, fall within most, if not all, of the land-use categories—from Semi-Permanent, or even Permanent, Cultivation soils to Shifting Cultivation and useless land: but there is little information, and no data are available, on the regime of cultivation and fallow required to maintain fertility on any of these soils.

The Gogo, who live in this environment, and whose main crops are bulrush millet, sorghum, groundnuts, and some maize, now commonly cultivate for about six years and follow this with a fallow of similar duration, or of longer duration if this is possible. But the ratio of fallow to cultivation sometimes falls as low as 3:6, and in a few centres of higher population density the stage of virtually continuous cultivation has been reached. Crop yields are generally low, the area is unquestionably overstocked, and the signs of erosion are evident. Whether this situation arises wholly from the pastoral proclivities of the Gogo, the deliberate reservation of land for stock to the detriment of cultivation, is debatable. The area may be one in which poor Recurrent and Shifting Cultivation land predominates. There is a high proportion of leached, pallid soils derived from granitic gneiss, and skeletal formations. The Cultivable Percentage of the area as a whole is probably low or very low, not only on account of soil poverty, but also because of the occurrence of areas of erratic rainfall—known to the Gogo if not to the original "groundnutters"—too uncertain to allow of cultivation with safety under simple subsistence practices. Annual rainfalls varying from 6 inches to 25 inches have been recorded at Kongwa.

I have seen little of the region, and that mainly during a visit to Kongwa in the early years of uncritical enthusiasm, when Mr Strachey was proclaiming the certainty of his conviction that "in a very few years the Groundnut Scheme will be one of the acknowledged glories of the British Commonwealth." My chief impressions were of dust, drought, and climatic uncertainty.

3. THE MIOMBO WOODLANDS

The dry *Brachystegia-Julbernardia* woodland country of south-central Africa (the *miombo* of Tanganyika, the plateau woodland of Northern Rhodesia, and the "sandveld" of Southern Rhodesia) stretch, with many breaks and inclusions, from the Lake Province of Tanganyika into the Rhodesias. In Tanganyika this type of country occupies two great lobes, one in the west and the other in the south-east, separated by a narrowing corridor of tree grassland, bushland, and thicket. Gillman (63) has estimated that these two great lobes, exclusive of the *miombo*-free country within them, occupy nearly half of Tanganyika's land surface. He also points out that this distribution "fits in well with the idea that *miombo* woodland is a function of climate—more specifically, rainfall distribution" and, he adds, "to talk of *miombo* soils is grossly misleading." This is true if one speaks of *miombo* soil as an unvarying entity: there is, of course, much variation, which is generally indicated by changes in the specific composition of the woodland, the understorey, and the ground cover: but on the whole the soils associated with these woodlands are unproductive and of low human-carrying capacity, at least for unaided subsistence agriculture. Long-term Recurrent Cultivation and Shifting Cultivation, low or at best very moderate population densities, and widespread distribution of the common tsetse (*Glossina morsitans*) are typical of much of these vast woodland regions. The prevalence of tsetse may, I suggest, be due to intrinsic soil poverty, which has prevented population densities reaching the level necessary to alter the environment, and the distribution of game, to the detriment of the fly.

The variation within the *miombo* woodland is illustrated by the differences between the two other centres of the Groundnut Scheme: Urambo, some fifty miles west of Tabora in the Western Province, and Nachingwea in the south-east.

Urambo is a fairly typical *miombo* environment, an area of advanced peneplanation and impeded drainage. The tops of the ridges are "planed" off to an even height, while the silted valley bottoms form large flat *mbugas* of sandy clay. The land between the valleys carries rather poor woodland, with *Julbernardia* dominating the higher ground and *Brachystegia* on the lower slopes, and the vegetation of the valleys consists usually of scattered *Brachystegia boehmii* and combretaceous scrub or open grassland. The soils are mainly yellowish and grey sands, with reddish well-drained soils on the ridge tops, and there are many termitaria into which the clay from the grey sands has been concentrated, so that these ant-hills seem to have collected and imprisoned most of the fertility.

Here the main problems derived less from unreliable rainfall than from low fertility and insect pests and diseases. Groundnuts failed as an economic crop, a failure attributed mainly to Rosette disease, and experience has shown, as might be expected, that flue-cured tobacco is the most suitable annual crop.

At Nachingwea the environment is more complex and fertility is, in general, higher, probably as a result of geologically recent elevation of the land, following a period of advanced peneplanation, and consequent rejuvenation of the drainage and regrading of soils. The most extensive soils—the Nachingwea series—are red or reddish-brown sandy loams and loams, sticky when wet but hard and massive when dry, with the common tendency to "cap" after heavy rain. They carry a vegetation very like that of some of the light but fertile Upper Valley soils of Northern Rhodesia: woodland or scrub of *Combretum spp.*, *Pterocarpus angolensis*, *Ostryoderris stuhlmannii*, and *Sclerocarya caffra* with tall *Hyparrhenia* and *Andropogon* grasses, and bamboo communities on moister sites. Similar soils of lighter texture, probably of fairly high agricultural value but very susceptible to erosion—the Nagaga series—are found in lower situations. *Brachystegia-Julbernardia* woodland occurs on ridges of brown and grey sandy soils, but woodland growth is noticeably more vigorous than at Urambo and there is usually an understorey of *Combretum* and a good ground cover of grasses.

It is the soils of the Nachingwea series that have mainly been put to use, and, though deficient in nitrogen and phosphates, they have proved suitable for groundnuts and a considerable range of other crops. This was to have been the major centre of development of the Groundnut Scheme, served by a new deep-water port at Mtwara and 120 miles of railway construction.

These Nachingwea soils do not carry *miombo* woodland and they are clearly of a different category from the general run of soils associated with such woodland. In traditional agriculture they would probably be used for Semi-Permanent or short-term Recurrent Cultivation as the Mukuwa people of this region use the light but stronger soils of their environment which carry mixed woodland.

4. THE MUKUWA SYSTEM OF TUNDURU

The traditional agriculture of the poorer *miombo* environments may be illustrated by the Mukuwa system of Tunduru, a district west of Nachingwea and bounded on the south by the Ruvuma river and the Portuguese border. Here is typical *miombo* woodland on weak pallid sandy soils: but there are some stronger soils, including red and red-brown loamy sands of better structure, and fertile dark-grey loams on seepage sites in bottom lands capable of dry season cropping. Traditional crops are sorghum and cassava, with a range of minor crops including rice, maize, groundnuts, pigeon pea, green gram, and cowpeas.

The weak, light sands of the *miombo* woodland are cultivated for a maximum of three years, and a subsequent fallow period of twenty years or more is recognised as necessary for the restoration of fertility. On the red and brown sandy soils, on the other hand, cultivation periods of up to six years are customary and traditional fallow periods are probably of the order of ten to twenty years, while the moist and fertile bottom lands are cultivated more or less permanently with only occasional short fallow breaks for the control of weeds. Where they are moist enough these bottom lands are planted to a dry season crop of maize and cowpeas which is planted in June and harvested in October.

The stronger and more fertile land is, however, too limited to provide more than subsidiary gardens, and the great prevalence of rapidly depleted soils of low cultivability results in a system which has been described as "an example of the most primitive of all forms of shifting cultivation." Population densities are, naturally, low, the general density for the district being 9 per square mile, according to the Royal Commission Report, but the Critical Density appears to have been exceeded in some areas where fallow periods on the weaker soils are said to have been reduced to six or eight years.

5. THE MAKONDE THICKET SYSTEM

In the extreme south-east of Tanganyika, just north of the Ruvuma river and extending westward from the coast, there is a peculiar environment which has been described as "not greatly dissimilar" to that of Tunduru. The similarities include climate and general soil poverty. Rainfall averages some 36 inches, over the period December–April, and soils are typically free-draining sandy loams of good moisture-retaining capacity, often pale orange in colour, but of low agricultural value judging by the rapid decline of fertility under cropping. But there are marked differences in vegetation and in the systems of land-use.

This is the Makonde plateau, an area of some 3,700 square miles, which rises from about 200 feet above sea level near the coast to an altitude exceeding 2,600 feet at the highest point of the terminal escarpment in the north-west. The vegetation and system of land-use of this region have been described by the younger Gillman (64).

Remnants of the original vegetation indicate that it consisted largely of high woodland in which *Pteleopsis myrtifolia*, *Albizzia gummifera*, and probably *Chlorophora excelsa*, were dominant: but the last species has been exploited to the point of rarity. Associated with these dominants are other large trees, including *Bombax rhodognaphalon*, *Cordyla africana*, *Trichilia emetica* and *Dialium holtzii*. Variations from this type of woodland occur, especially at higher and lower altitudes in the north-west and near the coast, and there are also limited areas of *miombo* woodland, with *Brachystegia spp.* and *Julbernardia globiflora*, on light-coloured sands.

Much of the original high woodland, but not the *miombo* type, has been transformed into man-made thicket in which regenerating trees and saplings are intertwined with climbing, scandent, and upright shrubs of many genera, including *Grewia, Dalbergia, Markhamia, Landolphia, Rhus*, and scandent forms of *Combretum*, to form a tangled and impenetrable mass of vegetation some 9 to 12 feet high when fully established. The composition of this "Makonde" thicket varies with locality, but it is very uniform in appearance and density.

Gillman has suggested, from observations on thicket invasion of woodland clearings, that the change may be completed after four or more cycles of cultivation and long-term fallow, starting from the original woodland. The first crop taken in cleared woodland is usually groundnuts and ground beans, sometimes with sesame. Sorghum and a little maize may be taken in the second year, but pulses and cassava are generally preferred; and in the third year cassava alone is grown. The land is then left for a period of perhaps fifteen or twenty years during which small colonies of the thicket species establish themselves in the regenerating woodland. These thicket communities extend in each fallow period following subsequent cycles of cultivation, until finally the whole area is occupied by thicket.

In fully established thicket the cycles of cultivation and fallow are quite different. The tangled mass is cut with bush knives, during the dry winter months, and allowed to lie where it falls, leaving a cover of timber and leaves over the garden area; and in late November, just before the rains, it is burned. The firing of this mass of highly combustible material probably has some of the effects of the *citemene* burn, creating a transient fertility which allows of cereal cropping in the first year, not only with maize and sorghum but also with rice. In contrast with cultivation of the original woodland, where a strong grass growth springs up after clearing, the cleared and burnt thicket land requires no hoeing. Seed is simply planted with the hoe: first maize followed by sorghum, widely spaced, and then a hill variety of rice which is sown after the first two crops have germinated. Thus, three intermixed grain crops are taken in the first year, and they ripen in the sequence maize, rice, sorghum over the period March to July.

In the second year fertility is too low for rice: sorghum and maize are the main crops, intermixed with cassava and a range of pulses and cucurbits as minor crops. Again, no hoeing is necessary. Coppice growth is cut back just before planting and the hoe is used to remove the stover of the previous crops, but the soil is not turned. In the third year cassava is grown alone, or with some of the subsidiary crops, for fertility is now so low that the risk of failure of grain crops is too great to be taken. The most important food crop is rice, and as this can be grown only in the first year, a regular system of annual extensions is maintained, so that one-third of the cultivated area is always in the first year of cropping.

When the end crop of cassava has been harvested, the garden is left and the thicket regenerates with great rapidity, reaching a height of five feet or more and becoming dense and impenetrable within a matter of two years. In from six to nine years after cropping has ended the stage of full "Makonde" thicket has been reached and the land is cleared and cultivated again. The change of vegetation, it seems, has greatly shortened the period required for restoration of soil fertility.

The conditions which permit, or dictate, reversion to secondary thicket in this environment are unknown, and the reasons for its beneficial effects on soil fertility have yet to be clarified by research and experiment. More rapid restoration of organic matter and soil structure, protection of the land from erosion and fire, transfer of nutrients from lower soil levels by the deep-rooting thicket species, and *citemene* effects, may all enter into the complex of factors determining the rate of fertility recovery.

The Makonde people practise this thicket-fallow system in country where permanent surface water is almost non-existent. Domestic supplies have to be carried over long distances, from the very few water holes and seepage lines or, usually, from the foot of the scarp and the valleys of the Ruvuma and other rivers. The keeping of livestock is, of course, out of the question. A number of reasons have been given for the endurance of this tremendous handicap but the most probable explanation is contained in a Makonde saying quoted by Gillman: "We prefer to have food in plenty and go far for our water rather than to sit by the water and starve." Any large population might well starve if they lived by the water, for movements of entire communities between villages and distant cultivation sites would involve much greater wastage of labour than the carrying of minimal domestic supplies, and much of the unguarded crops would probably be lost. One cannot leave gardens in the African bush to the mercy of game animals, birds, baboons, and other marauders. Disease hazards in the valleys, which appear to be at the root of some tribal legends, may also be a factor which discourages a regular wet and dry season transhumance.

According to Gillman's estimate, "present land requirements on most of the plateau appear to be approximately 15–20 acres per family," presumably of cultivable thicket: but without adequate data on the composition of the "family" and the proportion of suitable land one cannot hazard a guess at the possible carrying capacity of the system in this environment. If the area is 3,700 square miles and the population was "over one hundred thousand" (64), the general density may have been something of the order of 30 per square mile at the time of his survey. There was some local congestion of population, for he records that "in certain regions, especially near Mahuta and Newala, the population density has been rising, largely as a result of the improved birth to mortality ratio. Here the pressure of population has already encroached on the fallow period, and the natives report that they are having to curtail the bush fallow period to as little as four years." But, in general, food supplies appear to have been well maintained and the plateau retained its reputation as the granary of the surrounding plains country. Gillman concludes, however, that "the Makonde plateau cannot afford the luxury of any great increase in its population." Nevertheless the system is capable of supporting considerably greater populations than one would expect of shifting cultivation in such an environment, and this, one must suppose, is due to the remarkable soil rejuvenating effects of the secondary thicket.

6. The Mashokora Cultivation of the Coast

Similar situations are found elsewhere, where conditions favour the establishment of secondary thicket communities. For example, a form of land-use practised in the coastal hinterland behind Dar-es-Salaam, known as "Mashokora cultivation," bears a good deal of resemblance to the "Makonde" thicket system. This type of cultivation has been described by Hartnell and Fuggles-Couchman (76) as it was practised more than twenty years ago in

the central area of Dar-es-Salaam district, an extensive hill region
stretching practically the whole length of the district. This is an
area of good rainfall with the heaviest falls in March–May, driest
conditions during August and September, and somewhat unreliable "short" rains towards the end of the year.

The main cultivated soils of the hills and hill slopes are deep
red loams of light texture which formerly carried high woodland
or forest, now to be found in well-developed form only in the
Forest Reserves. Elsewhere, the vegetation on the cultivated soils
has been reduced to scrub forest or thicket containing *Erythrophloeum guiniense*, *Chlorophora excelsa*, *Syzygium guiniense*, and
Afzelia quanzensis, with species of *Albizzia*, *Ficus*, and *Grewia*, all
interwoven with woody climbers and scandents.

The sequence of cropping is somewhat similar to that of the
Makonde. In the first season of cultivation, early-planted maize
grown with the short rains is followed by a main crop of upland
rice sown in late January or February before the maize is ready for
harvest, unless garden preparation has been delayed or the rains
are poor, when the maize crop may be omitted. The field is
cleared for replanting in October or November and an early maize
crop, for harvest in late February or March, is again taken with the
short rains: but the main crop in this second year of cultivation is
determined by soil fertility. If the soil is judged to be sufficiently
fertile, a second crop of rice is taken, often intermixed with
sorghum, but if this is thought to be too risky sorghum alone is
grown as a main crop. In the third year maize is sown again, interplanted with cassava as an end crop on the less fertile soil which
carried sorghum in the second year, while on the more fertile soil
a main crop of sorghum is taken in the third year followed by
cassava as an end crop in the fourth year. A number of minor
food plants, such as pigeon pea, cowpea, and green gram are also
included in the crop associations.

After three or four years of cropping the garden reverts to
fallow. A rapid grass growth, in which *Panicum trichocladum* is
commonly dominant, submerges the remaining cassava, and this
is followed by secondary bush which in a few years assumes the
character of "Mashokora" thicket. Soil regeneration, however,
appears to be considerably slower in the Mashokora environment.
According to information collected by Hartnell and Fuggles-
Couchman, fertility has not returned to the level required for rice

cultivation after a fallow of ten years duration, though maize, sorghum, and cassava may be grown on land cleared at this stage. One rice crop is sometimes taken on soil which has rested for fifteen to twenty years, but land is not generally regarded as suitable for rice until it has lain for twenty years or more under fallow.

The reasons for the different rates of soil regeneration in the two environments, and the extent to which they derive from basic soil factors, differences in the growth rate and nature of the secondary vegetation, or from deliberate management, are still uncertain and have been little investigated.

The Mashokora environment probably has a lower human-carrying capacity than that of Makonde, since a Land-Use Factor of 6 or more would appear to be appropriate for the Mashokora system as it is, or was, practised. Hartnell and Fuggles-Couchman estimated that about one-sixth of the area consisted of scrub forest on suitable red soils and if this is taken as an approximation to the proportion of land cultivable under the system one would expect the Critical Population Density to be somewhere in the region of 15 per square mile, for a people wholly dependent on this form of cultivation. Mashokora cultivation is, however, frequently part of a composite system practised by peoples with access to poor lowland sands, on which the villages are often situated. The sands are, in general, suited only to cassava and coconut culture and the people rely on hill cultivation for their grain supplies.

CHAPTER XIV

FOREST LANDS OF THE CONGO BASIN
AND GHANA

1. The Equatorial Forest Environment

A key factor in the tropical forest environment is the extra-ordinarily rapid growth of secondary vegetation, in which *Trema guineensis* and *Musanga cecropioides* are often dominant, following the retirement of land from cultivation. Ross (143) has described some growth rates for south-western Nigeria. An area cleared from tropical rain forest had developed a dense growth of *T. guineensis* two to three feet high within six weeks of clearing, while a sample plot on which cultivation had ceased some five years previously had an almost completely closed canopy of *M. cecropioides* about 33 feet high, and on a plot of fourteen years regeneration *Musanga* was over 75 feet in height. The prevailing conditions of constant warmth and moisture are, of course, highly favourable to plant growth, but, as Richards (140) has pointed out, the physiological problems presented by these exceptionally fast-growing species are still largely unsolved.

It does not follow, of course, that conditions are suited to the growth of all plants, or to permanent farming. Soils are generally weak, leached, and acid, and although they are stable so long as the vegetation cover is undisturbed, fertility declines rapidly under cultivation. This was discovered by the Belgians when they opened their station at Yangambi, where such excellent work has since been done in the steaming fields and the air-conditioned offices and laboratories. They cleared and stumped the forest and attempted permanent farming on the principles of temperate agriculture. Yields of every crop fell rapidly and the land had to be abandoned after a few years. From this they learned a salutary lesson and some respect for traditional African management of the forest soils.

2. The System of the Bakumu

The system of the Bakumu, who live in the Stanleyville district west of the Congo, may serve as an illustration of traditional land-use in the great forests of the Congo basin. The area in which I saw something of this system was, in fact, a *paysannat*, but customary practice had not been much altered, merely regulated and controlled. Cash cropping had not upset the balance, for production of the cash crops of the region—oil palm nuts, robusta coffee, and rubber—was discouraged in a wide zone round Stanleyville from which food for the city is drawn. Food crop production was, of course, encouraged, and the area under cultivation to these crops may have exceeded a normal subsistence acreage. There was much unemployment in the city and the Department of Agriculture was only too glad to help any man who wanted to open a food garden and to give him axes, hoes, and seed: but, they complained, the young men preferred to be unemployed.

We started out from what looked like, and probably was, a model village, almost unbelievably neat and clean against its background of oil palms—for food—and small, well-kept groves of mango, pawpaw, citrus, bananas, and plots of pineapple. There was a school, a dispensary, a chief's court, a community hall, and a communal grain bin, for this was the centre of a group of *paysannats* serving, I was told, about 250 families. From this village we followed a narrow path through the semi-darkness and foetid heat of the old forest where the trunks of *Gilbertiodendron* and other giants, draped with trailing lianas 70 feet and more in length, formed solid walls 150 to 200 feet high on either hand. Yet the soil underfoot was light, almost a sand, with a pale lifeless look. I felt some sympathy for the young men who preferred unemployment. It seemed incredible that the forest peoples could have cleared such tremendous vegetation with no better tool than the small iron axe. Yet they did; for most of the vast forest of the Congo basin is now of secondary growth.

The clearing of secondary forest is a less forbidding but still highly laborious task. A "good man," I was told, clears about an acre and a quarter every year, but the average is considerably lower and may be rather less than an acre.

The initial fertility must be fairly high, for rice and bananas are major crops: but the first crop to be planted in the new garden is maize, which also has a high fertility requirement. Maize is sown in March as a rule—though I saw much later plantings—and harvested in July. This is followed by upland rice, sown in the same garden in July immediately after the maize harvest, or among late-planted maize; and later in the year banana shoots and cassava cuttings are planted in the rice land. Bananas are planted among the growing rice over the period August–October, a little at a time so that the yield is spread, and the cassava cuttings go in during December after the rice has been harvested. Minor crops in the main gardens are generally restricted to yams placed by tree stumps, scattered capsicums, occasional cocoyams, and a few *Lycopersicum*, a plant similar to the tomato but capable of bearing fruit and resisting mildew in the steamy jungle heat.

In the second year the cassava and bananas take possession of the garden, but the harvest is small since cassava needs about a year to mature and bananas eighteen months. These two crops give their full yield in the third year, and with its termination the cycle of cultivation comes to an end. Already, before the end of the third year, the secondary vegetation has gripped the land, and the broad leaves of a giant form of *Aframomum* make their appearance—or rather, a form which appeared gigantic to me, accustomed to the stunted growth of this plant on the Northern Rhodesian *chipyas*.

Thicket takes rapid possession of the land, with the aggressive *Trema* dominating and the taller *Musanga*, the umbrella tree, beginning to push above it. On a plot in its seventh year after retirement from cultivation I saw a solid and even growth of thicket some 10 feet high, with umbrella trees projecting above it to a height of 18 or 20 feet and forming a thin but almost closed canopy. After fifteen years of regeneration, with the establishment of secondary forest in which well-grown umbrella trees are often the most conspicuous element, the fertility of the soil has been restored to its previous level and the cycle of cultivation can begin again. No doubt, recovery is more rapid on some of the alluvial and other heavier soils of limited extent, but the research work of INEAC has established that this period of fifteen years is safe for the great range of cultivated forest soils in this region. The Kumu show a pronounced sense of soil selection: they speak of fertility in terms of suitability for bananas and they make use of trees and other plants as indicators, but I was unable to obtain a translation of their botanical vocabulary.

The general Land-Use Factor for the system and environment is, therefore, of the order of 6 garden areas; and, as I have already suggested (pp. 62–3), the Cultivation Factor may be about half an acre per head of population, on a subsistence basis. As far as I could judge, from questioning and rough measurements of a few examples, the Kumu were cultivating about o·6 of an acre per head of population, or very little more.

This relatively small acreage suffices because two cereal crops, giving a total of a ton or a ton-and-a-half of grain per acre, are obtained in the first year of the main garden, while cassava and bananas yield three to four tons of roots and fruit together in the third year.[1] There are also small village gardens for fruit, vegetables, and pulses, which are manured with ash, other household refuse, and the droppings of the few fowls and goats; while palm oil from wild and cultivated trees, and cocoyams grown in little plots in moist bottom lands, also augment the food supply.

In this region of climatic stability there is, probably, no great seasonal variation in the surplus from subsistence and semi-subsistence cultivation, which may amount to about 25 per cent of total production. Rather more than 20 per cent of the total production of main food crops in the Orientale Province now enters into commerce and goes to feed the towns, mainly Stanleyville. Rice, however, has acquired more of the character of a cash crop in some regions and over half the total produce is sold, with increasing reliance on bananas and roots for home consumption.

A family of five may therefore have about 3 acres of land in cultivation at one time, and this will require the clearing of an acre or so of secondary forest each year, for the system of annual extension must be strictly observed in order to maintain the balance of the food supply. This extent of clearing may be somewhere near the average physical limit and one may conjecture that the equatorial forest environment would be uninhabitable for subsistence cultivators with traditional equipment if an appreciably larger food crop acreage were required. As it is, the forest zone is surprisingly sparsely populated in relation to its apparent carrying capacity. Even if no more than one-third of the land surface is cultivable, a system such as that of the Kumu should be capable of supporting population densities of the order of 50 per square mile. A considerable proportion of the land is occupied by swamps, streams, and rivers, and there are areas uncultivable by reason of soil poverty, as evidenced by old abandoned *paysannats*

---

[1] Estimates based on *Statistiques*; *Principales Cultures Indigenes; Province Orientale*, 1958 (unpublished).

and the soil selection of the Kumu, but on the whole there is an impression of uniformity, and the proportion of cultivable land may well exceed one-third over much of the region. This is suggested also by the fact that in an area about Stanleyville, within 20 miles or so of the city, the density of rural population has reached, and probably exceeded, 50 per square mile; yet there is no evidence of impending land shortage.

3. POPULATION DENSITIES IN THE CONGO BASIN

In a few places in the Lower Congo, about the larger settlements and bordering important waterways and other routes, local population densities as high as 250 to the square mile have been reached. In these circumstances, fallow periods appear to be reduced to five or six years, and this suggests that the proportion of cultivable land exceeds 50 per cent, including the marginal zone of unsatisfactory soils used only under extreme pressure. But high, or even moderate, densities are rare in the forest region and a fundamental feature of the human background is great sparsity of population, ranging from 5 to 10 per square mile over great areas. The Eastern Province of the Congo has been described as "well populated."[1] Standards vary with circumstances: the province has an area little short of 195,000 square miles and the general population density is probably less than 12 per square mile. Rural density in terms of African cultivators is considerably less, since the population figure includes the urban concentration in Stanleyville and employees on European plantations and in other enterprises. In the Equatorial Province rural densities are no higher: the general figure appears to be about 10·5 per square mile. Indeed, the former Belgian Congo as a whole is among the most sparsely inhabited of African territories, and human numbers are commonly well below the apparent carrying capacity of the land for the traditional systems of land-use. The reasons for this, and the extent to which historical factors and disease factors—and infertility such as appears to be characteristic of the Kumu and Zande, as it is of the Ganda—have determined the present demographic pattern, are yet to be determined.

Farnell (55), who studied this problem among the section of

---

[1] "La Province Orientale est abondamment peuplée. Suivant les derniers recensements, elle compte 2.311.813 indigenes. Les populations agricoles sont particulièrement nombreuses." (22)

the Zande in the Southern Sudan, points to epidemics of sleeping sickness, combined with a low child/adult ratio, a marked preponderance of females, a high infant and child mortality, and sexual habits which inspire "wonder rather than horror." He concludes that "none of the aetiological factors reviewed are in themselves sufficient to account for a lowering of the reproduction rate," and that the Zande, though not so prolific as in the past, are managing to reproduce themselves: but "much more work is required to assess the incidence of venereal disease and of tubal occlusion among the women." On the other hand, it has been stated that the Vungara Azande in the north-east Congo are continuously declining in number, and it has even been suggested that the poor country they occupy should be abandoned and the inhabitants—about 250,000—regrouped in a district that is economically viable.

Certainly no part of Africa suffered more from the slave trade. According to a Belgian estimate, 30 million slaves were taken from the Congo and large areas were entirely depopulated. There was a further population decline of three millions, according to Roger Casement, during King Leopold's regime.

Whatever the reasons for the relatively low population density, and its corollary, abundance of land, this situation has certainly influenced the intensity of land-use, in the direction of shifting agriculture and moving populations; and it was a primary determining factor in the formulation of Belgian agrarian policy in the Congo. The situation would, no doubt, have altered in the course of time. Although a few tribes are no more than holding their own, or, perhaps decreasing in numbers, there has been a very considerable upsurge of the general population in the post-war years, at a rate exceeding 1·5 per cent per annum according to official population estimates. The effect on this trend of the disruption which followed independence has yet to be seen.

4. FOREST REGIONS OF GHANA

The forest belt of Ghana may be divided into a number of regions which vary in their agricultural potential and suitability for the main economic crop, cocoa. Overall, the high closed forest with its marked three-storey structure has much the same general appearance. In the central forest zone the smaller trees make a canopy at about 60 feet, while the taller species rise to well over 100 feet and form a higher canopy above which the great crowns of the forest giants project, like bosses on the flat green surface of the upper canopy as one sees it from the air. But the dominant species vary, and there are wide differences in climatic and soil conditions.

In the south-west there is true rain forest. Here rainfall ranges from 70 to 120 inches and humidity is very high throughout the year. Vegetation is evergreen and the type trees are species of *Cynometra*, *Lophira*, and *Tarrietia*. The typical soils are poor, leached, highly acid oxysols, and conditions are generally unsuited to cocoa.

The remainder, and by far the greater part, of the forest belt has a lower and less continuous rainfall. Annual precipitation is of the order of 50 to 70 inches and there are two well-marked rainfall peaks, in May–June and September–October, with short spells of comparatively dry weather between. Some of the tree species, mainly components of the upper canopy and emergent storey, are deciduous. This region of semi-deciduous moist forest may again be divided into three zones, two of which are transitional.

Between the leached oxysols of the rain forest and the more fertile moist forest region lies a zone characterised by the *Lophira-Triplochiton* association, according to Taylor.[1] Here soils are generally poor, and cocoa is grown mainly on restricted belts of alluvium. On the typical soils the plant is difficult to establish and comparatively short lived.

This ecotone grades into the central forest zone of typical ochrosols characterised by the *Celtis-Triplochiton* association. Under a lighter and well-distributed rainfall, these soils have been subjected to little leaching. They are of good physical condition and water-holding capacity; they do not dry out under the conditions experienced in the region, yet they remain well-drained even in the wettest periods. Initial fertility is fairly high, but it is restricted to the top foot or so of soil. Tree roots do not penetrate deeply; even the roots of the forest giants, with their buttress supports, often go down no more than four or five feet and their underground system has been described as "an enormous collar-stud" fastening the tree to the soil. But the main reserves of plant food are in the form of organic matter and fertility is poised in a

---

[1] This association was recognised by Taylor (162), but Ahn (4) considered it doubtful if such an association is present to any extend on the forest oxysol-ochrosol intergrades of the Tano basin where he made his surveys.

delicate equilibrium. The most important characteristic of these soils, from the point of view of Ghana's economy, is their extraordinary suitability for cocoa, under the climatic conditions of the moist forest region. The plant establishes itself readily on the upper level of the catena from the mid-slope upwards, virtually as a secondary growth replacing the original forest understorey, and once established it is maintained by periodic slashing of the regrowth. The present economy of Ghana is based on this relatively small part of the country.

North of this fortunate area there is a zone of drier forest which is subject to the desiccating effects of the harmattan and which is characterised by an association of *Antiaris* and *Chlorophora*. The soils are still typically ochrosols but conditions are generally too dry for cocoa which is relegated to the moister bottom lands and then disappears completely as savannah conditions are approached.

Food production in the moist forest region was, and to a large extent still is, based on an association of bananas and cocoyams. The conditions suited to this association are also those best suited to cocoa. Rice is not a main crop here, though it is grown in small depressions where water lies and more extensively on wet lands bordering streams. Maize too is grown, and two crops a year can be taken, but it is not a popular crop because of the damage caused by forest rodents, or so the cultivators said. This seems to be a valid reason, for Agricultural Officers told me they could rarely get reliable results from maize experiments because of the extent of rodent damage. Cassava is a traditional crop of the coastal savannah and the Volta plains rather than the forest, but it is now commonly grown on the poorer forest soils, on exhausted land about towns and villages, and in abandoned cocoa plantations.

Clearing for new food-crop gardens starts generally in April and planting in June. Cocoyams spring up spontaneously almost everywhere when secondary forest is cleared. The commonest form of cocoyam is the comparatively recent introduction *Xanthosoma sagittifolium* which is believed to have been brought in by the Basel Mission in 1843, but the much older and probably indigenous *Colocasia esculentum* is also to be seen. Mixed cropping is usual in the first year. Bananas are interplanted with the cocoyams and a number of subsidiary crops are added, including yams on small mounds scattered throughout the garden, chillies, okra, maize, beans, peas, tomatoes, onions, cassava, and the solanaceous fruit called garden eggs. Cocoyams are harvested in the second year and the main crop of bananas is taken in the third year. On the better soils bananas may go on yielding for another year or more, while on poorer variants only the first one or two suckers mature, but in traditional practice the cultivation period on the main run of soils probably did not exceed three years. This period is still commonly observed on "food farms," though the general pattern has now become complicated and confused by cocoa planting and by population pressure in some areas. There are exceptional soils, as there are in most environments, capable of supporting much longer periods of cultivation, but the fertility of the typical forest soils is transient. It seems, however, that they regenerate fairly rapidly under secondary regrowth after this short cropping period.

The general consensus of opinions given to me by cultivators in Ashanti and neighbouring parts of the Eastern Region was that most of the soils used for food production could be maintained at a satisfactory level of fertility on a basis of two-and-a-half to three years of cultivation alternating with rest periods of seven to ten years. It may be, and this was the view of agriculturalists with experience of the environment, that such cycles of cultivation and rest do not maintain fertility at the original level, but they may, nevertheless, result in a balance of fertility at satisfactory yield levels of the main food crops, and they are commonly used in areas where there is no obvious land shortage. I had an opportunity of inspecting figures showing acreages under food crops and regenerating bush which had been obtained in the course of a swollen-shoot disease survey of part of the Eastern Region, some 435 square miles in extent, bordering on Ashanti. This area was divided into blocks, varying from under 100 to over 1,000 acres, for the purposes of the survey and the subsequent disease control operations. The ratio of land under food crops to resting land varied widely between blocks, with a range from 1:1 in the case of blocks bordering towns or large villages, where the food acreage is small and the land mainly in cocoa, to 1:20 or even more in a few obviously atypical blocks of escarpment hill regions, but ratios in the range 1:3 to 1:5 were most commonly represented in more typical situations.

These observations suggest that the general Land-Use Factor

for the traditional system of subsistence food production in the central forest region may not have been higher than 5, and the Cultivation Factor may have been as low as 0·5 of an acre (pp. 62–3) in this environment where, to quote Beckett, "the staple food crops are comparatively uniform croppers (and, one might add, high yielders of bulk foodstuffs) and the chance of food shortage, as among grain eating communities, is remote" (26). Here too the proportion of land suitable for the staple crops is high: taken over-all, the proportion of cultivable land certainly exceeds one-third and it may approach or even exceed 50 per cent. On this basis, one may suppose that the Critical Population Density for the old subsistence agriculture was somewhere between 85 and 130 people per square mile, with a probability that it approached the higher figure. Much of the cultivable land has now been given over to cocoa while the system of food production remains virtually unchanged. The Critical Population Density for the present method of land-use must therefore be lower than that for the purely subsistence system, in the sense that fewer people can be fed from the reduced area available for food crops.

The introduction of a permanent crop such as cocoa does not increase the land requirement to the same extent as an annual cash crop imposed upon a system of Recurrent Cultivation. If, for example, we suppose the area under cocoa to amount to one acre per head of population, which it certainly does in some areas, the requirement of cultivable land will be 3·5 acres per head compared with 2·5 acres for a simple subsistence system (0·5 of an acre in food crops and 2 acres resting, taking the Land-Use Factor as 5). Assuming that the proportion of land cultivable for food crops and cocoa is somewhere in the region of 40 per cent, the Critical Population Densities with and without cocoa will approximate to 70 per square mile and 100 per square mile respectively. When the cocoa boom started, population densities in the central forest zone were far below the critical levels and there was ample room for a great expansion of the crop without serious repercussions on the food supply, despite population increase and the influx of "stranger farmers." The first cultivators were convinced that cocoa could be successfully established only on virgin soils under high forest and this view is still commonly held, although in a few cases the crop has been successfully replanted on some of the stronger and more fertile soils. The fact that great areas of high forest were available for cocoa is indicative not only of low initial population densities, in relation to the Critical Density for the system of food production, but also of relatively short-term Recurrent Cultivation practices which left much of the forest untouched.

The ease of food production and the high human-carrying capacity of this forest zone is illustrated by Beckett's study of a Gold Coast village. In the 1930s when he made his surveys, his "modal cocoa village" of Akokoaso in the Western Akim district of the Eastern Region had a population density of 31 per square mile, and the cultivated area was slightly less than 3 square miles out of a total area of 38 square miles of village lands. The village was then in a phase of rapid expansion of the cocoa acreage, with 762 acres in bearing trees and 951 acres in young plants. As nearly all the non-bearing cocoa land was planted to food crops the area of such crops amounted to something like 0·9 of an acre per head of population. This was obviously far beyond village requirements. Much of the bulk food was left in the field to rot, probably more than half and quite probably much more, since rather less than a ton per acre was harvested whereas bananas and coco-yams may produce four or five tons per acre. At that time the cost of transport from this particular village to the nearest large market was greater than the value of the foodstuffs. Yet, in spite of this superabundance, considerable quantities of expensive imported foods were used and the consumption of these luxuries was an important contributing cause of chronic indebtedness.

The general range of population densities throughout the central forest zone, according to the latest distribution map (23), is from 10–25 per square mile in the west to 50–100 per square mile in the centre and east, with areas of greater concentration mainly in the east and about the town of Kumasi in Ashanti where densities reach and exceed 200 to the square mile. The pattern of population distribution, decreasing in density from east to west, is due in large degree to the fact that cocoa-growing spread through the forest from eastern foci of establishment, often following the tracks and clearings made by timber extractors. Destruction of cocoa in the older areas, by swollen-shoot disease and the cutting out operations necessary for its control, has accelerated the process as new areas have been opened up in the west to compensate for the loss of the old.

Labour comes mainly from the Northern Region of Ghana and

from Upper Volta beyond the Ghanaian border. In addition to ordinary wage-workers there are *abusa* labourers—from a Twi word, meaning division into three parts—who look after the cocoa gardens of absentee owners. The *abusa* labourer usually does all of the work: clearing the undergrowth once or twice a year, harvesting, fermenting, drying, and sometimes even marketing the crop. For this he receives one-third of the cocoa he produces. The practice is said to be decreasing. All of the cocoa growers I met in Ashanti and neighbouring parts of the Eastern Region employed wage labour, with one interesting exception. A fairly large planter in Ashanti gave me an evasive answer when I asked him how many workers he employed and how much he paid them. Afterwards a Ghanaian Agricultural Officer told me: "That man doesn't have to pay his labour. He is a famous ju-ju man and people who want to consult him must work on his cocoa farms." Judging by the state of his plantations, he must have had a flourishing practice.

As yet there is no general shortage of land to halt this process of forest exploitation. There are areas of heavy overpopulation, mainly in the east and about towns and large villages, where the fallow period of the food-crop cycle has been greatly reduced and a decline of fertility is obvious, but in the west the land is underpopulated and considerable reserves of high forest remain. Between these two extremes is a great area comprising a complex mosaic of cocoa plantations, food gardens, and regenerating land, with small and shrinking remnants of the original forest, where the population-land balance is still in equilibrium and some limited scope for further expansion remains. It has been estimated that the largest remaining area of forest land suitable for cocoa, in the Bia area of the Tano-Bia basin, will be used up in some fifteen to twenty years if the present rate of clearing continues (4).

The rain forest of the south-west is, however, likely to endure for a longer period. On the generally weak and heavily leached soils of this region yields of bananas and cocoyams are poor. Cassava is often used as a first crop and gardens are commonly abandoned after one or two years of cultivation. The soils appear to be poorer than those of the Congo basin on which the Kumu practise their sequence-association of cereals, cassava, and bananas, and the regeneration period is probably longer. The forest itself has a rather stunted look, with fewer very large trees and more pole growth; it is not as high as the semi-deciduous moist forest of the central zone, for the two rather irregular canopies are formed at heights of some 40–50 and 70–90 feet and the emergent storey is less vigorous. Most of the land probably falls within the long-term Recurrent Cultivation or Shifting Cultivation categories. Oil palm, which is tolerant of conditions such as these, might be developed as a cash crop, and there are also possibilities for rubber, and for rice in some of the valley bottoms, but as yet no great interest has been shown in the limited potentialities of this desolate region. Cultivation is mainly on the relatively small areas of alluvial soils and tertiary sands, and the latter are being planted fairly extensively to coconut palm.

Under the lower rainfall conditions of most of the coastal belt, forest gives place to scrub and grassland. The commerce and industry of Ghana is still largely concentrated in this region of long-standing trade connexions with Europe, and population densities are high throughout, ranging generally between 100 and 200 per square mile and exceeding the higher figure in some areas, notably on the Accra plain and about the port of Takoradi. West of Accra the coastal belt is relatively narrow and vegetation is mainly close scrub, a curious mixture of forest and Guinea savannah species, on soils of the forest ochrosol type which appear to be capable of yielding little but cassava. Very probably they have been exhausted and degraded by long over-cultivation in the past. East of Accra lies the much wider and more complex grassland region of the south-eastern savannah and the Volta river outlet. Here, in addition to fishermen and cattlemen, there are dense cultivating populations on the Volta alluvium and on red earths which are said to be capable of supporting Semi-Permanent cultivation on a basis of three years' cultivation to maize and cassava followed by five years' rest. Rice projects in the lower Volta and cattle improvement schemes are being evaluated, but the coastal region as a whole is at present far from self-supporting in food.

Much of the food required by the large coastal population is drawn from the forest hinterland and this demand has resulted in the emergence of a considerable number of farmers who derive their cash income from sales of foodcrops rather than cocoa. Their "farming" is little more than an extension of subsistence cultivation. The implement of tillage is the hoe and maintenance of fertility still depends on adequate periods of bush fallow, but the area under cultivation at any one time is increased, often to two or three times the subsistence acreage. The increased acreage is maintained, as in cocoa planting, by employing poorly paid wage labour from the north, when peak labour requirements exceed the capacity of the family. This, of course, increases the burden on the land in much the same way as an annual commercial cash crop, but the consequences have been partly offset by the loss of cocoa, with reversion of the old cocoa lands to food farming, and by the fact that the new plantations yield food crops in the early stages of establishment.

A later stage of somewhat similar processes is to be seen in parts of the neighbouring Ivory Coast. Here, in the country of the Dida and Bete peoples, conditions generally allow of only two years' cultivation—to rice, cocoyams, yams, cassava, and bananas—after which a minimum period of six years' rest is said to be necessary to restore fertility to a satisfactory level for arable cropping. Continuous planting of land to cocoa and coffee after food cropping, combined with population concentration by settlement of villages along motor roads and immoderate sales of land to immigrant planters, has resulted in locally acute land shortage with the inevitable consequence of a shortening of the fallow period and a decline in food production.

CHAPTER XV

THE NORTHERN SAVANNAH

1. THE FOREST MARGIN AND THE VOLTA PLAINS

In the transitional forest zone of Ghana, north of Kumasi and south of Mampong, the cocoyam-banana food crop association continues, but cocoa cultivation decreases and gives place to more prosperous-looking coffee. Further north, as the forest weakens under the effects of decreasing rainfall and the assault of the harmattan, maize appears as a conspicuous crop and good yields of 1,000 to 2,000 lb per acre are said to be obtained. But conditions are still too moist for easy drying. The problem of storing grain in bulk formerly inhibited development of maize as a cash crop, but this difficulty has been overcome by the establishment of co-operatively run drying plant and handling services. Grain prices, which were previously depressed by the dumping of the crop on the market after harvest, are now maintained by continuity of supply at levels which, at the time of my visit in 1959, growers clearly found very attractive. Maize has become a main cash crop in the region about Mampong.

Even in this outer margin of the forest, cocoyams and bananas persist as staple food crops, supplemented by maize. In traditional practice, two maize crops were grown among the young plants in the first year and cocoyams and bananas were harvested in the second and third years. Three years of cultivation seems to have been usual, extending to four or five years on the best soils, followed by bush and secondary forest fallow of indefinite period. Some of my informants maintained that a bush fallow of five to seven years would restore fertility after three years' cultivation while others said it had been customary to rest the land for a long time and to return to well-grown secondary forest. Re-cultivation to cassava for a couple of years after a short break of three to four years, followed by a long period of fallow, may have been a traditional practice, and a crop of maize may have been taken in the first year of recultivation. The uncertainty regarding fallow periods does, however, suggest an abundance of land in the comparatively recent past. If this was so, the situation has been altered by population increase, attraction of immigrants to this area of economic opportunity, and extensive cropping of maize.

Re-cultivation is now commonly practised. The traditional sequence of maize, cocoyams, and bananas is usually followed, but the land is then rested for a short period of three to four years and re-cultivated for commercial maize, generally for two years during which four maize crops are taken. In the meantime, new gardens for food-crops are opened in "virgin" or well-grown secondary forest wherever this is to be found, while in some instances such land is opened to maize and cultivated to the point of exhaustion under a succession of commercial crops. There are few livestock and neither manure nor fertiliser are used. It is said that pressure on the land is not yet acute and considerable reserves of good re-growth remain, with some vestiges of climax forest, but these reserves are probably diminishing rapidly and the stage of general soil degeneration is unlikely to be very far off if present practices continue. The harmattan has a new ally in its endless assault on the weak and crumbling outer wall of the forest. Dead trees make an impressive feature of this area, stark skeletons of forest giants usually draped with half a dozen or so drab and melancholy vultures.

On the road from Kumasi to the north, just south of Ejura, the main forest ends on a sharp little escarpment up which one climbs into a different world, the lighter, more open world of the Guinea savannah-woodland. Here sunshine averages 6·70 hours a day, compared with 2·25 hours in the forest region. The ground cover is an almost continuous layer of grass, with generally short and widely spaced trees, but in this southern zone remnants of forest persist as isolated outliers and riverain forest along drainage lines. The shanty towns and villages of the south, with their roofs of rusty metal sheeting, disappear and give place to the typical thatched mud huts of Africa, while the agricultural pattern changes almost as abruptly. Cocoyams and bananas are still to be seen but they have lost their place in the main crop sequence and become subsidiaries. Yams, groundnuts (a crop little grown in the forest where the oil palm is the supplier of edible oil), cereals, and cassava become the dominant crops.

In this zone the main crop of the first-year garden is yams, grown on mounds with stakes to support the vines. Groundnuts follow in the second year and a crop of maize, or rice on wetter land, may be taken in the same year, for conditions still allow of double cropping. Cassava is also planted in the second year and the reaping of this crop in the third year generally ends the sequence. Fallow periods are said to be relatively short, ranging from five to ten years, but adequate. Re-cultivation to cereals and cassava, with a longer second fallow period, may, however, be a fairly common practice. The pattern, it seems, has become somewhat confused by the immigration of alien peoples, Hausa and others from the north.

North of this forest-savannah transition lie the great Volta plains of Ghana, a puzzling region of very sparse population. There are extensive areas of seemingly untouched and uninhabited savannah-woodland: elsewhere population densities of 10 per square mile or more are reached, and the general figure is about 5 per square mile over a region which has all the appearance of being able to support much greater numbers. Many reasons for this sparsity of population have been suggested: slave raiding and wars in a marcher zone which lay between the dominant and aggressive tribes of north and south, tsetse fly and sleeping sickness, yellow fever, and shortage of surface water. All of these factors may have played a part in maintaining population densities at a low level in the past. But the continuing desolation of the region is difficult to understand, even though surface water is certainly rare on the Voltaian sandstones away from the rivers, in contrast with the granitic lands of the north where water is abundant at shallow depth, and even though the main sandstone soils may be capable of supporting no more than long-term Recurrent Cultivation under traditional methods of land-use. The Volta and its confluents and tributaries carry an impressive volume of water through the region.

Here rainfall is of the "single peak" type, with maxima in August–September, and there is a marked dry season at the end and the beginning of the year with grass and bush fires in the period January–April. All vestige of forest has gone and riverain forest is replaced by riverain woodland. Yams are still a major crop, but maize as a main cereal is progressively replaced by sorghum—locally known as Guinea corn—and bulrush millet.

North of the Volta and in the neighbourhood of Tamale one comes into the country of the Dagomba people whose reputation as excellent agriculturalists seems to rest on the fact that their relatively simple traditional system remains little altered and has not as yet been complicated by cash cropping or population pressure. The original Dagomba were conquerors, like the Wala and Mamprussi to the west and north of them, who came from the Western Sudan and imposed themselves and their system of chieftainship on the people they subjugated. It may well have been that the central Volta plains was a buffer zone, constantly raided and harried, between these warriors of the north and the power of Ashanti in the south.

2. The Dagomba System

The Dagomba country shows considerable soil variation. A range of medium silty soils, sandy loams, and gravelly light loams are selected for the main gardens, with avoidance of low-lying silts liable to waterlogging in the rains, poorly drained sandy loams, very light sand soils and areas of extrusive ironstone. Vegetation is typical of the Guinea savannah. There is good grassland in which *Andropogon gayanus* is often dominant, and fairly widely spaced trees among which *Parkia filicoidea*, *Butryospermum Parkii*, and *Daniellia Oliveri* are conspicuous, while *combretums* and *terminalias* are more prominent in areas of poorer drainage.

Land is cleared early in the dry season and new gardens are prepared by a thorough hoeing off of the vegetation, which is collected and burned. The soil is then built with the hoe into mounds each of which is some two-and-a-half feet high and four or five feet in diameter at the base. The process looks laborious, but it is said that a Dagomba man normally makes 100 to 200 such mounds in a day. These are for yams. Small "seed" tubers are planted in the sides of the mounds, usually during the dry-season month of January, and a mulch of dry grass or leaves covered with earth is placed on each mound to conserve moisture and maintain an even temperature. The Dagomba have a number of yam varieties and different varieties are used on different soils and for early and late maturity. Early yams are lifted in August and the later harvest may be taken at leisure from September until the middle of the dry season. In the meantime, before the first yam harvest and generally in June or July, a late variety of bulrush millet is planted between the mounds which have now become somewhat reduced by rain wash and cultivation.

Yams are the main crop and bulrush millet a secondary crop of the first-year garden, but some subsidiaries are also included. Roselle, okra, and calabashes are quite commonly grown on the sides of or between the mounds, and occasionally there is a little sesame and an odd cotton bush or some other useful plant. Most gardens have an outer row of cassava or pigeon pea or both, or a few lines of them among the other crops. But most of the minor crops (ground beans, chillies, okra, and sesame) are grown by themselves in little first-year gardens cleared from bush or grassland.

Standards of cultivation are generally high. Indeed, the first-year Dagomba garden is often quite a remarkable example of skilful and painstaking horticulture. It is almost entirely the work of men: women's work is mainly confined to helping with the harvest, threshing grain, and carrying crops from the field. I did not once see a Dagomba woman hoeing or even carrying a hoe, but when I visited a first-year garden the man was there more often than not, busy about his plants. At times of peak labour requirements the help of kin and neighbours is called upon, as in almost all African societies, and they are rewarded with beer, food, and services in return.

Although land is normally cultivated for three years the first-year garden is the most important part of the sequence, both in terms of the labour expended on it and the return. Yield data (5, 110) indicate that the yams alone generally give two to three tons of food per acre, and yields up to five tons are not uncommon, although the Dagomba country is near the northern limit for the crop. The late millet, however, is widely spaced between the mounds and usually gives a light yield of some 200–300 lb of grain per acre.

The second-year garden provides most of the grain and pulse requirements. This too is well cultivated though it does not get the meticulous care of the first-year garden. The yam mounds are broken down and the land is ridged. Red sorghums for making beer and white varieties for food grains are invariably sown, sometimes alone but more commonly with an intermixture of maize. Groundnuts are planted in lines at a wide spacing between the cereals, and also (though far less frequently in the areas I saw) ground beans, common cowpeas and a variety of cowpea known as sanza bean. Details of practice vary locally and on different soils.

The third-year garden gets little cultivation and it is not usually ridged. After the land has been cleared of weeds and crop refuse, sorghum or bulrush millet is planted on the flat, and some groundnuts or other legumes may be inter-planted. As a general rule, sorghum and some legumes will be sown if the residual fertility is judged to be high enough for a satisfactory crop, but if fertility is thought to be low bulrush millet will be substituted.

Cultivation may sometimes be continued for a longer period on the strongest soils, while on weak soils the third-year garden is omitted, but the common pattern is this three years' sequence of (1) yams and bulrush millet, (2) sorghum, maize, and pulses, (3) sorghum or millet, followed by a period of fallow. In the *Andropogon* grassland the rest period is determined by the time required for the re-establishment of a good cover of *Andropogon*, which is regarded as indicating the restoration of fertility to a satisfactory level, and this is said to vary from six to ten years after the customary three-years' cropping cycle. It is possible, therefore, that the land of this environment is capable of sustaining short-term Recurrent Cultivation, with a Land-Use Factor of about 4 for the customary Dagomba system.

The Cultivation Factor appears to be low, probably because of the high yield of yams. Sampling data given by Akenhead (5) show an average figure of 1·66 for the number of persons supported by one cultivated acre, while Masters (110) obtained a figure of 1·40 people per cultivated acre. These data indicate Cultivation Factors of 0·60 and 0·71 of an acre respectively. The latter survey was restricted to two villages only, but it is very probable that the cultivated acreage has been increasing in response to market demands, especially in areas nearer the markets. The traditional subsistence acreage may have approximated to the lower figure. Such an acreage should be adequate, according to yield indications, to give a considerable normal surplus of yams, a sufficiency of pulses, and some surplus of grain when rice is taken into consideration.

Rice is grown on a small scale as a minor cereal but is never included in the main crop sequence. It is cultivated as a pure crop in swamp lands and, sometimes with yams and even maize, in wet areas. The planted acreage is increasing under encouragement from the Agricultural Department but it is still very small in relation to population, though yields are probably fairly high. In addition, some Dagomba have "compound farms." These are small gardens very close to the village which are manured with the droppings of livestock and village refuse. Livestock are not numerous. There are cattle of the small West African shorthorn type, but they are owned by relatively few. A few Dagomba also have riding horses, many more have goats and sheep in small numbers, and nearly all have small flocks of guinea fowl and ordinary domestic fowls. But manure is applied only to the "compound" gardens. Some villages in the west are said to grow "prolific maize crops year after year" on these gardens, but they are mostly used, where they are used at all, for tobacco only. We shall discover presently that the "compound farm" is a prominent and essential feature of neighbouring land-use patterns to the north, but it has very little practical significance in the Dagomba system of food production.

Thus, the requirement of cultivable land for the main food-gardens appears to be much the same as in the central forest zone, about 2·5 acres per head of population; but the Cultivable Percentage of the land in the Dagomba region is undoubtedly lower. A considerable proportion of the land is avoided for main gardens, if it is possible to do so, because of seasonal waterlogging or for other reasons, and consequently these gardens are often at some distance from the village—as much as five miles away in extreme cases. But even if the proportion of "cultivable" land—that is, land which would be freely selected as suitable for main gardens—is rather less than 25 per cent, the Dagomba system may still be capable of supporting a Critical Population Density of the order of 50–60 persons to the square mile in the areas which allow of short-term Recurrent Cultivation. Parts of Dagomba probably have lower carrying capacities. I was told that in remote areas of low population fallow periods are prolonged indefinitely, but I was unable to discover whether this was due to voluntary Shifting Cultivation under conditions of abundant land or to the necessity of a long fallow.

Present population densities appear to fall mainly in the range 25–50 per square mile, with lower densities in places and higher concentrations in the neighbourhood of urban settlements, mainly around the chief town of Tamale. Here there is a wide ring of obviously degraded land, due mainly to part-time cultivation by town workers: almost any soil capable of bearing the most meagre crop is brought into cultivation, and fallow periods have been reduced to short breaks of two to three years. But, apart from these local concentrations, population densities are probably in general below, and sometimes well below, the critical level. According to all accounts there is little if any pressure on the land and the system of production ensures not only an ample food supply for the cultivating family but also a surplus for sale. This surplus is mainly absorbed by the growing population of Tamale, but some is bought by traders for the Kumasi market in the south.

Here, it seems, we have a traditional system which has altered little but is capable of supporting a considerable degree of urban development and of providing the cultivator with a satisfactory income, on present African standards, in addition to his food supply. An economic survey of two Dagomba villages (110) showed the average annual cash income per adult male to be over £58 in both cases. About 73·5 per cent of the income came from sales of food crops and livestock (the trade in which is small) and the products of hunting and collecting, while the remainder derived from local employment, petty trading, and remittances. This compares favourably with incomes from cash cropping in many countries and with the £31 a year (in addition to food, housing, and working dress) which cocoa planters in southern Ghana told me they paid to labourers from the Northern Region.

The owners of cocoa plantations can, of course, make much more money, though the return varies from year to year with yield and prices. Polly Hill found that average net incomes from cocoa in ten places where she made investigations varied from £575 in the most prosperous to £65 in an area badly affected by swollen-shoot disease (81). This was in 1954–5 when the market price of dry cocoa was 72s. a load, as compared with 60s. a load in 1958–9. The economic attraction of the south, with its opportunities for comparative wealth, may have played a part in maintaining the population-land balance in the Dagomba region. Of the two villages studied by Masters, the population of one had decreased over the period 1948–55, a decrease attributed to migration, while the population of the other did not seem to have increased.

Whatever the demographic situation in Dagomba may be, the southward migration has not been sufficient to restore a population-land balance in the problem areas to the north.

3. Concentric Ring Cultivation

North of the Dagomba country there is an abrupt change to another region with a wholly different agriculture. The geology changes, from the sandstones and shales of the south to granite, granodiorite, and lava formations, and this transition is marked in places by an escarpment which reaches imposing dimensions in the Gambaga scarp to the east. There is no great change in rainfall, but the climate is probably more typically "Sudanian," with greater extremes and a harsher dry season. The rain starts in March or April and continue, with an August–September maximum, until early November; then, as the long dry season sets in, the desiccating harmattan blows steadily from the north-east.

Acacias become more prominent in the vegetation, including *Acacia arabica* and the beautiful *A. albida*, as also do baobab and tamarind. Few trees survive in the densely settled areas and they are mainly of useful species such as the baobab, the tamarind, and the acacias, with *Butyrospermum Parkii*, *Parkia filicoidea*, and *Diospyros mespiliformis*; and all the uncultivated land of this open countryside carries a grass cover. But cattle are numerous, a very high proportion of the land is in cultivation, and overgrazing has reduced and degraded much of the remaining grassland, often to a thin cover mainly of *Heteropogon contortus*.

This is, on the whole, a region of higher soil fertility. There are dark-brown soils and red earths of considerable fertility and strength, associated with greenstone of the Upper Birrimian formation, which may well fall within the Permanent and Semi-Permanent Cultivation categories, while the granite soils, though much lighter, are inherently fertile and may be capable of sustaining Semi-Permanent and short-term Recurrent Cultivation. On the other hand, the soils associated with the Lower Birrimian formation are generally very poor and have been described as "hardly worth cultivating," since yields are too low to give sufficient food by hand cultivation. These are, perhaps, to be regarded as areas of Shifting Cultivation or Partial Cultivation land.

Here, however, the terms we have been using lose some of their significance, for agriculture is no longer "shifting." This is a region of fixed and continuous agriculture with the use of manure, which is so highly valued that every scrap is often collected from cattle paths and grazing areas and laboriously transported in head-loads to the field. It is also the most urgent problem area of Ghana, a region of poverty and malnutrition which is among the worst in Africa.

The peculiar concentric ring system of cultivation has features reminiscent of the old in-fields and out-fields of Scotland. Each homestead is surrounded by its "compound" garden—for the peoples of the north, the Builsa, Nankanni, Fra Fra, Kusasi, and others live in separate family homesteads or "compounds," unlike the Dagomba who live in compact villages. Another fundamental difference in the agricultural pattern is the absence of yams. Here, in the extreme north of Ghana, yams cannot be grown, or so I was told, because temperatures are too high at the time the first rains come and the seed tubers rot in the ground: if they are planted late enough to avoid this period yields are miserably low. The main food crops are restricted to cereals, chiefly sorghum and bulrush millet of early and late maturing varieties, with subsidiary legumes.

The typical homestead garden surrounding the family dwelling shows three concentric rings of cultivation, clearly defined by differences in fertility and cropping. Bordering the homestead there is a very narrow ring of kitchen garden maintained in fertility by regular manuring and the addition of compound sweepings, household refuse, and night soil. Next comes a very much wider ring, the compound garden, which received a fairly regular dressing of whatever manure can be had, from cattle, small-stock, and poultry. Beyond this is an outer ring, the semi-compound garden, to which manure is applied only occasionally when a surplus happens to be available. The manure is obtained from night droppings, augmented by what can be collected from cattle tracks and grazing grounds, and it is transported in small basket headloads. Bedding is not used to increase the supply except by the few modern "plough farmers," probably because the additional labour this would require is more than the family is willing or able to supply.

Another garden form persists, the "bush" garden which is generally at some distance from the homestead. This is never manured. In the past these bush gardens were probably rested for a considerable period—about ten years according to one account—after a short cropping cycle, but the cultivation period has become extended and fallow breaks are commonly brief and in-adequate. Many families now have no bush gardens, because, they say, there is no bush accessible to them, while others appear to assert long-standing fallow rights over land they do not cultivate. I was told that when grazing areas are demarcated cultivators sometimes come forward and claim fallow rights over parcels their fathers once used as bush gardens but which they themselves have never cultivated. This probably happens where former "bush" areas have come into use for grazing, and holders of cultivation rights do not exercise them for fear of damage by livestock and friction with the graziers.

Cultivation follows a fairly definite pattern in each of these garden forms. In the little kitchen garden ring, "industrial" crops for home use are grown as well as food plants. Tall *Hibiscus cannabinus*, the Ambaria hemp, is conspicuous: this is the main source of fibre for string, ropes, and nets. Calabash cucurbits, cotton, tobacco, and other useful plants are included in the mixture, together with sesame, early sorghum, pumpkins, cassava, and maize which is used as a vegetable rather than a cereal since most of the cobs are eaten green. Sometimes there is also a bed of sweet potatoes or egg plant.

In the compound garden a mixture of early bulrush millet and sorghum is alternated with a mixture of early and late millet year after year, while in the semi-compound garden sorghum is usually alternated with late millet. As a rule, early millet is excluded from the semi-compound garden but it is sometimes planted in the year when manure has been applied. Cowpeas and cucurbits are sown as ground crops with the sorghum and millet and an area of the semi-compound garden is often reserved for groundnuts to give an early crop or to provide the main supply for families with no bush garden.

Cropping of the bush gardens is rather more variable. Ground-nuts are often planted as a pure crop followed in the next year by sorghum or late millet, or one of these cereals may be planted in each year with cowpeas, groundnuts, and ground-beans, or cow-peas may be alternated with sorghum. Whatever the sequence, it is generally continued to the point of soil exhaustion and the land is then left to recuperate for a few years. Other subsidiary gardens are used, but their extent is very small: they include rice patches in wet valley lands, little beds of sweet potatoes and coleus pota-

A.H.—17

toes in moist places, and plots of groundnuts grown as a single crop on light soil.

Only a small part of the cultivated land is manured in any one year, 12 per cent according to Lynn's surveys (1932–6), and 11·8 per cent of the homestead garden according to a survey conducted in Zuarungu some twenty years later, while the rates of application are probably of the order of 2 to 4 tons per acre. Labour, especially, and the quantities of manure available, are limiting factors. In spite of the universal use of manure, the system is incapable of maintaining fertility at the level necessary to ensure an adequate and reliable food supply. Lynn reported in the early 1930s that, with the exception of the inner compound ring, the bulk of the land had been reduced to a basic minimum of fertility and yields were precariously low. Conditions are, on the whole, no better today, in spite of a great deal of agricultural improvement work and the adoption of "plough farming" and the bedding of live-stock by a few. Hunger is the common lot and in many years famine is averted only by the selling of cattle to make good the food deficiency.

Here, it seems, we have an exception to the general rule that traditional systems of land-use are capable of maintaining the food supply without damage to the land, up to a certain level of population density. Or is there another explanation? We may, perhaps, find a clue if we look to the west, to the savannah country south of Lake Chad. This is more than a thousand miles away, in a drier region with a rainfall of 28 inches all of which comes in the period between mid-May and late November; yet the land-use pattern, as Dumont has described it for a cereal-growing village near the river Shari (52), bears a striking resemblance to that of North Ghana. Here, again, are the concentric rings of cultivation.

There is a little "home field" or kitchen garden by the hut which is heavily manured and planted to maize, mainly for green cobs, together with the same "industrial" crops as one finds in North Ghana. Beyond this is "the first concentric ring of cultivation," as Dumont calls it, the equivalent of the compound garden: this is manured occasionally and it bears an unbroken succession of sorghum crops. Beyond this again is an outer ring, analogous to the semi-compound garden, which is more extensively cultivated on a rotation of two years of mixed cultivation, with lines of sorghum interspersed with groundnuts or ground-beans, followed by two or three years of fallow. The Ghanaian practice is more intensive, a development one would expect under conditions of population pressure and land shortage, and there are differences of cropping which may reflect differences of soil and climatic conditions, but otherwise the resemblance is close. It does not end there. In the system described by Dumont there are also "bush fields" at some distance from the homesteads. Bulrush millet appears as a cereal crop in these gardens, "either grown for two or three years in succession or, more frequently, alternating with sorghum. After this the land remains fallow for three to five years, which is barely long enough, especially as there are tracts of virtually empty land a little farther to the east."

The cultivated land deteriorates, except for the most heavily manured fraction. But in this case there is an explanation, which Dumont gives. "The rapid impoverishment of the surrounding land which is brought on by over-frequent cultivation was formerly counteracted by moving the whole village to a fresh area as soon as serious soil deterioration set in. Here, on the east side of the Shari, there is no lack of land. The density of population is only three or four per square mile. . . ." This, it seems, is really a Recurrent Cultivation or Shifting Cultivation system which has become "fossilised" at a low level of population density because, as Dumont puts it: "When the *Service Geographique* has determined the position of a village on the map, the Administration does not take kindly to the idea of subsequent changes of location. The official pressure which is exerted to avert such changes is thus an important factor in the impoverishment of land, and until a scientifically devised system of perennial cropping can be introduced, permanent forms of rural settlement should be strongly discouraged." But he makes it clear that the mere devising of a system is not enough, for he comments: "With its distance from the coast and from possible sources of equipment, the region will probably have to wait a long time before the intensive methods presupposed by permanent occupation of land can be applied."

Such a changing system of land-use would allow of temporary local grouping of population, in homesteads or dispersed "villages," at densities well above the carrying capacity of the land, and this grouping may have been necessary for defence. It was so explained to me by some of my African informants in North Ghana. Each homestead of this region, with its enclosing walls, looks like a miniature fort and is generally within bow-shot or double bow-shot of its neighbours. The whole pattern has the appearance of an effective device for defence in depth, provided the enemy is sporting enough to stay away at the time when high-grown crops screen the "forts." Warfare, or, at least, long distance raiding in strength, was usually a dry season occupation, to be engaged in after harvest when the granaries were full. On this supposition, we may regard the manuring which is practised not as an attempt to maintain permanent fertility but as a device to prolong the period of occupation of one area and defer the need for a general move by the whole community. A community in process of moving must have been almost as vulnerable as a hermit crab changing its shell.

It seems possible, indeed probable, that the land-use pattern we now find in North Ghana derives from such a changing system which became "fossilised," not by recent administrative pressure but by enclosure and growth of population in the more distant past.

In these districts of North Ghana, Navrongo, Zuarungu, and Kusasi, a form of filariasis transmitted by the insect vector *Simulium* and known as "river blindness" is endemic in riverain areas. Country where the disease occurs is avoided and there is a curiously contrasting pattern of dense over-population and empty bush, some of which is also infested with tsetse. There are traces of former habitation in this now empty bush and the people say that their ancestors—some say their "grandfathers"—went to live there, but they were stricken with disease and some died while many became blind. Population therefore concentrated on the habitable land, hemmed in by the danger zones along the south-flowing tributaries and heads of the Volta, by the tsetse barrier to a stock-owning people, and by other tribes, so that a shift of land was no longer possible. Then came the restrictions imposed by international boundaries and the population growth that followed the peace of the suzerain powers. High densities of population have been reached in the inhabitated areas: these are generally of the order of 300–400 per square mile, with a range from as low as 40 per square mile on the poorest land, which is "hardly worth cultivating," up to 800 or 900 to the square mile on the strong and fertile soils. Meanwhile, grazing has been restricted by cultivation and confined to the poorer land, with consequent over-stocking and degeneration of the grass cover.

4. AREAS OF INTENSIVE AGRICULTURE

There may have been some intensification of practice under these conditions but no higher system was evolved, such as we have noted in parts of East Africa. The evolution of intensive systems seems to be characteristic of refuge areas in which natural conditions afforded some degree of protection against attack and disturbance. There are examples in West Africa. One of these, the system of the Hill Pagans of Dikwa Emirate in the north of the Cameroons, has been described by Stanhope White (184).

The Hill Pagans live in the Mandara mountains which rise to some 3,000 feet above the savannah south of Lake Chad, not far from the region of concentric ring agriculture we have noted. Here there was a marcher zone between the rival powers of the Madagali Fulani, the Mandara of Mora and the Kanuri of Bornu. The plains were uninhabitable for the Pagans. Not only were crops certain to be pillaged and destroyed but any Pagan found living or even wandering there was liable to be captured and taken into slavery by raiding bands of horsemen. Until the British occupation in 1919 they were confined to their hill refuge and there they evolved an agricultural system which, as White puts it, "contains practically every principle that Agricultural Departments throughout Africa are trying to instil in the 'backward' peoples" (184).

The present cultivators dispossessed an earlier people, remnants of whom remain, and took over an admirable system of dry-stone terracing of unknown date which, White estimates, must represent the work of centuries. The hills, he says, are covered from foot to summit with stone-walled terraces, so carefully built that they are "in no way inferior to the dry-stone walls of Northern England." Although they did not build this great system of soil conservation works, the present occupants are fully aware of its value and they tend and maintain the terrace walls.

The soil seems to be of low intrinsic fertility, for it is said that only two good crops can be taken on unmanured land, after which a fallow break is necessary. Manure is not only used but made by bedding down the animals, and the supply of soil-fertilising material is augmented from every possible source. White was impressed by this feature of their agriculture: "It is no exaggeration to say that these people destroy nothing that is of any possible value for their farm or their stock, and utilize everything that can be utilized."

The Hill Pagans have cattle, sheep, and goats, but, like the Kara of Lake Victoria, they do not collect cattle for the sake of possessing them, though they are used for bride wealth, blood money, and ritual sacrifice. They are highly valued as manure-making machines. The cattle are kept in huts at night and bedded down on grass which, as in Chaggaland, has often to be carried a long way. They are kept indoors and hand-fed throughout the rains but they graze out during the day in the dry season. Grazing is scarce at this time and some of the wet season flush is conserved as hay for supplementary feed, a very unusual practice in traditional African agriculture. Grass is cut towards the end of the rains and plaited into trusses which are hung on trees until required for use in the dry season. Cattle are also valued for quality, and selective breeding is practised.

The manure supply obtained by bedding down the animals is augmented by wood ash from the household fires, which is carefully collected and conserved, and by night soil from the latrines. Weeds from the cultivated land are collected and placed in heaps to form compost. All of this material is carried to the field and used to maintain the fertility of the terrace plots which are cultivated on a fairly fixed three-course rotation of (1) beans, (2) bulrush millet, and (3) sorghum. Subsidiary food crops are grown separately: ground-beans and sweet potatoes in small plots wherever land is available, finger millet on the terrace edges bordering the bean crop, and onions in irrigated streamside gardens.

It seems, however, that the manurial treatment does not keep the fertility up indefinitely. After a period of cultivation which may be as long as ten years a break is considered necessary and the land is left fallow for some two years. A curious treatment is then applied, though it includes the incorporation of cut grass as manure, a practice which, as we have seen, is not unusual. Soil is dug from the terrace plots to make holes in which the grass is placed together with quantities of wood ash and household sweepings. The soil is then replaced and planted with tiger nut (*Cyperus esculentus*) which is grown for two or three years. Fertility has then been restored, or so it is claimed, to a level which will allow of a repetition of the main cropping cycle.

In addition, there is a high regard for trees such as we noted among the Kara. The terrace villages, White says, are notable for fine trees, including *Balanites aegyptiaca, Acacia albida, Khaya senegalensis*, and *Borassus flabellifera*. The last of these is sown by hand and the others are allowed to propagate themselves under protection.

This is clearly an intensive and laborious system which should be capable of supporting a relatively high population density. The general density in the early 1940s appears to have been of the order of 170 per square mile, and at that time the Administration was anxious to move the Hill Pagans to the plains. This was not because of any question of land hunger but for ease of administration, since they are an independent and troublesome people. White considered such a move undesirable as it would lead to decay of the terraces.

On the other hand, what would seem to be comparable densities represent a considerable degree of over-population among the Cabrai of north-east Togo. This has long been recognised as a region of excessive population and from 1925 onwards the French carried out resettlement work for the alleviation of the problem. Yet, from all accounts, the agricultural practice of the Cabrai is as intensive as that of the Hill Pagans. The steep slopes of their poor and broken country are cut into terraces and these are faced with stone walls. Irrigation is practised, manure is used, all suitable household refuse is composted, and a high value is placed on human excrement as a source of soil fertility. The Cabrai are even said to carry fowls to their gardens to control insect pests. But there is one significant difference: the lack of cattle among the Cabrai. Manure production depends largely on relatively few small-stock, which are hand-fed, and it may be that the supply of manure is insufficient to maintain a level of fertility which will support high population densities. A lower proportion of cultivable land in this environment may also be a factor.

5. HERDSMEN-CULTIVATORS

We now glance briefly at a contrasting system, if one may call it such, in which abundant manure is used lavishly and wastefully without any expenditure of energy. In north-east Ghana, notwithstanding the need for manure, it is a common custom for owners of large herds to lend animals to Fulani herdsmen who are skilled in cattle management and have an excellent knowledge of pasture grasses and their qualities. These herdsmen grow crops, although, like other traditional pastoralists, they greatly dislike the drudgery of cultivation. As a rule they have no small-stock and few cattle of their own and they cannot rely on the bor-rowed stock since the owner may recall his animals at any time. Also, it is probably impossible for them to maintain a sufficient number of cows in milk throughout the year without long-distance movements to new pasture, and there is no room for nomadism in this overcrowded country.

These Fulani live in more-or-less fixed homesteads from which the cattle are driven out to graze and water during the day and to which they return in the evening. The cattle are kept near the homestead overnight, either tethered in an open camp or within a thorn-fenced kraal. When the rains come the camp or kraal is moved to another place and the old site is brought into cultiva-tion, with some variation of cropping in accordance with the depth of manure that has accumulated over the area. There is a recog-nisable kitchen garden in which maize is grown with Ambaria hemp, cotton, and calabashes of which a large supply is required for milking vessels. But practically the whole of the manured area is planted to cereals, without pulses or other subsidiary crops. Where much manure has accumulated and it lies several inches deep, a mixture of early bulrush millet and sorghum is sown. Most of the garden, generally about two-thirds of the area, which has had a moderate dressing of manure, is occupied by early millet alone, while in places where the accumulation is scanty late millet is substituted. In the following year the poorer part of the garden is abandoned and part of the second camp or kraal site is taken into cultivation.

The area cultivated per head of population probably averages no more than half an acre, but cereal yields are fairly high, as one would expect of land that has received the night droppings of twenty or more cattle per acre over many months. An Agricultural Department survey of one Fulani homestead showed a total grain yield of 6,500 lb of grain from 5·26 acres, in striking contrast with a normal Kusasi garden of the concentric ring type which yielded 3,490 lb of grain from 10·17 acres. In the one case the yield was over 1,200 lb per acre, and in the other only about 340 lb per acre.

Yields from the kraal site gardens would probably be higher were it not for the poor standard of cultivation. The weed growth is, of course, vigorous but the Fulani will not lift a hoe if he can help it. He relies on neighbouring cultivators who come to his aid in return for gifts of milk, fowls, and grain or payment in cash. If they do not come or are late in coming the weeds get away and many Fulani fields are choked with them.

In spite of the use of manure and the relatively high grain yields, this is very far from being an intensive system of land-use. If, for example, the ratio of cattle to cultivation is 20 head to one acre, and if the grazing requirement is 10 acres per head, the land requirement for each person will exceed 100 acres. The human-carrying capacity probably approximates to that of the pastoral systems which we will discuss presently.

PART III

HUNTERS AND HERDSMEN

CHAPTER XVI

HUNTERS AND FOOD-GATHERERS

1. Remnants of the Economy of Savagery

It may be of interest, and even of some relevance in the study of land-use problems, if we now consider how far these ideas of the limitations imposed on human numbers by the nature of environments and the ways in which they are exploited can be applied to the earliest systems of land-use—hunting, fishing, and the gathering of food. The story of humanity and sub-humanity probably goes back for the greater part of a million years,[1] and for all but a little fraction of this time there is no trace of any higher form of exploitation than the "robber" economy of savagery. Even today our own exploitation of the sea as a source of food remains, basically, at this level.

Practically all of the cultivating peoples of Africa supplement their diet by gathering food and by fishing where they may and hunting where there are still beasts to hunt. Indeed, in many systems, an important part of village subsistence is obtained by a full utilisation of the surrounding bush, woodland, or forest. Here and there one comes across more curious remnants of the old economy. In north-eastern Ghana an indigenous grass, *Dactyloctenium aegyptiacum*, is still laboriously collected for food, while in Sierra Leone, Guinea, and parts of Nigeria another grass, *Digitaria exilis*, which has not been found in the wild state, is cultivated as a grain.

At least until very recently, the Valley Tonga also harvested and sometimes even stored wild grasses, including species of *Brachiaria*, *Panicum*, *Dactyloctenium*, *Echinochloa*, *Rottboellia*, *Urochloa*, and *Sorghum*, the seeds of which were boiled as grain. These probably played an important part in alleviating the recurrent famines of the past.

But it is as regular sources of supplementary food and "relishes," and of raw materials, that collecting, fishing, and hunting activities

[1] A new method of age-determination recently applied to Dr Leakey's *Zinjanthropus* skull from East Africa suggests a very much longer period.

are of greatest importance to the agricultural peoples. The main meals, commonly of cereal porridge, are usually eaten with a relish, and these relishes are the main source of vitamins, minerals, animal and plant proteins, and fats. It is probably true of many peoples—as Scudder has shown for the Valley Tonga—that food-gathering, fishing, and hunting provide a much higher proportion of the relishes consumed throughout the year (and, consequently, of these vital elements in the diet) than agriculture and animal husbandry combined. They comprise a great variety of animal and plant products.

In addition to obtaining from it relishes and vitamin-rich supplementary foods, such as honey and wild fruits, the subsistence cultivator must rely on the uncultivated and uncultivable "waste" land for all of his raw materials. He needs a constant supply of wood for fuel, and of timber and thatching grass for the construction and repair of dwellings, outbuildings, and grain bins. More timber is needed for kraals and garden fencing, tools and weapons, canoes, stools, traps, bowls and spoons, drums and other musical instruments, stamping blocks and pounding poles used for making meal, and a variety of other artifacts. Different woods are selected and used for many of these purposes, and the satisfaction of all of these demands requires, in the aggregate, the annual consumption of a considerable area of woodland. Many other things also come from the waste land. The list includes materials for baskets and mats; fibres for ropes, twine, snares, and nets; skins and the materials for softening and preparing them; bird-lime and mastic; salts from plant ash for use in cooking; vegetable oils; plant poisons for fishing, hunting, and the destruction of vermin; medicines for the cure of sickness and for use in ritual and sorcery. Indeed, it may be said that many of the cultivating peoples depend almost as much on the waste land as on their gardens for their comfort and well-being. The urbanised African, richer in cash income but deprived of these resources, may well be poorer in terms of real wealth than his brother in the bush.

2. AFRICAN SURVIVORS

Peoples who have no agriculture and no livestock, and who live wholly by hunting, fishing, and food-gathering, still survive in the more inhospitable parts of the world, mainly in Arctic and semi-desert regions and equatorial forest. In Africa there are Bushmen,

Pygmies and pygmoid Batwa, Dorobo, or Wanderobo, and negroid hunting peoples known collectively as Wata, some of whom still lead the life of the Old Stone Age.

The Bushmen may be the most numerous of the survivors. They are scattered over a great area of the central and northern Kalahari and the sand-scrub and bush surrounding it, while a few small pockets of similar peoples, such as the Hadzapi and Sandawe of northern and central Tanganyika, survive elsewhere. At one time these Bush people ranged and hunted over much of south and south-central Africa, from the Cape to Rhodesia and from Angola to Mozambique: but they were slaughtered or driven from their hunting lands, first by Bantu and Hottentot invaders from north and south and then by a still more formidable enemy, the mounted Boer marksmen. In places they were peacefully absorbed and disappeared as a race by intermixture with the Bantu, a process which is still going on.

Yet, in spite of all the factors making for their extermination, the Bushmen survive in unexpected numbers. It is, of course, extraordinarily difficult to arrive at any estimate of these numbers, but Phillip Tobias (167) set himself this task. His first difficulty was in answering the question, what is a Bushman? At first sight this seems easy enough, since the Bush people have quite distinct physical characteristics: but if he had used race purity as his criterion he would have had to leave out many people commonly recognised as Bushmen but of mixed blood, even though they follow the traditional way of life and speak the language of the Bushmen. On the other hand, if he had included in his count only those who still live by hunting and gathering food he would have had to exclude the cattle-herding Masarwa and Bushmen servants on European farms, although some of these are the least hybridised of all. He did, in fact, use as his criterion language and the common recognition of individuals and tribes as Bushmen or Sarwa, the name given to the Bushmen by the Tswana-speaking people of Bechuanaland.

On this basis of definition—which omits some groups who, though of Bushman blood, speak other tongues—Tobias collected his information on the spot and from District Commissioners and official estimates where any existed. He reached the surprising conclusion that there must be more than 55,000 living Bushmen: about 31,000 in Bechuanaland Protectorate, 20,300 in South West

Africa, 4,000 in Angola, a few hundred just within the Rhodesias, and a very few surviving individuals in the Republic of South Africa.

No one had supposed there were so many living Bushmen. They were, and still are, commonly referred to as a dying race on the point of extinction, numbering no more than 2,000 to 7,500—though, as early as 1939, Schapera had revised his own previous estimates and suggested a population of 30,000.

The figures collected by Tobias do not tell us how many of the Bushmen still lead the life of their forefathers as wandering hunters and collectors of foodstuffs. Some of the groups are "fairly wild," others are "relatively tame," and of the "tame" Bushmen some keep cattle and some are in employment as herdsmen, though probably many of them are part-time hunters as well. The "wild" Bushmen are still dependent for food on what they can gather and the meat of the animals they kill, and on the skins of these animals for clothing. They are hunters of consummate skill in spite of their palaeolithic equipment, which consists of throwing-sticks, spears, bows, and arrows tipped with poison. Even in the Kalahari there is game to hunt, quite a lot of it in some regions: such desert-living animals as gemsbok and springbok and long-distance travellers like the giraffe, elephant, and ostrich which often go far from water; while in the less arid parts, and elsewhere during the flush that follows the rains, there are wildebeeste, kudu, buffalo, and wild pig. Parts of the Kalahari even have a fair rainfall, fifteen or twenty inches in the year: but this comes within two or, at most, three months and the rest of the year is a long period of drought and thirst, great heat and winter cold.

The collection of veld foods, in which women specialise, probably contributes more to the food supply than hunting. Even this semi-desert can provide, for those who have the knowledge and skill to seek and find them, a list of foodstuffs which is long and varied, if not particularly appetising. It includes a considerable range of edible roots, tubers, and melons—some of which also provide water, the only water available for part of the year—wild cucumbers, berries and pulses, honey, fungi, and green-leafed vegetables, and small creatures such as lizards, desert rats, hares, tortoises, termites, and snakes. But the Kalahari is, for the most part, a hostile and hungry country, where water is often an even greater problem than food, and the survival of the Bushmen in such an environment must be regarded as no small achievement.

A group of Hadzapi hunters and collectors, thought to number no more than 500, still survives near Lake Eyasi: but the remaining Sandawe, whom some regard as analogous to the Hottentots, have taken to cattle keeping.

The Pygmies of the equatorial forest may be as numerous as the Bushmen. They fall into three main groups: the western Negrillos in French Equatorial Africa, the central group in the heart of the former Belgian Congo where there has been much inter-mixture with Bantu elements, and the eastern group of the Ituri forest who have kept their culture in its purest form, though they are now beginning to settle and cultivate. Those who still lead the old way of life hunt with little bows, only two feet long, and poisoned arrows tipped with fish bone or with iron heads obtained from their Bantu "patrons," and they gather wild fruits, roots, fungi, snakes, bats, caterpillars, honey, and whatever else the forest has to offer. Although they are the smallest of human beings they hunt and kill even the elephant.

Some of the Pygmies still live in small, isolated groups and others in a sort of symbiotic relationship with Bantu peoples, their "patrons," with whom they exchange the products of hunting and forest collecting for grain and artifacts such as spearheads and arrowheads, knives, and pottery: but in the former Belgian Congo a good many have now been established in stabilised villages and drawn within the orbit of the money economy. As a Belgian Agricultural officer put it to me, "Les Pygmées eux-même sont devenus dans plusieurs regions des producteurs de viande pour certaines sociétés et ne peuvent plus etre considéré comme des élements normaux." Some also find a useful source of income by performing and posing for photographs along the tourist routes.

The Pygmies are not only being attracted to a new way of life; in many parts they are being driven out of the forests by disappearance of the game. This rapid fall in the number of game animals, outside the game parks, is attributed only in a very small degree to increased cultivation—the cultivated area is expanding at a rate of about 4·75 per cent of land surface per annum—and mainly to excessive hunting by Bantu with firearms. The number of hunting permits issued to Africans in the Congo increased from 7,800 in 1947 to nearly 44,700 in 1952.

Recently, for the first time, a count was made of the Pygmies settled in *villages stabilisée* in the Mombasa territory of the Congo. The result indicated a total population of 16,500—5,500 men, 4,100 women and 6,900 children—but the *administrateur* in charge of the count considered these figures to be underestimates. He thought that at least one Pygmy in ten had managed to evade the census.

In East Africa there are other hunting and food-gathering people known as Dorobo, a term which appears to have no ethnic significance. It is, or was, applied generally to people who live mainly by hunting and honey-hunting, and the pastoral Masai sometimes use it in a more general sense as a term of contempt for people who are not pastoralists, even for a subservient section of their own tribe. Joseph Thomson, however, refers to the Dorobo as a race of small people scattered over Masailand. At that time (1885), he says, they had no livestock and no agriculture. They hunted antelope, buffalo, and elephant, specialising in elephant hunting, and they were also craftsmen and traders who made buffalo-hide shields for the Masai and acted as intermediaries between them and the cultivating peoples. Hollis (82) also refers to them as hunters at the turn of the century, though by that time they had probably acquired flocks of goats. The Kikuyu say that the land they hold in Kiambu was bought from the Dorobo in exchange for goats, at a rate of about five acres for one goat, and old Kikuyu men still living maintain that as small boys they herded goats to the Dorobo in payment for land.

A few scattered groups of Dorobo still survive as hunters and honey-hunters in the Mau and Aberdare mountains and in northern Tanganyika, but most of them have now become cultivators and herdsmen or workers on European farms. Some have been settled on land that belonged to the Masai. Just before the last War the Kenya Government bought a considerable area of land from the Masai for the purpose of settling "resident labourers" who might be expected to leave European farms when the Resident Labourers Ordinance of 1937 was put into operation, and also for Kikuyu who had infiltrated into Masailand. This scheme was a notorious failure. The first settlers, mainly Kikuyu from Masai, "poor types not wanted by their own people" according to an official account (1), refused absolutely to follow the simple and necessary rules of rational husbandry imposed as a condition of settlement and, in the circumstances existing during the War, little supervision could be given. Only a few Dorobo, who happened to be included in the scheme, followed the officially approved behaviour pattern. In the end, after the matter had become a major political issue, the "poor types" were expelled and since 1955 the land has been used for the settlement of Dorobo.

3. Land Requirements of Hunting and Food-Gathering Systems

There is no knowing how many of the world's people still live wholly or largely by hunting, food-gathering, and fishing. In all, they cannot number more than a few hundred thousand—a minute fraction of a world population now not far short of three thousand million. The surprising thing is that the economy of savagery has survived at all, from Palaeolithic times into the second half of the twentieth century, even as so small a remnant.

The land requirements of people who live in this way must, obviously, be very high, but any attempt to estimate these needs in quantitative terms is almost hopelessly handicapped from the start by lack of data on yields of wild food resources and the enormous variations in these resources between different environments. One has only to contrast the frozen wastes of the Arctic, where the Eskimo have succeeded not only in surviving but in creating what Toynbee classes as an "arrested civilization," or the Canning desert of Australia where the Bindibu still lead the life of their ancestors of the Old Stone Age, with such almost paradisian environments as the Pacific coast of North America or some region of great grassland plains dotted with innumerable herds of game, to appreciate the magnitude of these variations.

We cannot hope to make anything in the nature of reliable estimates, but we may be able to get some indication of land requirements by relating actual populations to the land areas they occupied, in so far as these data are known or can be guessed at. For example, it is believed that the Aboriginal population of Australia numbered somewhere in the region of 300,000 when the first settlers from Europe went there in 1788 (166). This suggests an average land requirement, on the continental scale, of about 10 square miles per person if we assume that the Aborigines occupied the whole of the continent, as appears to be true, and that population densities in each environment approximated to and were maintained roughly at the critical level. We have considered the concept of critical population levels, or Critical Population Densities, in relation to subsistence systems of agriculture, but it is equally applicable to hunting and collecting systems, in as much as the yield of the wild food resources of any area cannot support in perpetuity more than a certain number of people. If the critical level of population is exceeded the food resources will be used up more rapidly than they can replace themselves and the human population must inevitably decline, either by migration of some of its number or by starvation and the incidence of an increasing death rate.

The average land requirement of the Aboriginal economies may, then, have been something of the order of 10 square miles per person over the whole vast area of Australia. But population densities must have varied enormously, though they would be exceedingly sparse everywhere when measured by our standards, or even by the standards of a simple agricultural economy, except perhaps in some coastal regions where the main food supply came from the gathering of sea foods, fishing, and the hunting of turtles and dugong.

Steward (160) attributes hunting areas of only 100 to 150 square miles to Australian hordes of 20 to 30 persons and it may be that the land requirement was something of this order in more favoured regions such as those described in Joseph Hawdon's diary of his discovery of Lake Bonney in 1838 (77). He writes of natural pastureland supporting great numbers of kangaroos and fine lakes of fresh water carrying thousands of duck and wild swans, and he was impressed by the number of Aborigines who seemed to live there. It is clear, however, from Hawdon's own account, that the Aborigines from a wide area had gathered to see and follow him and his companion, "disputing about this extraordinary inroad upon their territory," and admiring the milch cows the strangers had brought with them, which, according to Hawdon, they thought to be the white men's women.

Vogt says, on the other hand, that "the territory of a group of Australian Aborigines may include 8,000 to 10,000 square miles of arid country" (179), but he does not say what he means by a "group." If by this is meant the horde, which commonly consists of a few closely related families, these areas appear to be more than could, in practice, be exploited, though the land requirements of people who live in near-desert environments must be very high.

In areas of such low potential the practical upper limit of a group's size may be less than the theoretical critical number for it is set by the inability of more than a certain number to exploit the area effectively and still remain a group.[1] There must also be a lower limit size for a group, determined by the need for co-operation in an environment where the isolated family cannot survive.

The hunting territories of Australian hordes seem to have varied from about fifty square miles to a thousand square miles or more, suggesting land requirements ranging from a mere two or three square miles per head of population up to fifty square miles and more in steppe and desert regions.

Even in the steppe regions life was not miserable or generally hard, as Spencer and Gillen have pointed out (153). Kangaroos, rock wallabies, and emu were there for the hunting, and small animals such as rats and lizards could easily be caught by the women, who also collected large quantities of grass seeds, tubers, and fruits in their season. Where there was no surface water, supplies were obtained from sources such as tubers and tree roots. This impression, that a people with a very primitive technology can maintain themselves in relative comfort even in a seemingly inhospitable environment, is borne out by reports of the recent University of Melbourne and Royal Geographical Society expedition to the Bindibu, a group of about two hundred people who live on the edge of the Canning desert in the country around Lakes Mackay and Hazlett—desert salt "lakes"—on the border between Western Australia and the Northern Territory. Although there is little left for the Bindibu to hunt—in four weeks travelling the expedition saw only two kangaroos and two rabbits—and they appear to live mainly on desert rats, mice, lizards, and a sort of "bush tomato" which they pound into a loaf, and although it was a year of more than usual drought, the expedition found the people well-fed and contented, and, apart from a high incidence of trachoma, reasonably healthy. Their babies were the happiest and fattest the members of the expedition had ever seen.

These indications of the land requirements of Australian hunters and food gatherers are supported by data from other sources, including the more precise work of American and Canadian anthropologists. Hallowell (74), using his own work on the Bernes

[1] I am indebted to Dr Rodney Needham, of the Institute of Social Anthropology, Oxford, for pointing this out to me in a personal communication.

River Indians and Davidson's earlier study of the Grand Lake Victoria Indians, has estimated that the territories exploited by these hunters and trappers averaged 6·2 square miles per person for the former group and 55·6 square miles per person for the latter, while Kroeber's estimates of Aboriginal population densities (quoted by Hallowell) are 5·3 square miles per person in the region north of the Great Lakes and 34·6 square miles per person in the eastern sub-arctic zone.

A good many estimates of the size of North American Indian hunting territories have been made—so well recognised were the boundaries of these territories that it was possible until comparitively recently to map them with a fair degree of accuracy—but information on the relationship between areas and the populations exploiting them is usually scant or lacking. In general, however, these data indicate land requirements per head of population commonly ranging from four square miles to fifty square miles or more. Wissler's estimate (190) of the United States' Indian population in 1780 is 636,750, a figure which implies a mean population density of one person to less than five square miles, but this cannot be taken as representing the average land requirements of the hunting and food-gathering peoples, since the population includes tribes living largely by tillage or practising subsidiary cultivation, and their land requirements would be much lower.

The distribution of the Eskimo people suggests a similar range of land requirements for a habitable Arctic environment but with an even higher extreme. It is thought that there are now about 40,000 Eskimos, and past populations as high as 100,000 have been conjectured; but Rasmussen (135) estimated the total at no more than 33,000 and he considered that this "represents perhaps the outside number of persons who can gain their livelihood by hunting in a country so forbidding." Most of them live in Greenland, a vast area which is largely uninhabitable, so that the great majority are confined to the south and the western coast where general population densities appear to be as high as one person to three or four square miles. This relatively high concentration is possible only because their economy is based on fishing and the hunting of sea mammals. The economy of the inland Eskimos, who live by hunting caribou and moose, and musk oxen where any survive, has a vastly higher land requirement. Baffinland, with an area of 231,000 square miles, has a population of only about 2,000, all Eskimos, and over the whole vast region of the Canadian North-West and Yukon Territories, more than one and a half million square miles, the average density of the tiny Eskimo and Indian populations is not much greater. In Alaska as a whole there are about eight square miles to every person but in the regions inhabited by the hunting Eskimos, who make up only about a quarter of the total, population densities are far lower. According to Marshall (109) the population density of the Upper Koyukuk, a region of approximately 15,000 square miles, is 0·0085 per square mile! He makes the interesting observation that, although the rifle has completely replaced the bow and arrow, and in spite of more than thirty years of virtually uncontrolled hunting with this weapon, the big game animals, moose and caribou, appear to have increased. It would seem, therefore, that the population density—one person to nearly 120 square miles of country—is well below the critical level for a hunting economy in this particular region.

In Greenland, on the other hand, where the population densities of regions habitable for man and beast are much higher, reindeer and musk ox have been almost, if not quite, exterminated, and there is evidence that even the sea mammals are being over-hunted.

At the other ecological extreme, the rain forest environment of the equatorial regions may not be much more favourable for hunting and food-gathering economies than the frozen and arid deserts. Here the growth of vegetation is so rank as almost to choke out animal life: but, in spite of this luxuriance the plant foods eaten by men are by no means abundant. Game is scarce and the economy must generally be based more on fishing and gathering than on hunting. Nicholas Guppy (71), among the Wai Wai hunters and cultivators in the Amazon forest of British Guiana, noted evidence, which he found it hard to believe, "that fifty people could reduce the game in an area the size of Wales." The land needs of hunters and food-gatherers in such an environment may well be of the higher order, but there appear to be no data on which to base even the most conjectural estimates.

Nor is there any information about the land requirements of the hunting peoples of Africa, though anthropological studies of Bushmen and other groups have been made: but it may be assumed that these requirements fall within the wide limits indicated for other regions. An observation by Debenham (49) indicates a

land requirement of about ten square miles per person in a region
of the Bechuanaland Protectorate which supports a very considerable population of game animals. There seem to be, he says, a
thousand or more Bushmen living in an area of about 10,000
square miles between Lehututu and the district of Ghanzi, though
"they are only to be met in little groups or clans of a dozen or less."
According to Elizabeth Marshall Thomas, the territory of such a
group "may be several hundred square miles in area" (164).

4. LAND TENURE AND THE POPULATION-LAND BALANCE

The very high land requirement of hunting and collecting technologies implies the comparatively rapid build up of intense
population pressures even at low increase rates. If, for example,
we assume an average land requirement, on the continental or
world scale, of eight square miles for each person, and if we also
assume an increase rate that would double population only once
in every century, then within a matter of a millennium and a half
the descendants of one small hunting group of, say, fifty people
would require for their maintenance an area greater than all Africa,
and within another three centuries they would need a land area
greater than that of the whole of the Old World. The picture, of
course, would not be one of continuous, steady increase and expansion, but, rather, of advance and retreat and renewed advance
with changing climate and ecology, the spread and recession of the
great ice sheets, the alternation of arid and pluvial periods: but
always there would be this tendency of men to increase and to
press into every accessible and habitable corner of the earth under
the inexorable pressure of the need for land.

The problem of preserving a balance between population and
land must have presented itself at an early stage in the human story
and we may therefore suppose an ancient origin for certain customs
and devices of savagery that tend to maintain this balance. A concept of "land tenure", of exclusive rights over land or its natural
products, is found in many of the surviving and recent cultures,
and so too are ante-natal and other practices which have the effect
of restricting population growth.

It appears to have been true of most hunting and food-gathering peoples that each group within the tribe or larger corporate
community possessed exclusive right of exploitation over a specific
area defined by natural boundary marks such as hills, trees, rivers,

lakes, and swamps. These are the "hunting territories," the existence of which we have already noted, or implied, in considering land requirements. The group associated with each territory consisted usually of a small number of families—commonly three or four and sometimes more—individually related by descent, together with women married to men of their families. They inherited their rights and held them exclusively. The group might permit others to exploit their land but trespass was forbidden on pain of death or affliction by sorcery. In some cases even the rights of the group members were limited and controlled to prevent over-hunting and over-fishing. A sort of wardenship over the natural resources of the territory might be exercised by one member of the group, who was the titular owner, but his "ownership" was expressed merely in the giving of permission to other members of the group to exploit the resources. They had an inalienable right to do so and it was inconceivable that permission should be withheld.

Patterns of this general type, varying considerably with different peoples, and the ecology and resources of their environments, have been described for many North and South American tribes, Australian Aborigines, Bushmen, and other hunting, fishing and food-gathering peoples. Among the Australians, the horde, band, or local group, exercised exclusive ownership rights over a territory and all it contained, while the economic life of the group itself was strictly disciplined and controlled by kinship rules and institutions reinforced by social and ritual sanctions. The pattern is still discernible among the surviving bands. Each Bushman group "has a very specific territory which that group alone may use and they respect their boundaries rigidly" (164).

This pattern of land division among small groups was not, however, universal. Hoebel says of the Comanche that "they had no conception of land value. As herding hunters, land was a matter of unconcern to them being held neither individually nor jointly. One may speak of land merely as having been communally occupied": but, he adds, "trespass by enemy tribes meant death." In effect, the whole area occupied by the tribe comprised a single hunting territory, and it was a grazing ground as well, for the Comanche had acquired large herds of horses and become quasi-pastoralists by the middle of the nineteenth century. The man-land relationship may have altered as a result of this change in land-use, or it may not. There are obvious circumstances in which subdivision of the land among small groups would not be a very practicable system. It would not be practicable where the main food animal was a large species that ranged widely in great herds, like the American bison and caribou. Such circumstances call for concerted action by large hunting groups. In spring and summer, with the flush of the grazing, the bison concentrated and moved in great herds but in autumn and winter, as feed became poor and scarce, they split up and scattered. The hunters, of necessity, followed a similar regime. Farther north, the hunting pattern of Indians and Eskimos was determined by the migration of the caribou herds between their summer feeding grounds on the open Barrens and the winter shelter of the fringing forest to the south.

With the coming of the Europeans into the lands of the northern hunters, rights in land tended to become further subdivided, with the development of family hunting grounds within territories formerly exploited by the bands. Reduction of hunting territories and diminution of game, following European colonisation, and the importance of fur-bearing animals in the acquisitive economy that came with the trading posts, created a new concept of the importance of land ownership (101).

It is among the more purely food-gathering peoples, in regions with little or no game and fish, that one finds the clearest evidence of a lack of any sense of ownership in land and its products. The Shoshone Indians, who lived in the barren Utah basin, and other food-gathering tribes of west and central North America, seem to have recognised no sort of exclusive rights to exploit the meagre economic resources open to them—acorns and pine nuts, wild seeds and fruits, herbs, roots, and grasses. Lack of game and the stark poverty of their environment caused them to lead a nomadic life and to wander over a wide range in search of food, in contrast with the restricted range of the hunting band confined to a limited territory. Even today, in the age of atomic power, jet aircraft, and adventure into space, there are peoples who live on this lowest level of economic activity. The Penan of Borneo, or most of them, are still forest nomads. Though traditionally associated with certain river basins, they wander over vast and undefined areas of equatorial forest, recognising no boundaries and no exclusive rights to any natural product, edible or otherwise. Their staple food comes from the wild sago palm and their lives and migrations depend directly on the numbers, distribution, and flowering of this plant; for the trees cannot be exploited until they are about fifteen years old, when just before flowering a large quantity of starch is stored up in the pith of the stem. Reliance on a food supply as uncertain and variable as this may well have imposed the necessity of uncoordinated nomadic foraging, as the only means of exploitation open to a food-gathering people.

It does seem probable, however, that meat-hunting and collecting peoples did evolve some system of land-holding, or intratribal division of land, and that they did so in consequence of pressure of population on limited food resources. This would have the effect of maintaining a more-or-less stable relationship between population and land, at a level approximating to the critical density, when the picture is viewed in the wider perspectives of space and time: but there must have been constant change and adjustment within the larger framework as changing ecological conditions, drought and flood, movements of game, and disease among men or animals, brought disaster to some communities while others flourished.

Hallowell noted that the great differences in the size of Indian hunting grounds, measured in terms of the exploiting populations, "are difficult to explain in terms of purely cultural factors," as some anthropologists had sought to explain them, and he suggested that the deciding factor may be "the relative abundance of game and fur-bearing animals available within a given area," quoting in support of this view an earlier observation by Cooper: "It looks as if land tenure among hunting people is delicately responsive to ecology, especially to the fauna exploited as the staple food supply. It looks likewise as if tenure can and does adapt and change readily and swiftly in accordance with changing ecological conditions."

A stable man-land relationship in any one area would be maintained only so long as population and food supply remained static. Natural populations do not remain static. The motivations and controls of human fertility are complex—though, perhaps, not quite as complex as the demographers make out—but one may reasonably suppose that primitive populations tended to decrease under conditions of great duress and privation, or exposure to killing and debilitating disease, and to increase rapidly under favourable conditions. One may also suppose that the increase tendency predominated in the long run; otherwise it is difficult to explain the spread of men into almost every habitable corner of the earth accessible to them, and even into regions on the very margin of habitability. Wherever population increased up to and beyond the critical level, and there was no access to vacant land for the surplus, the community would be left with a choice of three alternatives—starvation, acquisition of additional land by force, or deliberate restriction of population growth. Perhaps warfare did play a part in the economy of savagery, but there is little evidence that it played an important part in adjusting the population-land balance within communities. Agricultural peoples can go to war or on foraging raids once the crops have been harvested, but fratricidal strife does not seem to be consistent with an economy which requires the individual to give almost all of his time and energy to the continuous hunt for food. It is recorded of the Eskimos that, though they would defend their hunting grounds against encroaching Indians, warfare among themselves was un-known, and Stow (quoted by Elliot Smith (149)) says of the Bush-men that "they never appear to have had great wars against each other; sudden quarrels among rival huntsmen, ending in lively skirmishes, which, owing to their nimbleness and presence of mind, caused little damage to life or limb, appears to have been the extent of their tribal differences." A later writer, Elizabeth Marshall Thomas (164), also remarks that the Bushmen "cannot afford to fight with each other and almost never do," and she adds a further reason that is strangely reminiscent of the present dilemma of the Great Powers. Their most effective weapon—the arrow poison capable of dealing death in a scratch, for which there was no antidote—was, she suggests, too terrible to be used in inter-necine warfare.

To hunting and food-gathering peoples faced with these alternatives the adoption of practices leading directly or indirectly to restriction of procreation may well have seemed the most ac-ceptable choice, and, perhaps, the only alternative to starvation. Culturally sanctioned devices of this sort are prevalent among the surviving remnants of savagery. They include the toleration of infanticide, the procuring of abortion by artificial interference or the use of medicines, and the abandonment of aged and infirm people under stress of economic necessity. Infanticide was not merely tolerated but sometimes prescribed in circumstances of ill-omen such as the birth of twins or a deformed child, or a difficult pregnancy and labour; and also in the event of the birth of a child to a nursing mother during the prolonged lactation period— extending to three or four years—made necessary by the lack of other suitable food.

Practices such as these, in varying degrees and combinations, have been recorded for Eskimo, Bushman, Australian, and other surviving and recent cultures. "It seems reasonable in these cases," says Lorimer (103), "to attribute such practices quite directly to the resources available for meeting these needs."

5. THE LAST OF THE OLD STONE AGE

Societies living in such a delicate balance with their environment are very vulnerable. Reduction of hunting territories by encroach-ment, slaughter of the food animals by invading peoples, and ab-sence of the active hunters for prolonged periods in defence of their lands, would rapidly disrupt the economy of food production. These factors came into play when the Europeans crowded into the last strongholds of the hunting and food-gathering peoples in America and Australia. To the early immigrants these continents must have seemed vast open spaces with immeasurable reserves of unused land, but in all probability they were already fully occupied to the limits of the delicately balanced economy of savagery.

The Indians of North America were in continuous retreat and their economy in a state of disruption from the time of the first considerable influx of European settlers in the late seventeenth century until the crushing of the last desperate attempt at armed resistance in the Sioux War of 1890. The bison and, at a slower rate, other game fell to the firearms of the newcomers; axe and fire destroyed the forests, and ploughs ripped up the hunting and food-gathering lands. Firearms in the hands of the Indians them-selves worsened the situation by intensifying inter-tribal wars, fomented by the general disruption, and hastening the destruction of game. Inevitably, population declined with the loss of food supplies—from 636,750 in 1780, according to Wissler's estimate, to 246,834 in 1891. The decline continued for a time after settle-ment of the remaining Indians in reservations as herdsmen-cultivators, but since the beginning of the present century this tendency has been reversed and numbers are increasing to an extent that appears to be taxing the resources of the reservations. The Blackfoot, with a commendably modern outlook, have recently offered rent-free sites for industry in their reservation to provide work for tribesmen who, they say, can no longer make a living from the land.

The effect of European contact on the highly specialised and finely balanced economy of the Australian Aborigines was even more disastrous. From an estimated total of about 300,000 in 1788, numbers declined year by year, at a rate roughly corresponding to the spread of settlement, to somewhere in the region of 50,000. In the case of the Tasmanians—who never numbered more than a few thousands—the process continued to the point of complete extinction. During the bad years of the 1830s there was much killing on both sides. Aborigines murdered stockmen and stole cattle, and they in turn were hunted down and shot. Some settlers did not shrink from poisoning the Aborigines, as one poisons vermin, with arsenic mixed in flour or concealed in the carcase of a sheep. Complete disaster came to the native Tasmanians even earlier. In 1805, only two years after their arrival, the European settlers on the island found themselves desperately short of food. They had already displaced the natives from some of the best hunting land; now, to save themselves from starvation, they hunted the kangaroo almost to extinction. In a last despairing attempt to preserve their means of existence the Tasmanians resorted to wholesale murder and the settlers responded with atrocities, accounts of which are starkly presented in the records of the Aborigines Committee of 1830. Attempts to save the few hundred survivors failed completely: they could not, or would not, adapt themselves. Sunk in an apathy of hopelessness, they soon died.

Much the same story is repeated wherever emigrants from Europe have invaded the territories of hunting and food-gathering peoples. The two ways of life are completely incompatible and the outcome is inevitable.

To the pioneering Boers—and, no doubt, in earlier times, to invading Bantu—the little yellow Bushmen with their murderous arrows, their inability or unwillingness to change and adapt themselves, and their propensity to treat the flocks and herds of the invaders as easy game for the hunting, must have seemed an intolerable menace—a menace to be eliminated as speedily as possible and by any means. Yet the Bushmen survive, in un-expected numbers.

They survive, as do the other remnants, only because temporary sanctuary remains to them in lands so desolate or difficult that neither cultivators nor herdsmen, nor the people of the advanced technologies, have yet found a use for them. There is little likeli-hood that these sanctuaries will remain inviolate much longer: the white man with his bore-holes and ranch cattle is advancing into the Kalahari and the marginal lands elsewhere, while hungry eyes are turned on the equatorial forests and the mineral wealth of Arctic and desert wastes. However much one may regret it, only one conclusion is possible: the hunters are faced with extinction at no distant date—not by shot and poison, but by intermixture with other races and absorption into the economies that have sur-rounded and defeated them. Their cultural patterns—sometimes, as in the case of the Australians, complex and beautiful—cannot be preserved without preserving also their isolation and their way of life by reserving vast areas in a land-hungry world, human "game reserves," to support tiny populations condemned by the limitations of their technology to remain static or starve.

CHAPTER XVII

FROM HUNTING TO HUSBANDRY

1. THE NEOLITHIC REVOLUTION AND THE GENESIS OF CIVILISATION

The Neolithic revolution, that fundamental change in the relationship between men and land which brought with it the seeds of civilisation and began the long-drawn-out martyrdom of the hunters, started at least seven thousand years ago; some authorities, with a good deal of reason, put the date at ten thousand years ago or even more. In spite of this tremendous lapse of time the revolution might be regarded as still in progress, since remnants of the preceding Palaeolithic economy still survive. Present evidence seems to point to a place of origin somewhere between southern Turkestan, the Iranian plateau, and the eastern Mediterranean, but speculations about dates and origins are as yet based on little factual knowledge. Archaeologists and prehistorians will have to dig a good deal more, and deeper, before these mysteries are resolved.

No doubt the husbandry of crops and animals was at first and for a long time quite subsidiary to hunting and fishing. Systematic agriculture as a staple activity, as the main or only source of food, may have begun in the flood lands of the great rivers—first by utilising the natural floods and then by controlled flooding or irrigation, for the step from one to the other is natural and not very difficult. Certainly the first civilisations grew from the alluvial soils of the great rivers, the Nile, Tigris and Euphrates, the Ganges, and the Yangtse. This is not at all surprising, for these soils are the most persistently fertile in the world; they have an almost inexhaustible supply of available plant nutrients brought down from the upper lands drained by the rivers. Such soils, with a sufficiency of water assured by irrigation and the annual floods, under suitable temperature conditions, can produce a surplus large and reliable enough to allow of the growth of non-agricultural classes, the accumulation of capital and the genesis of civilisation, even on a level of technology no higher than simple hand cultivation.

It may seem strange, at first sight, that these admirably en-
dowed cradle-lands of civilisation are now regions of poverty and
hunger—"underdeveloped" regions, in the euphemism of today.
In all probability, for the great majority of their peoples, they were
never anything else. This civilisation was a very thin veneer of
wealth, culture, and knowledge supported by inarticulate and
labouring masses—king's peasants, serfs of the gods and temple
priests, slaves of the land. Nevertheless, knowledge and techniques developed rapidly. By the beginning of the second millennium of the pre-Christian era most of the fundamental agricultural inventions and discoveries had been made. Oxen were
used to plough and draw carts, cows were milked, bread was made
by methods very similar to those of today, and the elements of
cheesemaking and brewing were known.

The first animal-drawn implement, a revolutionary invention,
was probably a sort of one-time cultivator not unlike the "plough"
with a wooden share and flat iron point that is still used in many
places from the Sudan to Sinkiang: but the mould board plough,
which turns over the furrow slice and so buries weeds, goes back
to fairly remote antiquity. The prototypes of implements still in
use are pictured on early Egyptian tombs.

With the invention of an efficient plough, civilisation could
spread beyond the areas of highly fertile, permanently cultivable,
and readily irrigable soils. Plough farming and the production of
a reliable surplus became a possibility on soils capable of maintaining their fertility under short periods of cultivation and fallow,
using some such system as the alternation of wheat and barley
crops with rest breaks of one, two, or three years, and supplemental irrigation from perennial streams and melting snow. This
is still the basis of arable farming in Cyprus and over much of the
Middle East, and there is no reason to suppose that it has altered
greatly since Bronze Age times.

More than three thousand years ago the main outlines of the
world land-use pattern had been drawn and many of the problems
that beset us today had already been posed. In Hammurabi's
Babylonian empire land was freely alienable: it could be sold or
leased or let on a profit-sharing or share-cropping basis. Sheep
and goat flocks, which, no doubt, grazed the waste, stubble, and
fallow land as they still do in Cyprus and other parts of the Middle
East, were of such importance to the economy that the conduct of

the shepherd was regulated by law. Landowners and lessees could not do as they liked: neglect of the soil and the vital irrigation works was regarded as a crime against the community, and the punishment was made to fit the crime: "If a man has taken a field to cultivate and has not caused the corn to grow, he shall be put to account and compelled to give corn like its neighbour. If a man shall neglect to strengthen his bank of the canal and the waters have carried away the meadow, the man who neglected the bank shall render back the corn which was lost. If one should leave his field or his garden or his house to waste, and they should be taken by another for three years, they shall not be given back to him who returns."[1]

These ancient land laws have a slight flavour of modern African Native Authority Regulations for the improvement of agriculture and the upkeep of anti-erosion works, made under the promptings of some zealous administrative or keen agricultural officer: but no doubt they were much more effectively applied. One of the problems of every agrarian society is to ensure a minimum standard of land use, for the bad cultivators, the lazy, neglectful, and improvident, are a danger to the society. All men are not good farmers, even though their abilities may amount to genius in other pursuits. Robert Burns and Isaac Newton were farmers: they were certainly not good farmers.

The Jews approached this problem, characteristically, by way of precept and moral suasion, very much in the spirit of the "extension" worker of today. The Book of Proverbs has much to say on agricultural matters such as the need for timely ploughing, planting, and weeding, the upkeep of terrace walls, and the preservation of fodder for the flocks. "The sluggard will not plough by reason of the cold: therefore shall he beg in harvest and have nothing. . . ." "I went by the field of the slothful, and by the vineyard of the man void of understanding; and, lo, it was all grown over with thorns and nettles covered the face thereof, and the stone wall thereof was broken down. Then I saw, and considered it well: I looked upon it and received instruction." ". . . Yet a little sleep, a little slumber, a little folding of the hands in sleep: so shall thy poverty come as one that travaileth; and thy want as an armed man. . . ." "Be thou diligent to know the state of thy

---

[1] From C. H. John's translation of the inscription on the stele of Hammurabi.

flocks, and look well to thy herds. For riches are not for ever. . . .
The hay appeareth, and the tender grass sheweth itself, and herbs
of the mountain are gathered. The lambs are for thy clothing, and
the goats are the price of thy field. And thou shalt have goats'
milk enough for thy food, and for the food of thy household, and
for the maintenance of thy maidens."[1]

This approach, it seems, was not very successful. Four
hundred years after Solomon, Haggai spoke with the voice of
Yahweh: "Thus saith the Lord of Hosts—consider your ways. Ye
have sown much and bring in little: ye eat, but ye have not
enough." Finally, the great prophecies of Isaiah contain passages
that suggest the renaissance of modern Israel: "They that shall be
of thee shall build the old waste places; thou shalt raise up the
foundations of many generations; and thou shalt be called The
repairer of the breach, The restorer of paths to dwell in."[2]

Throughout the centuries, as civilisations and empires waxed
and waned, there were all sorts of innovations and experiments in
agrarian organisation, in the relationship between the individual,
the land, and the community. Empires in their formative phases
might be built on a solid foundation of free farmers, as Rome was
built: but this was an ideal state that could last only as long as
there was ample land. Sooner or later, increasing population and
demands on land resources led to subdivision and fragmentation
and relapse towards a bare subsistence economy, unless these tendencies were checked by the re-organisation of agriculture on an
estate or feudal basis with the inevitable consequences of serfdom
and slavery and the growth of a landless, under-employed proletariat, which, unless placated with "bread and circuses," represented a continual menace to the ruling classes and the security of
the state. But, while there were all manner of attempts to solve
insoluble problems of organisation, there were no further revolutionary inventions or improvements in agricultural techniques
from the innovations of the early civilisations until very recently.
Even in Britain, which was in the forefront of change as profound
and disrupting as the Neolithic Revolution itself, all agricultural
work except ploughing was done by human labour until about two
centuries ago.

[1] Proverbs, XX. 4; XXIV. 30–4; VI, 10–11; XXVII. 23–7.
[2] Haggai I. 5–6; Isaiah LVIII. 12.

2. African History

Africa beyond the Nile did not remain a closed land, cut off entirely from the currents of historic change. In the last decade or two archaeological research has revealed a new and startling picture (48). No longer can we believe that "the Negro is a man without a past," or that Black Africa is "a continent where men by their own efforts have never raised themselves much above the level of the beast." In the soil of Africa civilisations germinated, took root, were fertilised by contacts from outside, and began to grow against all difficulties of environment and partial isolation from the rest of the changing world. The picture is just beginning to emerge, and much of the present detail is conjectural. We have yet to learn how and when agriculture came to sub-Saharan Africa.

Some five or six thousand years ago, it seems, the once fertile Sahara became a major obstacle to human migration, traffic, and contact. But the barrier was never complete. Cultures could and did spread southwards from the ancient civilisations of Carthage, Kush, Axum, and southern Arabia. They were carried by way of the Nile valley and the park-land south of the desert, and even, with difficulty and at great hazard, across the dead waste of the Sahara. In the early centuries of the Christian era migrants from east and north-east penetrated to the western Sudan, among Negro people who had probably long been there, and stimulated the foundation of such relatively advanced states as Ghana, Mali, and Songay.

Knowledge of the smelting and working of iron and other metals, and of agriculture spread slowly southward during the first millennium A.D., bringing the fundamental change from Stone Age hunting and food-gathering techniques to early Iron Age civilisation, with no interregnum of copper and bronze. And in the same period the Sahara was outflanked by sea-borne contact between the East African coast and the developing maritime countries of the Indian Ocean and the Red Sea. When the Portuguese rounded the Cape and reached East Africa in the late fifteenth century, they found flourishing and populous city ports, ocean shipping manned by sailors who knew the sea routes to India and beyond, and a coastal civilisation little if at all inferior to that of contemporary Europe.

During the most formative period in the history of the sub-

Saharan cultures, between 500 and 1000 A.D., while Europe
suffered the ravages of Barbarian incursions and struggled out of
its age of darkness, nascent civilisations developed in eastern and
south-eastern Africa. These, it seems, were the creation entirely
of men of African stocks, though they probably supplied and depended upon the ocean trade. Behind the coast, in what is now
Kenya and Tanganyika, was the Azanian culture—so called after
the "dry land" of the ancient Greeks—remnants of which may
have survived into the seventeenth century. It was destroyed so
thoroughly that little is known of the "Azanians." There was
probably an important division of labour in their society between
food-producers and specialist craftsmen skilled in mining, in the
working of metals, in masonry, in building, and in road-making.
They mined and worked iron and other metals, they used stone to
make buildings and terrace walls, and they built towns and made
roads with cuttings and embankments. It is possible that they
even had a trunk road running from near the head of Lake Nyasa
northward by Arusha, much as the Great North Road now runs, to
the highlands of Kenya. Their agriculture may have attained a
fairly high level. They reared cattle and raised grain crops, they
terraced hill slopes, and it is very probable that they had an advanced technique of irrigation. Similar practices of today, such as
the irrigation of the Suk, the water-distribution system of the
Chagga, and the terrace cultivation of the Nyakyusa, may be
surviving remnants of this vanished culture, as is often supposed;
or these modern practices may have been evolved later, perhaps by
the people who now use them, as the Matengo evolved their
remarkable system of erosion control. The evidence of ancient
terracing is there to be seen, but there is nothing to show whether
the Azanians had achieved an integrated and balanced agriculture,
or how they maintained fertility at the level needed to feed the
urban populations.

Engaruka, on the scarp of the Rift Valley south of Lake Natron,
is thought to have been one of the last of the Azanian settlements.
It has been described as "a large ruined city" in which thirty or
forty thousand people may have lived. The maintenance of an
urban population such as this in tropical or sub-tropical Africa
poses very difficult problems not only of food supply but of sanitation and public health and water supply and distribution. How did
the Azanians solve these problems?

It is true that some modern African peoples do build what may justly be described as towns, notably the Bechuana. Serowe, the chief town of the Bechuana, probably has a maximum dry-season population of about twenty-five thousand, and others have maximum populations of more than ten thousand. But these are agro-towns, fully occupied only for part of the year and many people spend more time at the distant gardens or far afield with the herds than they spend in the towns. Furthermore, though the towns are permanent, the houses are temporary structures of perishable material. They can be rebuilt frequently and the old sites can be cleansed by fire. Permanently occupied stone-built cities are another matter.

On the plateau of south-eastern Africa, mainly between the Zambesi and the Limpopo, cultures similar to the Azanian reached a higher level of development. Their relics include a great number of old mine workings and stone ruins, hillside terracing which in the aggregate covers many square miles of land, and such spectacular monuments as the high walls, the "temple" and the "acropolis" of Great Zimbabwe, and the "golden burials" of Mapungubwe. Here the Iron Age civilisation of southern Africa grew and flourished with the ocean trade and reached its climax. It was flourishing when the Portuguese adventurers came to Mozambique. They may not have reached Zimbabwe but they knew of it and of "the great kingdom of the Benametapa pertaining to the heathen whom the Moors call Kaffirs" of which Barbosa wrote in 1517. All the evidence goes to show that this was a native African civilisation which endured for centuries and that there is no substance in the romantic tales of Ophir and the mines of Solomon, but the evidence of African origin is not yet universally accepted. A recent publication of the then Federation of Rhodesia and Nyasaland informs us that "the origin of the Zimbabwe ruins near Fort Victoria is unknown. Their fascination for the tourist is unlimited."[1] Such reluctance to accept evidence of African achievement in the past has drawn sharp comment from a Nigerian scholar, Dr Onwuka Dike. "The point is not that Africans have no history but that there is profound ignorance concerning it, and an almost pathological unwillingness to believe the evidence of it when presented."

By the time white men came to explore and settle in these regions beyond the coast there was nothing left of the Azanian and

[1] *Inside the New Africa: Portrait of the Federation of Rhodesia and Nyasaland.*

southern cultures but ruins for adventurers to pillage, tourists to wonder at, and scholars to ponder over. Three-fold disaster had fallen upon them and destroyed them utterly; the Portuguese intervention, the impact of the overseas slave trade, and the incursion of barbarian nomadic herdsmen. The Portuguese were the first from renascent Europe to come with their firearms and to seize the terminal ports and take the wealth of the ocean trade for themselves, but the Dutch, the French, and the English were not slow to follow. They too started the overseas slave trade that for four centuries drained the life-blood of much of Africa and brought war and devastation to the heart of the continent: but at the peak of this grim commerce Britain controlled more than half its total volume.

The final blow to the sedentary metallurgical cultures was delivered, it seems, by warrior herdsmen. A southward movement of pastoral peoples, Galla, Somali, Hima, Luo, Masai, and others, may have started as early as the fourteenth century and it went on into recent times. It is probable that these warlike pastoralists first pressed upon and finally overran the nascent Azanian civilisation, destroying the towns and settlements as completely as our Anglo-Saxon ancestors destroyed the remnants of Roman urbanity in Britain. At a later date migrant regiments of Nguni warriors dealt the same fate to the remnants of the Zimbabwe culture in the south, where the Portuguese, with an army of "250 men and 30,000 Kaffirs their vassals," had already broken the military power of the Monomotapa. These Nguni were a backwash from the region that is now Natal, where they had found further southward penetration barred to them by the guns of the advancing Europeans.

"Thus," says Davidson, "the Portuguese, having found peoples in South East Africa who were confident and prosperous, and strong in their own evolving civilization, dragged them gradually down to helot misery." And, he adds, "it was into this wilderness that Europeans of the late 19th century would push their way and would imagine, as well they might, that what they saw was not the work of yesterday but had endured, in simple desolation, since time began."

Earlier writers are often more disparaging of these mining, stone-building cultures. "The south, being dry and inaccessible, received little if any stimulus from outside," says MacMillan

(108), "from Arabs or Indians of the east or even from the slave traders. It is at most possible that some of the southern peoples may have lost a more advanced culture when driven out by the wars, so freely postulated, into more arid and difficult country. The lost culture of Zimbabwe may perhaps be an example and that of the Bechuana another. In exceptionally difficult and almost arid conditions some Bechuana agriculture is respectable." Others prefer to regard the evidence of a greater past as the work of some mysterious "higher people who have now vanished," a people "comparatively civilised, more so than modern Africans, and seemingly of Hamitic origin," from whom the moderns have acquired nothing, "unless the irrigation systems used by some tribes such as the Suk are a legacy of the past" (88). Yet the Portuguese of the fifteenth and early sixteenth centuries were far from contemptuous of what they found in Africa. "The lord of Monomotapa is the lord of an exceeding great country," wrote Barbosa, and his countryman Diogo Cao was equally impressed by the power and extent of the Kingdom of the Congo. They broke and destroyed what they had found, with a ruthlessness and brutality strangely matched by the highest courage and endurance and a consuming faith.

The pioneers who in the late nineteenth century came into the land between the Limpopo and the Congo were shocked by its untidiness and by the seeming indolence of the African. They came, of course, with an eye to the "main chance," for it was believed that a new El Dorado lay beyond the Limpopo, but it was clear to them that they also had a civilising mission. The African must be made to labour, under European tutelage of course, for his own salvation. Sir Harry Johnson, writing in 1899 (95), put it all rather neatly. "In this world natural law ordains that all mankind must work to a reasonable extent, must wrest from its environment sustenance for mind and body, and a bit over to start the children from a higher level than the parents. The races that will not work persistently and doggedly are trampled on, and in time displaced, by those who do. Let the Negro take this to heart: let him devote his fine muscular development in the first place to the setting of his own rank, untidy continent in order. If he will *not* work of his own free will, now that freedom of action is temporarily restored to him; if he will not till and manure and drain and irrigate the soil of his country in a steady, laborious way as do the Oriental and the European; if he will not apply himself zealously under European tuition to the development of the vast resources of Tropical Africa where hitherto he has led the wasteful unproductive life of a baboon; then force of circumstance, the pressure of eager, hungry, impatient outside humanity, the converging energies of Europe and Asia, will once more relegate the Negro to a servitude which will be the alternative—in the coming struggle for existence—to extinction. The Negro has been given back his freedom that he may use it with a man's sense of responsibility, not that he may squander away his existence with the heedlessness of these anthropoid apes to whom in a minute fractional proportion he is more nearly allied than are we, his present guardians."

This was written when little was known of the Central African environment, and practically nothing of the history, social organisation, and agriculture of its people. The same belief in this civilising mission, and it was no hypocrisy, is implicit, a decade earlier, in the formal petition of Rhodes and his associates for the British South Africa Company's Charter. "Your Majesty's Petitioners believe that if the said concessions, agreements, grants, and treaties can be carried into effect, the condition of the natives inhabiting the said territories will be materially improved and their civilisation advanced, and an organisation established which would tend to the suppression of the slave trade in the said territories, and to the said territories being opened to the immigration of Europeans, and to the lawful trade and commerce of Your Majesty's subjects and of other nations."

The Chartered Company, as an instrument of commerce and government, was in harmony with the cautious and parsimonious spirit of the new imperialism, for by this device the Empire might be extended with a minimum of public expenditure and involvement. This point is made in a contemporary Parliamentary Paper. "The example of the Imperial East Africa Company shows that such a body may to some considerable extent relieve Her Majesty's Government from diplomatic difficulties and heavy expenditure."[1] The British South Africa company was duly constituted and incorporated, Her Majesty's advisers being satisfied that the intentions of the petitioners were "praiseworthy and deserving of encouragement, and that the enterprise in the petition

[1] C5918, No. 88 of 1889.

described may be productive of the benefits set forth therein."
With the extension of the Company's rule to the borders of the
Congo Free State in the north and of the Portuguese dominions in
the east and west, the partition of Africa between a small number
of European states was virtually complete. The land and the people had been shared and divided and set in new and rigid political
frameworks.

3. MOVEMENT AND MIGRATION

Previously there had been much movement and migration of
peoples. The land was not yet full. Beyond the regions of the
sedentary mining cultures and such foci of power as the Balunda
Empire, the Kingdom of the Congo and the states of the Bashonga,
there was probably much habitable land unoccupied or sparsely
held by small cultivating groups or Pygmy and Bushman hunters.
Wherever agricultural people increased in numbers beyond the
capacity of the land to support them, groups and sub-tribes could
hive off and move to fresh land on which to establish a new focus
of settlement. After the disruption and collapse that came with the
Portuguese intervention and the overseas slave trade the scope for
such movement was doubtless increased. Many of the present
peoples of the central and southern continent are comparative
newcomers whose tenure of the lands they now occupy goes back
no more than a century or two, and some have shorter histories.
The folk lore of Africa is full of stories of movement and migration, and very often the reason for the movement is given as population increase and a growing shortage of land in the old environment. Two examples must suffice to give an idea of the legendary
accounts that are still current. One tells of a tribal migration,
probably on a considerable scale and over a great distance, the
other of a mere village fission. According to the traditions of the
Chewa, as recorded by one of their own people, they came from a
country called Urua somewhere to the west or north-west of Lake
Tanganyika. "In Urua the land for cultivation was not measured
off in farms and plots, as is done in European countries. When the
land for cultivation became too small for the people they used to
find other gardens nearby. Therefore there was not enough good
and fertile soil for all the different tribes. Because of that, Karonga
and Undi, leaders of the Mulavi tribe, led their people out to the
east and arrived at *Nyanja Ya Malawi* [the 'Lake of Flames,' Lake

Tanganyika]." They formed a new focus of settlement by the
Lake of Flames, and then, when all the fertile land in the neigh-
bourhood had been occupied, the ancestors of the Chewa and
Senga moved out and travelled southward along the shores of Lake
Nyasa to their present homes in the Eastern Province of Northern
Rhodesia. There, according to the story, they took the land from
a small people—presumably of bushman or pygmoid stock—who
were living entirely by hunting and collecting wild produce.

The second story is from a distant and very different part of
Africa, north-western Ghana, where you will find the Dagarti
villages of Tie and Eremon. There is a legend of how Eremon
came to be established and this is how it goes: "In the time of our
great-grandfathers the land around Tie became overpopulated.
There were so many people that they could not find enough land
on which to grow food. One day a man called Toola said to his
brother Katon Toola, 'My brother, I can no longer live in Tie; my
farm is too small to feed my children and there is no land for my
sons when they grow up. I have made up my mind to go away
with my wives and children and find a new country.'

So at dawn the next day, the families of Toola and Katon Toola
set out. First went the men with spears in their hands ready to
fight any wild beasts who attacked them. Then came the women
and children with loads on their heads. Even the small children
carried little pots or bundles of sticks. They walked on to the
south-west for about twenty miles, then Toola said 'Let us stop
here.' There were few trees and the place looked very bare. The
women grumbled and said 'This place is no good. Where shall we
find fruit to pick? Where can we grow our peppers?' But Toola
would not listen."

Toola, it seems, was no ecologist: he had made a poor choice
and the community would certainly have come to grief but for the
intervention of a hairy fairy with a highly developed sense of land
selection. This apparition, "a strange-looking creature covered all
over with hair," appeared when the people were almost at the stage
of starvation. Toola, rather surprisingly, at once recognised it as
a fairy and when the apparition said "Bring your loads, and follow
me," he and the two families did so. The fairy led them to a land
where there was waving grass and tall trees, herds of antelope and
bush-cows (buffalo), wild fruits in abundance, and much good land
for cultivation. There they settled and built the village of Ere-

mon: but the fairy, having done its good deed, disappeared and was never seen again (125). Is this, perhaps, a folk lore account of the genesis of a knowledge of ecology and land selection?

Some tribes, like the Tonga of the Mazabuka district in Northern Rhodesia, have no tradition of any former home, perhaps because they have remained for long in one locality, while others have stories that seem to tell not of migrations but of the coming of agriculture to a people on a hunting and food-gathering level, or of new crops to a people with no more than supplementary cultivation. The Lamba, who live near the Copperbelt of Northern Rhodesia, have such a legend. Long ago, they say, there were few Lamba and they had no proper food; they ate mostly wild fruits, leaves, and roots, and whatever else they could gather in the bush. Then a stranger came to live among the Lamba "a superior man" called Chipimpi, who brought with him seeds of maize, sorghum, groundnuts, and other crops unknown in Lambaland. Chipimpi did not come alone; his household came with him and his sister Kawanda Shimanjemanje and her household. The crops they brought to the Lamba were not known in Chipimpi's own country, which lay somewhere to the west of Lambaland. Kawanda Shimanjemanje was something of a traveller; she and her son had been to Lubaland on the Lualaba river where they had seen the great variety of crops grown by the Luba people, and, by a stratagem, obtained seeds of all of them. With this seed Chipimpi and his households planted gardens in Lambaland and gave food to the people. This, says the legend—or, rather, one version of it—was the beginning of Lamba agriculture and also of the institution of chieftaincy; for Chipimpi, the giver of food, became the first of their chiefs.

Is it not possible, or even probable, that such stories are tribal memories of the spread throughout Africa of crops from the New World? Some of these are specifically mentioned by the Lamba as having been brought by Chipimpi, though he is also regarded as the bringer of sorghum, their present staple, a crop which may have originated in North Africa. It is not difficult to believe that some of the older crops spread into regions where they were not yet known at the same time as the new arrivals of American origin. The Lamba, in their pre-Chipimpi days, may have been small-circle *citemene* cultivators with no crops except finger millet and ground beans, and no implement but the axe.

CHAPTER XVIII

THE PASTORALISTS

1. ORIGIN AND SURVIVAL OF PASTORAL COMMUNITIES

It is no longer fashionable for economic anthropologists and historians to treat pastoralism as a more primitive form of land-use than cultivation and therefore to be regarded as a sort of halfway house between hunting and farming; they now tend to regard it as a specialised and often highly developed way of life which may have been even more difficult of achievement than agriculture because it implies mastery over more intractable material. There is a wealth of speculation about the first domestication of animals, but little factual knowledge. Toynbee sees the origins both of cultivation and herding in responses to the challenge of dessication, and in support of this contention he cites the evidence produced by the excavations at Anau: "Here we find the challenge of desiccation, in the first instance, stimulating certain communities which had previously lived by hunting to eke out their livelihood in less favourable circumstances by taking to a rudimentary form of agriculture. The evidence shows that this agricultural phase definitely preceded nomadism." Later in the story of the Anau communities, after they had acquired sheep and cattle, "Nature gave her screw of dessication a second turn," and cultivation was no longer possible in that region. The response to this new challenge was two-fold. Some of these early cultivators used the mobility conferred upon them by the possession of flocks and herds to migrate in step with the changing climate and to continue their way of life as cultivators. Others, more daring, "cast themselves loose on the inhospitable steppe with their flocks and herds and staked existence on the new art of stock-breeding." They became the first wandering herdsmen.

Their way of life survives. Evidently it has attractions. A few years ago I met in Turkey two urbane and well-educated young men, survivors of the epic trek of the Kazaks from Sinkiang to Kashmir, employed in the unlikely occupation of hotel receptionists. For their first twenty years they had lived the life of the herdsman, a period of which they told me much—both spoke excellent English they had "just picked up" in Kashmir—and on which they looked back with very evident nostalgia. They were, however, comforted by a firm belief in an approaching world cataclysm that would destroy the Communist powers and, in some mysterious way, return them to the free life of steppe and mountains and restore their flocks and herds.

People who obtain all or a large part of their livelihood by pastoralism still occupy an enormous region of the Old World stretching from the Atlantic coast across North Africa, Arabia, and the Middle East through the heart of Asia to the boundaries of China, from the Himalayas to the Arctic and from the Sudan through East Africa to the south-west of the continent. There have, of course, been profound changes in the Russian-dominated part of the Asiatic heart-land, but, all things considered, the area given over to the herdsmen and shepherds can hardly be much less than ten million square miles; an area much greater than all the cultivated land, and, quite probably, greater than can be permanently and economically cultivated on the basis of present techniques. Unlike the hunters and food-gatherers, the herdsmen and shepherds are no vanishing remnant; they have not been counted but they are certainly to be numbered in millions.

Any attempt to estimate numbers would meet with difficulties of definition such as we have already encountered. It is far from easy to draw a line between pastoralists and agriculturists, nomads and sedentaries; indeed, it is not possible to draw any hard-and-fast line at all. These economic classes are not mutually exclusive. Some nomads have sedentary sections and many predominantly pastoral people also practise agriculture. Again, true pastoral nomadism may be combined with cultivation, as where a tribe sows its crops in a suitable locality and then moves out with the animals, leaving a section to tend the crops until harvest, or where a subservient people do the cultivating. Most of the traditional cattle pastoralists of Africa have now adopted cultivation and some must be classed as predominantly agricultural.

In the great marshes and savannah regions of the upper Nile, herds of long-horned cattle are reared by the Nilotic peoples (Nuer, Dinka, and Shilluk) whose ancestors, according to Toynbee, became herdsmen in response to the original challenge of dessication "and were driven into Equatoria." They are pastoralists by tradition, holding cattle in almost religious esteem, but they also engage in agriculture and fishing. The extent of their reliance on agriculture varies; some of the Dinka often neglect to grow enough grain to last them from one season to the next, and when they have a hungry year they trade cattle for grain with the Humr section of the Baggara Arabs to the north at rates very favourable to the Humr. The Shilluk, on the other hand, have become entirely sedentary and predominantly agricultural, and are no longer rich in cattle. These Nilotic peoples extend into Uganda and Kenya as the Acholi, Lango, and Luo, all of whom now cultivate, though they preserve the remnants of their herds and their pastoral traditions.

The Nilo-Hamites or half-Hamites include the Turkana and Masai of Kenya and Tanganyika and the Karamojong of Uganda who remain nomadic herdsmen, as no doubt all their congeners once were. Of the other Nilo-Hamitic peoples, the Jie of Uganda now have a mixed economy, while the Nandi and Suk of Kenya and the Teso of Uganda depend largely on agriculture, though all of them still have large herds of cattle. The Teso have become ploughmen and some of the hill Suk have an irrigation system which, as we have noted, is commonly thought to be a legacy from the past, because "the Suk are too primitive to have invented such a thing for themselves" (88). The Suk, or Pokot, who live in the dry plains as neighbours of the Karamojong and Turkana are still semi-nomadic pastoralists, while of those who live in the hill region some practice an intensive form of irrigation agriculture and some have a mixed economy. Other Nilo-Hamites are regarded as more progressive, notably the Kipsigis, a section of the Nandi who occupy one of the finest areas of the Kenya highlands. They have taken to farming of a sort on enclosed holdings. In Buret, which is probably the most fertile of the lands they hold, there are some five hundred square miles "of neatly hedged farms with managed pastures resembling Dorset from the air" (1). This is very impressive from the air, but less so when one comes down to earth.

A Nilo-Hamitic strain persists also among the Hima of Uganda, the giant Tusi of Ruanda, and the pastoral Fula, or Fulani, who are scattered over great tracts of northern Africa from the Senegal to French Equatorial Africa and the Cameroons. The Hima and Tusi were formerly cattle-owning aristocracies who disdained agriculture and relied for supplies of grain and beer on subservient Hera and Hutu tribesmen. At the time of writing, the Hutu seem to be set upon the extermination of their Tusi overlords, in spite of the intervention of Belgian military forces.

The dry "horn" of Africa is occupied mainly by Hamitic pastoral peoples. The Somali, who may be comparatively recent immigrants from Arabia, live within an area of about 350,000 square miles stretching from Eritrea to Cape Guardafui and southward along the Indian Ocean into Kenya, an area in which there are twice as many camels and ten times as many sheep and goats as there are people. Kenya's vast Northern Province, rather more than half the total area of the country, is an arid zone with an annual rainfall of only five to fifteen inches in which Hamitic peoples, Somali, Gurreh, and Boran, as well as the Nilo-Hamitic Turkana, rear great flocks and herds of camels, fat-tailed sheep, and goats of excellent quality, and Boran cattle, commonly regarded as the best native stock in Kenya both for meat and milk.

Throughout eastern and central Africa where conditions are suitable for cattle, many agricultural peoples of Bantu stock preserve the traditions of a pastoral past or have adopted the social and cultural values attached to cattle by the pastoralists. Some were pastoralists in the recent past and a few, like the Ila of the Kafue Flats in Northern Rhodesia, might still be regarded as herdsmen rather than cultivators: but most of the Bantu people are, and have long been, agriculturalists rather than herdsmen, depending on cultivation for all or most of their livelihood. Some of these cattle-owning agriculturists value their beasts mainly as a durable and transferable form of wealth, for in the primitive economy cattle were one of the few forms in which durable goods could be acquired, but very few value them, as we do, primarily as producers of meat, milk, and manure.

In areas where the plough, and less commonly the cart, has come into use, cattle have acquired a new value as plough and draught animals. Such a development has come about very recently among the Valley Tonga of Northern Rhodesia who formerly owned large flocks of sheep and goats but few cattle. With the control of game and reduction of tsetse and trypanosomiasis, their cattle have increased, and they are now valued mainly as plough animals, while the flocks continue to be regarded as a major form of wealth. The Plateau Tonga, on the other hand,

PLATE V

CONTOUR CULTIVATION IN A DENSELY POPULATED AREA OF
KABALE, UGANDA

Reproduced by permission of the Director of Surveys, Uganda.

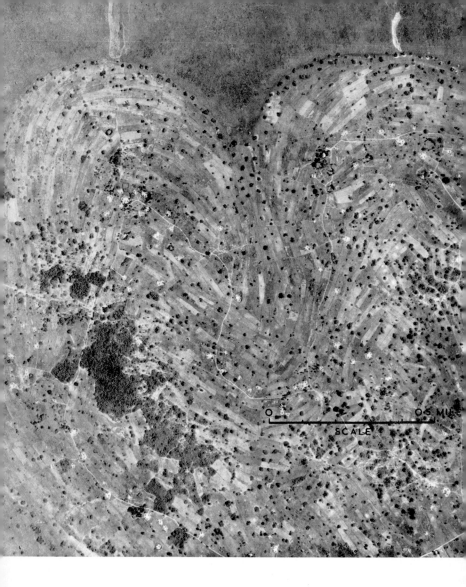

PLATE VI

PLOUGHED FIELDS ARRANGED ALONG CONTOURS,
SOUTHERN TESO DISTRICT, UGANDA

Reproduced by permission of the Director of Surveys, Uganda.

have long owned large herds of cattle, which they use as plough
and draught animals and value as wealth, but they have only
negligible numbers of smallstock.

As a general rule, sheep and goats are kept only in small numbers by the traditional cultivators and they appear to be most
numerous among comparatively recent converts from pastoralism
and peoples in a stage of transition. They play no part in ritual
observances, except where they are used as sacrificial animals.

2. THE LIVESTOCK CARRYING CAPACITY OF RANGE LAND

The land requirements of a purely pastoral society are determined by two factors; the number of livestock needed for the
subsistence of a family or an individual and the stock-carrying
capacity of the grazing or browsing land. Neither of these factors
can be readily ascertained and the latter is, of course, enormously
variable.

The carrying capacity of land for cattle and other grazing livestock depends on the average acreage of pasture land which is
capable of maintaining an animal for an indefinite period without
deterioration of the pasture and this, in turn, depends mainly on
soil and climate and partly on the system of management. Really
good grassland capable of carrying a cow to the acre, or of even
higher carrying capacity in the case of improved and well-managed
pasture, is found only in the more temperate regions under cool
and perennially moist conditions. Where a long dry season
scorches the land, and on the leached, acid soils of the tropics,
there is no formation of what farmers in temperate regions know
as a sward. There are no leguminous companion plants, such as
the clovers which add value to temperate pastures, and the grasses
are generally tall and tussocky. Growth of these grasses is rapid
for a few weeks of the year when the feed value is generally high,
but after reaching maturity the nutrient status of leaves and stems
falls quickly as nutrients are transferred to the seeds, or the roots
of perennials, and when the rains are over the plants dry off and
become tough, wiry, and fibrous. There is a surplus of feed during
the flush: but as the dry season reaches its climax the nutrient content of the food intake becomes insufficient even for maintenance
and the animal has to draw on its own reserves of fat and flesh.

Problems of management are much more difficult than those
of temperate grasslands. During the two or three months of very

rapid growth, the tall grasses of the one-season rainfall zone, such as the *Hyparrhenia* and *Cymbopogon* species, are very liable to "grow away" from stock and this results in uneven grazing and pasture deterioration. Grazing areas are limited by the incidence of tick-borne diseases, tsetse or other biting flies, and, in the dry season, by the distribution of the generally poor and localised water supplies for livestock. This leads to overstocking. Hornby (83) has pointed out that overstocking—"the maintenance of animals on a piece of land to the detriment of its carrying capacity"—is a necessary evil for the African pastoralist. "It is the only way by which he can maintain a high standard of health among his herds and has been deliberately made use of by him from time immemorial. Persistent vegetation favours ticks, flies and worms while overstocking favours aridity and reduces the incidence of parasitic diseases."

These conditions, seemingly so unfavourable for livestock, obtain over most of the regions inhabited by nomadic and semi-nomadic pastoralists. Their carrying capacity for livestock is, with rare exceptions, very low in comparison with that of the grassland in more temperate zones. No one can say with any certainty what these carrying capacities are, for there is little factual evidence and there is need for a great deal of experimental work on a wide range of pasture types. The work carried out so far has been concerned mainly with selected types of grasses and improved methods of management rather than with the nutritive value and carrying capacities of natural grazing under traditional systems of usage.

Since the amount of precise information on stock-carrying capacities is usually insufficient for practical purposes, such as de-stocking and the regulation of livestock numbers, empirical formulæ based on observation and experience are commonly used. One such formula for cattle, which has been used in the former Belgian Congo, is based on a minimum grazing requirement for an adult beast of as many hectares as there are months in the dry season. On this basis, the average requirement of grazing land in an area which is rainless for half the year would approximate to 15 acres per head of adult stock. French workers have estimated that the general stock-carrying capacity of Madagascar is of this order: an average grazing requirement of 6 hectares (14.82 acres) per adult ox. Work in the southern savannah of Ghana has also placed the cattle-carrying capacity of this region at 15 acres to the beast, which, it is thought, may be reduced to 10 acres under rotational grazing. Estimates for Southern Rhodesia and South Africa range from 10 acres per beast in the better areas to 15 or 20 acres where rainfall is less, and even 40 acres on the poorest grazing under very dry conditions. Somewhat similar figures have been given by Troup (177) for the dry ranching areas of Kenya. The natural herbage which, he says, must form the basis for ranching, is generally of low feeding value and the capacity at the time of his investigation varied from one head of cattle to 25 acres in a low rainfall and newly alienated area such as North Laikipia to the other extreme of one beast to 6 acres in certain low rainfall areas adjoining the Rift Valley where permanent star grass sward had developed in consequence of regular rotational grazing. But, he adds, this heavier stocking was made possible only by the use of irrigated lucerne and, or alternatively, silage and hay from fodder crops.

In regions of high and more reliable rainfall where the dry season is shorter and less severe, carrying capacities for livestock are, of course, higher. Fulani herdsmen on the Guinea savannah of northern Sierra Leone may require no more than 7 acres to support a cow (121) but a figure of at least 12·5 acres has been estimated for the Fulani of Bamenda in the Cameroons, on their present system of management, even though they alternate plateau and lowland grazing. This figure of 12·5 acres is an estimate of the actual density of stocking with cattle and there is evidence of overstocking in the more frequently used areas even at this low overall figure, but this is due rather to methods of management than incapacity of the land to carry more animals. Experiments on rotational grazing have indicated that with really good management the carrying capacity might be increased to 4 or 4·5 acres to the beast. It might, of course, be said of any pastoral system that it does not make the best use of the land, and the whole issue is affected and confused by questions of grazing management and control: but it is impracticable to assume intensive land-use where it is not in fact practised, and where there is neither the will nor the means to adopt such practices. The present discussion is concerned with traditional pastoral systems as such.

In regions with a well-distributed double rainfall, where green grass growth is maintained throughout the whole or the greater part of the year, one would expect the carrying capacity for live-stock to be at least double that of the more arid zones with long dry seasons. Such comparable estimates as it has been possible to find for the moister parts of Kenya and Uganda lie between 3·5 and 7·5 acres to the beast, in terms of cattle. These figures, like the others, are largely conjectural and based on observation rather than experimental data. It is very difficult to arrive at any really reliable conclusion in this way, as is well illustrated by recent ex-perience in Uganda. Attempts have been made in the course of detailed surveys of Uganda agricultural systems to determine the amount of land given over to grazing and the amount required for each head of stock, but with little success owing to the fact that a herd is not confined to the area of its own *mutalla* (hamlet) but frequently ranges over the lands of others, while in seasons of dearth the cattle are taken to graze in distant swamp lands. So indeterminate are the grazing patterns of pastoralists and agro-pastoralists that it is a matter of great difficulty to relate numbers of stock to clearly defined and measurable areas. This may derive from the attitude to tenure and rights in land common among pastoral peoples.

3. LAND TENURE

It appears to be true of African pastoralists, or most of them, that they recognise no specific grazing rights of any sort. All the land of the tribe is, in theory at least, open grazing for the animals of all members of the tribe. Every one of my Masai informants, both in Kenya and Tanganyika, told me that all Masailand was open grazing for all Masai, and that there never had been any recogni-tion among them of exclusive rights to pasture held by individuals or groups. In practice there is a fairly clear association between groups and grazing areas. The tribe is divided into sections (*loshun*), said to represent successive waves of migration, and each section is associated with a vaguely defined area. The clans which compose the sections also tend to move within limited areas, but these associations are regarded merely as matters of con-venience and not as implying any exclusive rights. The livestock of one section or clan may, and do, graze in areas associated with others, and in years of drought cattle from badly stricken sections are admitted to the areas of the more fortunate. Some of my in-formants said that they would not graze their beasts in an area associated with another section, because, though they were free to do so, the people would make fun of them and laugh at their accent and manner of speech; others denied this. All were emphatic that Masai never quarrel among themselves but freely share water and grazing. This is not the experience of District Officers who sometimes have to deal with violent quarrels over access to water, but rarely over grazing.

A similar pattern has been described by Brown (32) for the Somali of the British Somaliland Protectorate who are primarily nomadic pastoralists, though recently there has been some enclosure of land for agriculture in the very limited areas where rainfall is sufficient for cropping. Their attitudes are conditioned by a devout adherence to Islam; land belongs to God alone and only its products, surface water, grass, and trees are subject to human ownership. But ownership of the products of unenclosed land is tribal in the widest sense; these are common property of the people as a whole "and no individual or group may claim an exclusive right to a particular piece of grazing or surface water supply."

Somali society is based on clans which habitually graze their stock within certain areas, but these areas are vague and ill-defined except in time of war and feud when the clan contracts and consolidates for defence. A season of drought also causes the clans to contract about the remaining water supplies, but even in these circumstances a group may be joined by others from more severely stricken areas. When rains are adequate the flocks and herds of the various clans and groups—which are formed at various levels in the genealogy of the clan—intermingle freely and make common use of grazing, browse, and surface water.

This concept of grazing land and surface water as free goods of the tribe is found also, according to Gulliver (70), among the Karamojong, Dodoth, Jie, and Donyiro of Uganda and the Turkana of Kenya. Nevertheless, "owners" of herds—the head of a nuclear family among the Turkana and a group of full brothers among the Jie—tend to move their animals in an established annual grazing cycle over country with which they are familiar and they are likely to resent encroachment by other groups in time of dearth. Gulliver says that fights over grazing do occur in seasons of drought and scarcity, although in theory "no man should be denied pasturage and water for his animals."

The same concept persists among peoples with a mixed economy, where it applies also to gardens after harvest and fallows, until acute shortage of land makes free grazing for all members of the tribe a practical impossibility. The Humr section of the Baggara, who combine nomadic herding with cultivation of millet and cotton, recognise no ownership or rights to grazing land except in the very wide sense that the whole of Dar Humr belongs to all the Humr, and the herdsmen can and do graze their cattle wherever they will within a country more than twice the size of Wales. There is even an area of overlap between the grazing lands of the Humr and those of Ngok Dinka to the south, so that no clear boundary between the two can be distinguished (44). Among the Tonga of Northern Rhodesia, on the other hand, an agricultural people who have been conscious of increasing shortage of garden and pasture land for a good many years, grazing is restricted to a division or *cisi*—a segment of the tribal land now replaced by the modern chieftaincy. As a general rule any member of the *cisi* has the right to graze whatever number of cattle or other stock he pleases anywhere within the *cisi*, but no cattle of one *cisi* may graze within the boundaries of another (10). Restriction, or localisation, of grazing rights has reached a more advanced stage among the Chagga of Kilimanjaro who are acutely short of land. Some of the Chagga are former pastoralists, though few now own more than two or three head of stock, and the Siha section were leading a predominantly pastoral existence until a few decades ago. Although the tribal area consisted of three virtually autonomous divisions, Hai, Vunjo, and Rombo, there was a tradition of free grazing over all; now, with increasing pressure on the land, rights of pasturage are becoming rapidly localised and limited. Herds from Vunjo may no longer be taken across to Hai, as was the former custom, and in Rombo each minor chieftaincy has its own exclusive grazing and grass-cutting reserve. Private rights to grazing are being asserted and these mingle and conflict with public rights in a medley of confusion.

4. Nomadic Patterns

Movements of nomadic flocks and herds are determined by a number of factors of which seasonal distribution of water and grazing are commonly most important, while other less obvious factors such as the incidence of tick-borne and fly-borne diseases, prevalence of biting flies which may make life almost intolerable for cattle, and the occurrence of natural salt, modify the pattern and are of major importance in some areas. The Masai pattern is essentially a simple expansion and contraction dominated by distribution of water supplies. The binodal rainfall averages from 8 to 25 inches in different parts of the region but the annual fall is very variable, and partial or almost complete failures of the long or short rains are not infrequent. During the dry season the stock must remain within range of the limited permanent water supplies from rivers, wells, and springs, but with the rains the bulk of the flocks and herds move out, each clan tending to follow a definite pattern which must, of course, be modified in accordance with rainfall and the consequent distribution of surface water and grazing. During this outward movement, the *moran* of the warrior age-group act as scouts who locate water and grazing and sites for the thorn *bomas* in which the cattle are kept at night. Areas within range of tsetse fly and where east coast fever is endemic are avoided. Not all of the livestock move out with the rains. Considerable numbers remain near the permanent water sources throughout the year with the result that these areas are never rested and they deteriorate rapidly. Thus, though the Masai practise a rough grazing rotation, the general picture is one of very uneven land-use.

A somewhat similar pattern, determined by distribution of water in the dry season, has been described by Gulliver for the Jie of northern Uganda, but here a rainfall gradient increasing from east to west results in a rhythm of movement with the regularity of a transhumance. Conditions on the black clay plains of Jieland appear to be better than over most of the Masai country. Rainfall averages about 25 inches but increases to 30 or 35 inches in the west near the Acholi border. Most of the permanent water is in the west and the herds concentrate about these points during the dry season, spreading out over the whole of the western region when the rains come in April. Here the grass cover, dominated by *Hyparrhenias*, is tall and coarse and by mid-June it has "grown away" from the livestock which then move to the east where there is now surface water and fresh grass. At the end of the rains in September this transient water soon dries up and the herds must return to the west, where surface water is more persistent and they can remain dispersed, feeding on such components of the grazing as remain palatable, until December when they must again concentrate about the permanent water points.

The nomadic pattern of the Turkana, who live in the Rift Valley to the east of the Jie, is less influenced by water supplies, in spite of the fact that much of their country is sub-desert with a low and very unreliable rainfall. The main water courses, which carry run-off from eastern Uganda and the highlands of Kenya to Lake Rudolf, provide dry-season water from pools and shallow wells, and the alkaline water of the lake is thought to contribute greatly to the condition of the animals that drink there. Few areas are seriously short of water, by African standards, and the main determining factor of Turkana nomadism is poverty of grazing and browse for livestock. The region is a great plain broken by scattered hills and a few mountain massifs, over which rainfall ranges from a mere 6 inches in the central desert lands to 16 inches on some parts of the plain and more in the mountains, while the environment varies from bare sand and rock through desert scrub with a sparse and transient cover of annuals to permanent grassland in the better regions and relatively good grazing with feed throughout the year in the mountains above 4,000 feet and along main water courses.

This environmental complex determines patterns of movement and imposes a dichotomy between grazing and browsing stock. Camels and goats, which browse and graze, are mainly confined to the plain though there is a tendency to move to the mountains at the end of the dry season. The flocks and herds concentrate on the areas of better and more persistent feed during the dry season, spreading out to utilise the transient grazing brought by the rains and falling back again on the better areas as the dry season advances. Cattle, on the other hand, stay in the mountains for most of the year, moving to the plains when the grazing there is at its best and retreating to the mountains at the start of the dry season in a more or less regular transhumance.

Movements of sheep and goat flocks and camel herds in the British Somaliland Protectorate are again determined mainly by seasonal water supplies. The high edge of the interior plateau fronts the Gulf of Aden, forming two parallel mountain ranges behind the narrow, arid coastal strip, as seen from the sea. In the mountains, where there is a mist zone of evergreen vegetation, rainfall reaches 20 inches, while the upper plateau behind the mountains has a fall of 12 to 18 inches. The remainder of the plateau, by far the greater part of the country, is semi-desert with an uncertain rainfall averaging about 8 inches, most of which comes in May–June and September–October. The altitude of the plateau decreases and aridity increases to the south and east. Vegetation, including the dominant species of *Acacia*, is determined by rainfall, altitude, and the presence or absence of gypsum which is remarkably prevalent. Vegetation, in turn, determines the details of the pastoral pattern but the main nomadic movement is a rapid and extensive spreading out from the permanent water supplies in the regions of higher rainfall, followed by the inevitable retreat and concentration as surface water dries up and feed becomes scarce. Homesteads move with the animals which graze around them in two concentric zones, an inner ring of smallstock and an outer ring of camels, so long as conditions allow of this. Later in the season there is a pronounced dichotomy in the grazing regime; young men go out with the camels and may range more than fifty miles from the homestead during an absence of several months while the smallstock remain near the homestead. The outward movement ignores international boundaries and carries the flocks and herds over traditional grazing lands far into Ethiopia, while the retreat brings all of the livestock once again within the boundaries of the Protectorate (61, 87).

The Humr section of the Baggara Arabs in the Sudan combine cultivation with nomadic pasturing of cattle and smallstock in a pattern that has been described by Cunnison (44). Here conditions dictate a regular sequence of movements north and south, and the pattern is greatly influenced by seasonal plagues of mosquitos and other biting flies. The heartland of Dar Humr might be described as an oasis in a sea of sand and scrub. It is an area of red clays in which are deep pools of permanent water and sandy ridges used for cultivation. The clay and the area as a whole are called *Muglad*. North of the *Muglad* is an area known as *Babanusa* because of the prevalence of the bush *Dalbergia melanoxylon* which has this local name, and to the south a region called the *Goz* used by the Humr as little more than a passage way to the river system in the south, the *Bahr*, where the Dinka live. The *Babanusa* and the *Bahr* are the main grazing areas, used in the rains and the dry season respectively, with short stops in the *Muglad* during the northerly and southerly movements. Rain falls mainly in summer, starting

in April and ending in October, with the heaviest fall generally in
August.

In December the herds of the Humr leave the *Muglad*, where
the grazing has dried up; they move rapidly southward across the
Goz, while enough surface water remains, to the river system
grazing in the *Bahr*. There they remain throughout winter and
early spring, moving north again before the first rains bring a
plague of biting flies from which the cattle get no rest during the
day or night. The Nilotic people who live in this region have
adapted their methods of animal husbandry to these conditions;
they protect their cattle against mosquitos by tethering them in
smoke houses at night, but the Humr do not do this and their
beasts seem to be more sensitive to insect attack than those of the
Nilotes. During this northerly move the transit of the *Goz* is more
leisurely, probably because they have to wait for sufficient water
ahead, and the herds may take upwards of a month to reach the
Muglad, where they are used to manure the garden lands. Their
stay here is short because conditions for cattle deteriorate rapidly
with the advancing rains; the clay turns to mud, and horse flies,
midges, buffalo gnats, and mosquitos plague the beasts. The herds
then move north again, to the *Babanusa*, where there is little mud
and flies are few, remaining in this more favourable environment
throughout the rains and returning to the *Muglad* as late as possible in the season to avoid the flies. After a few weeks in the
Muglad, during which they graze the millet stover and provide
further manure for the gardens, the herds start off once more on
the southerly movement to the *Bahr*.

The nomadic pattern of the pastoral Fulani, who are scattered
over the vast West African savannah zone, is also, in general, a
movement southward in the dry season and northward with the
rains, within limits circumscribed by desert in the north and
tsetse-infested country to the south. In the dry season, as the
northern pastures and water supplies fail, the herds of cattle dis-
perse southwards, returning again and concentrating in the north
to avoid the seasonal spread of tsetse in the rains. Local variations
of environment determine the range and intensity of these movements and modify the general pattern. Under favourable conditions movements may be reduced to a minimum, or they may follow a more definite and limited pattern of transhumance between
hill or plateau and valley or flood plain (158).

Conditions in the Bamenda province of the Cameroons contrast strikingly with those of the dry pastoral regions of East Africa. Rainfall approaches and frequently reaches 100 inches in the year, falling mainly in the period April–November; while the dry season, though severe to the point that surface soils dry out and the winds are dust-laden, is comparatively short. The grazing lands of the Bamenda Fulani consist of high plateau grassland and dissected valleys which are flooded by the overflowing streams during the heavy rains. In the wet season the herds move and graze over the high plateau, generally above 4,000 feet, but in the dry season, when the upland grasses have become dry and fibrous, they move down to the valley plains as the flood waters recede leaving good pasturage there—though it is limited and less valuable than the plateau grazing at its best.

The Fulani of the Guinea grassland in northern Sierra Leone, who are "shifting cultivators" as well as cattle herdsmen, follow a system of "shifting pasturage" which may have originated in a need to group as closely as possible together for defence. Their practice is to over-graze one area with a heavy concentration of stock for two or three years and then to move to another area in a cycle which takes them back to the first grazing ground after a long period, sometimes fifteen or twenty years (121). This form of "rotational grazing" has nothing to recommend it from the land-use point of view. The heavy stock concentration tends to destroy the palatable grasses, allowing unpalatable and woody vegetation to become dominant and tipping the ecological balance from grassland to scrub brush.

When disaster strikes the herds of the pastoralist, he must change his way of life. This has happened to the Fulani of northeastern Ghana. They are no longer cattle nomads, for the beasts they own are far too few, but they preserve an association with their pastoral past by acting as herdsmen for the Kusasi cultivators among whom they live. Thus, a Fulani family may have the care of a large herd of cattle, but it is an uncertain source of livelihood since the owners may at any time call on their cattle "banks" for the settlement of dowry transactions or to meet other social obligations. In more recent years this uncertainty has been increased by the official drive for mixed farming which puts constant pressure on the cultivators to retain their cattle. The Fulani themselves have therefore become cultivators—reluctantly, since they dislike farming—and dwellers in more or less fixed homesteads from which the herds go out during the day, returning in the evening to be tethered or kept in thorn-fenced kraals which are later used for cultivation. Though the cultivated area is small, compared with that of the agricultural peoples, it is fertilised by the night droppings of many cattle (quite commonly twenty or more beasts to the acre) and yields are high. The bulk of the food supply comes from these gardens and the main role of the herd is to produce manure, with milk as a minor supplement to the diet and a source of cash income.

This type of change, towards at least partial reliance on cultivation or some form of livelihood other than pastoralism, is bound to be set in train when the ratio between livestock and human populations falls below a certain level. Reduction of the ratio below this critical point may be brought about by epidemic disease among the stock, on so wide a scale as to preclude rebuilding of individual herds by the customary means of loans and gifts, or by a general increase in the human population at a greater rate than the livestock.

There is, then, a certain minimum requirement in the size and composition of the herd or flock of a pastoral group. We may refer to this as the "basic" herd and define it as the minimum number of animals, in the required proportions, that will suffice for the subsistence of an individual.

5. Land Requirements of Pastoralists

The size of the basic herd will be determined by the type of animal, by the way in which the herd is exploited for food, and by the environment, to the extent that environmental factors affect the productivity of the animal.

Practically all accounts of pastoral peoples are agreed on one point: that meat constitutes only a small fraction of the regular human diet. The slaughter of large stock represents a reduction of the family's capital and killings are restricted to relatively rare occasions such as periodic festivals, ceremonies, and sacrifices, or the arrival of a particularly important guest. The occasions and their frequency vary in different societies. Animals are also slaughtered when it is thought that they are about to die and meat is eaten on these occasions and when a beast dies naturally or is bitten by a snake or killed by a carnivore. In the aggregate, these occasions may represent the consumption of quite a considerable quantity of meat, even though it is not eaten in the form of regular meals. For example, with the present numbers of cattle owned by the Masai, consumption of beef on such occasions might well amount to an annual average of 100 or 150 lb per person, if we attribute a herd mortality of 4 or 5 per cent to occasional killings and deaths of cattle which are subsequently eaten; and this takes no account of the contribution made by the great flocks of sheep and goats. The meat need not be eaten all at once; drying is an easy and obvious means of preservation in an arid climate. The Baggara, for example, make biltong from the flesh of a cow or ox which has died, and this is subsequently pounded and used as a sauce ingredient over a long period.

The importance of milk and milk products varies in different pastoral societies and environments, but it is generally regarded as an essential staple. It appears to be true for most of the wholly pastoral Fulani that the family lives on milk, either by consuming milk and milk products or exchanging them for other foods, but reliance on these products implies large cattle herds with a high proportion of milking cows and an environment which will allow of a sufficient number remaining in milk throughout the year. In regions with a long dry season when water is scarce and the nutritive value of the food intake barely enough for maintenance, milk cannot be a general staple for more than part of the year. Thus, Gulliver says of the Turkana that, though milk is a staple food, it is relatively scarce for much of the year and "the whole supply is pooled for the benefit of the younger children" (70).

Cattle which may not be slaughtered and cannot be milked are no great asset from the point of view of food supply. Perhaps it would not be too fanciful to see in this dilemma an economic origin for the custom of bleeding cattle, a custom universal among Nilotic and Nilo-Hamitic herdsmen and practised also by some of their Bantu neighbours. The same method is common to all of these groups: a leather thong is used as a tourniquet to congest the great vein of the neck which is then pierced with an arrow the head of which has been specially designed and the shaft blocked to avoid serious injury to the beast. Considerable quantities of blood can be taken from an animal in this way without doing it permanent harm, provided the operation is carried out only at fairly long intervals.

Bleeding is still practised—in addition to cattle, the Turkana bleed their camels and the Masai take blood from sheep by piercing the vessels above the eyes—but it is difficult to assess the extent to which blood is used as food or was used in the past. The accounts of earlier observers suggest that blood was an important and popular element of diet among the Masai, but my informants in Masailand all denied this. They said that blood was not "food," except for women in the last stages of pregnancy and the earlier weeks of nursing, and that, apart from this, cattle were bled only infrequently and for ritual purposes. Even the older men maintained that this had always been the custom. The Chagga gave a similar account; they said that the blood of cattle was given as a supplement in the diet of women for three months after the birth of a child but was not otherwise used as food. A custom so striking and unusual as the bleeding of animals may, of course, have attracted the attention of observers to a greater degree than was warranted by its economic importance: but it is equally, if not more, likely that the modern Masai—or, at least, the more sophisticated among them, from whom my informants were mainly drawn—now tend to deny a custom which the questioner may regard as uncivilised. My informants, in fact, went to considerable pains to present me with a rather unexpected picture of the Masai as a peace-loving and humane people, the "good neighbours" of East Africa—an account difficult to reconcile with the records of their forays or the views of the peoples formerly subjected to them. Even today, the Moran, for whom life must be rather dull, especially in the Game Parks where lion may not be molested, occasionally indulge in a little cattle lifting from European estates and the herds of their neighbours. While I was in Kenya a band of Narok Masai raided the Kipsigis and stole a herd of their cattle, but they were pursued and defeated by Kipsigis spearmen after a sharp battle in which two Masai were killed. Returning with reinforcements, they routed the Kipsigis and went off again with about five hundred head of cattle. The incident ended, as usual, with the arrival of the District Commissioner and Tribal Police.

Hollis (82), writing at the beginning of the present century, says that the Masai formerly ate no food except that produced by their cattle, including blood drunk pure or mixed with milk: but after the great rinderpest epidemics of the 1880s and 1890s they were forced to eat the "food of savages" such as maize, rice, and

bananas, and even game meat, like the Dorobo. They still disdain
game meat and hunt only the lion, with such persistence that the
unfortunate beasts have developed an anxiety neurosis. Lions on
a fresh kill and obviously hungry will immediately abandon it and
bolt for the bush on the first sight or scent of a Masai, such is their
terror of the Moran.[1]

Merker, writing in 1910, gives a similar account of the use of
blood foods by the Tanganyika Masai. They bled cattle, sheep,
and goats—as they still do to some extent—and drank the blood
fresh or ate it in a coagulated form. It was also added, fresh or
after cooking, as a food for invalids (111).

If, in fact, blood was used as a major food it follows that the
capacity of the cattle as blood donors would be an important factor
in determining the size of the basic herd. According to Leakey
(102) the blood of two cattle is required to provide a meal for a
family of five or six people, and the animals must not be bled more
frequently than once in five or six weeks, if they are to remain in
good health. Consequently, a herd of about 80 cattle would be
required to provide a daily meal for such a family, or 13 to 16
animals for each individual. These figures approximate fairly
closely to the numbers of cattle actually owned by the Masai; the
averages are about 16·3 cattle per head of population in Kenya and
13·9 in Tanganyika according to the more recent estimates of livestock and population. The *ingan*, or homestead, commonly consists of from 3 to 8 families, averaging between 5 and 6 members,
associated with a herd of 300 to 700 cattle. The main factor holding the families together is their ability to agree among themselves;
if the families quarrel the group will split. Thus, though the
families comprising an *ingan* are usually closely related, this is not
always the case.

If we assume a basic herd of 13 to 16 cattle and a grazing requirement of about 15 acres per beast, which may be on the low
side for Masailand as a whole, then the Critical Population Density
as determined by the land requirement would be of the order of 2
or 3 people per square mile. Increase of population beyond this
level would result in over-grazing by the additional stock, with its
inevitable consequences, or reduction of population density by
acquisition of more grazing land, or a change in the system itself.

[1] According to Mervyn Cowie, Director of the Royal National Parks of
Kenya.

Present population densities are approximately 4·3 people per square mile in Kenya Masai, which is seriously over-stocked, and 2·0 in Tanganyika Masai which appears to be rather under-stocked as a whole, though local over-stocking is very evident.

Whatever may have been the case in the past, the use of blood as a food no longer dominates the Masai economy and the argument is of very doubtful validity, even though it appears to explain present human and cattle population densities rather neatly. Apart from uncertainty as to the economic importance of bleeding cattle, and possible changes in diet, the argument ignores the existence of great flocks of smallstock and the fact that livestock numbers are not necessarily related to strictly economic needs.

Some idea of livestock requirements might be obtained by comparing the flocks and herds of pastoral peoples with those of others who have a mixed economy or depend wholly on agriculture, but the value of this approach is vitiated by the uncertainty of the data for both human and livestock populations. In some cases, where regular cattle counts are made for veterinary or tax purposes, fairly reliable figures are available, though it is not always clear whether they refer to total stock or to adult animals only: but figures for sheep and goats, where they exist at all, are usually no more than very approximate and variable estimates. Estimates of the sheep and goat population of British Somaliland vary from four million to thirteen million, and for Kenya Masailand from one million to as much as six million. Human populations are also uncertain since it is no easy matter to make an accurate census of pastoralists who see no reason why they should co-operate in such an undertaking and sometimes resent the counting of their live-stock.

The data which can be used are therefore meagre and the figures given in the following table are intended only as a very general comparison between the numbers of animals owned by pastoral and agricultural peoples.

For practical purposes it is customary to regard one ox as the equivalent of five head of smallstock in terms of grazing require-ments, and this is usually referred to as a "livestock unit." A camel is often taken as the equivalent of two oxen and is therefore counted as two livestock units. Of course, it does not follow that the value of camels, cattle, and small-stock as food producers is in the same proportion. Sheep and goats may well provide a more

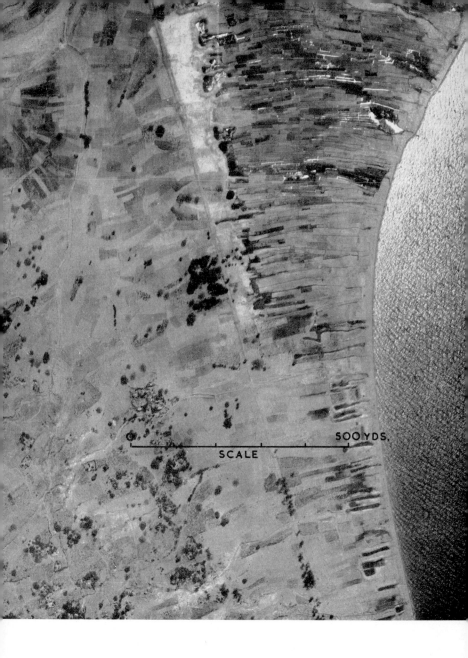

SCALE 500 YDS.

PLATE VII

LAKE-SIDE IRRIGATION AND DRY-LAND FIELDS ON
UKARA ISLAND, LAKE VICTORIA, TANGANYIKA

Reproduced by permission of Sir Alexander Gibb and Partners.
Enlargement by Directorate of Overseas Surveys.

PLATE VIII

THE KIKUYU CONSOLIDATION PATTERN NEAR MUGUGA,
TEN MILES NORTH-WEST OF NAIROBI, KENYA

· LIVESTOCK OF PASTORALISTS AND CULTIVATORS:
SOME COMPARISONS

	HUMAN POP. (*Thousands*)	LIVESTOCK PER HEAD OF POPULATION			
		Camels	*Cattle*	*Small-stock*	*Livestock Units*
PASTORALISTS:					
1. Masai (Kenya)	60·6	—	16·3	16·7	19·6
2. Masai (Tanganyika)	46·0	—	13·9	16·3	17·2
3. Mukogodo	3·3	—	10·2	11·5	12·5
4. Somali (Brit. Somaliland)	640·0	2·0	0·4	15·6	7·5
5. Turkana	80·0	1·0	2·5	10·0	6·5
MIXED ECONOMIES:					
6. Baggara Humr	48·0	—	6·0	1·1	6·2
7. Jie	18·2	—	3·6	3·8	4·4
STOCK-KEEPING CULTIVATORS:					
8. Kipsigis	159·6	—	2·0	1·9	2·4
9. Teso	455·6	—	1·5	0·6	1·6
10. Tonga Plateau	9·0	—	1·2	—	1·2
11. Tonga Valley	45·8	—	0·8	0·5	0·9
12. Mambwe	9·5	—	0·9	0·1	0·9
13. Ngoni	14·4	—	0·8	0·5	0·9

Sources

1. Population from (1), p. 66. Cattle from Vet. Dept. estimate (1958). Smallstock taken as 1,000,000 only.
2. Figures supplied by officers of the Tanganyika Agric. and Vet. Depts. (1959).
3. Census (1955), quoted in (1), p. 104.
4. No census has been made, either of humans or of livestock. The 1958 estimate of population was 750,000, of whom 640,000 were assumed to be nomadic. Livestock estimates: based on Hunt (87), and revised in consultation with Director of National Resources, British Somaliland.
5. P. H. Gulliver (70).
6. I. Cunnison (44), and personal communications. Smallstock numbers very uncertain and probably underestimated.
7. P. H. Gulliver (70).
8. (1), p. 159.
9. General figures for Teso District supplied by officers of Uganda Dept. of Agric. (1959).
10. Allan, Gluckman, etc. (10), p. 121. Figures refer to Sianjalika *cisi* only.
11. The "grassland-cultivating" Aisa Mambwe. Figures from W. Watson (181).
12. Population estimated and livestock counts for 6 chiefdoms in Gwembe District (1956).
13. Priestley and Greening (132). Population estimates and livestock counts for 4 Ngoni chieftaincies in Fort Jameson District, N. Rhodesia.

adequate and regular food supply, in relation to their numbers, than cattle which yield little milk and which may not be slaughtered except on comparatively rare occasions, but no quantitative comparison can be made since there is very litttle information on the productivity of flocks and herds under traditional systems of nomadic management. The numbers of livestock required to maintain a wholly pastoral existence probably vary considerably with environmental conditions and also with the type of animal and the way in which it is used. Fulani who live almost entirely on milk and its products and who keep no small-stock must maintain a very large number of cattle for each human unit, and it seems that at least some of the Fulani of Bamenda have more than 20 cattle for each head of population. Yet in some regions a minority of Fulani have few or no cattle and they depend largely or even wholly on sheep and goats. This is true also of the Masai, among whom there are poor families with few cattle and some with none. Camels are of great importance in the semi-desert lands of Turkana and Somaliland, where they are prized for their milk yield and prolonged lactation. But some of the people of these regions have no camels and very few of the Somali own cattle. They too must depend wholly on their flocks, as do the shepherds of North Africa, Cyprus, and the Middle East.

It seems probable that the economic role of sheep and goats in pastoral economics such as that of the Masai has been obscured by the high social and prestige values attached to large-stock and has therefore escaped the attention of most observers. Apart from occasional and irregular meals of meat, the present diet of the Masai consists mainly of the flesh of smallstock, grain which was formerly obtained by trading and raiding but is now bought at the store, and milk from cows and ewes. There is no strong evidence of any marked change since the time of the great rinderpest epidemic and it is probable that, at least since then, sheep and goats have played a dominant part in the food economy both as direct providers of regular meat supplies and as currency exchangeable for grain. Otherwise, it is difficult to understand why the Masai should have maintained enormous flocks, which competed with cattle for water and grazing, and to which they attached no non-economic values.

We must expect considerable variation, and on our present knowledge we can arrive at no satisfactory figure: but let us sup-

pose that that the minimum number of animals required per head
of population to maintain a wholly pastoral existence—the factor
I have referred to as the "basic herd"—is represented by six livestock units which is rather less than the number on which the
Turkana still maintain their pastoral way of life. If we again
assume a grazing requirement of 15 acres for each of these units,
we might conjecture that the Critical Population Density of pure
pastoralism is likely to be something of the order of seven people
to the square mile, at least in the drier parts of eastern Africa
where it is still practised.

6. POPULATION DENSITIES IN PASTORAL REGIONS

All that has been said in the preceding section amounts merely to
a suggestion, based on conjecture and a few approximate data,
that pastoral populations in the drier and less favourable regions
are unlikely to exceed a general density of seven per square mile.
It would seem that population densities of surviving pastoral peoples are usually well below this figure, even in the more favourable
of the regions they still occupy. Estimates of the total areas
utilised and general population densities for some examples are
summarised below:

	TOTAL AREA OF RANGE (Sq. miles)	HUMAN POPULATION DENSITY (per sq. mile)
PASTORALISTS:		
Masai (Tanganyika)	23,000	2·0
Fulani (Bamenda)	4,116	2·4
Turkana	24,000	3·3
Masai (Kenya)	14,000	4·3
Somali (Br. Som.)	110,000	5·8
Mukogodo	550	6·0
MIXED ECONOMIES:		
Baggara Humr	18,150	2·6
Jie	1,300	14·0

Again, these figures are no more than approximations. Pastoral
populations are not static, they follow what might be called a

"repetitive kaleidoscopic" pattern of change. At some seasons population is relatively concentrated while at others it is widely dispersed, and there are many intermediate changes between these two extremes. The general population density is, therefore, a gross figure based on the whole area over which livestock range during the year and the total population supported by the flocks and herds.

In addition to uncertainty regarding human numbers, the areas over which their livestock range are generally unsurveyed and vaguely defined, while attempts to estimate areas utilised by nomadic herds are often complicated by the intermingling of pastoralists and agriculturalists and of different pastoral peoples. Nevertheless, the figures serve to illustrate the low human-carrying capacities of pastoral systems. Population densities are limited by the large number of livestock required, the low stock-carrying capacity of much of the grazing under primitive systems of use, "bottlenecks" in the grazing cycle, the extent of ungrazeable land within the range, and the tendency to maintain more stock than is necessary for subsistence.

The Humr range over an area so extensive that they have probably well over 30 acres of land for each livestock unit, but there is a "bottleneck" in the cycle during the wet months when the prevalence of biting flies restricts cattle grazing to the limited area of the *Babanusa*. Harrison has estimated that at present stock numbers, Baggara country is 20 per cent overstocked (75). Similarly, dry season grazing is a "bottleneck" in the regime of the Bamenda Fulani. The lower limit and general extent of this grazing, which is poorer than that of the wet season, is limited by the distribution and dry season range of tsetse. Again, land capable of maintaining stock may be excluded from use because of the incidence of tick-borne—or fly-borne—disease or distance from water, and in every large area of range there is a varying proportion of land intrinsically useless for grazing. Thus the land needed to support livestock and human populations may be considerably greater than the theoretical grazing requirement. It has been estimated for Masailand as a whole that something like one-third of the total area cannot be used because it is near-desert, too arid for cattle, or on account of disease hazards or lack of surface water. In regions such as Turkana and Somaliland, with large areas of sheer sand and rock desert, and unusable vegetation such as

Euphorbia, the proportion of useless or virtually useless land may well be even higher.

Of the examples we have considered, the Masai and Mukogodo appear to have an excess of livestock in relation to the economic requirements of simple pastoralism, while in the case of the Somali and Turkana the ratio of livestock to humans may approximate to the minimum. The relatively small numbers of animals owned by the Jie, and their comparatively high population density, reflects the importance of agriculture in their mixed economy.

The Humr present an interesting example of a pastoral people who once lost their herds. At one time they were camel herdsmen, but when they were forced to move into country unsuitable for camels they took to cattle and used these beasts much as their ancestors had used camels. Cunnison says that "only for a short time in their history, as far as is known, have they been virtually without camels or cattle; this was during the Mahdiya, when many of them moved to Omdurman, and the few who remained were bereft of cattle and practised agriculture and the collection of wild fruit in the Bahr El Arab region. After the reoccupation they lost no time in restocking: they did this mainly by hunting elephants and selling ivory to merchants who took cattle with them and installed themselves in trading posts in the south of the country" (46).

Agriculture is still an important part of the Humr economy, though they are reluctant cultivators. In common with other cattle people, they dislike the tedious labour of agriculture that was once the lot of their slaves, and the extent of this dislike is evidenced by the fact that it has been found necessary to give the courts power to compel a man to cultivate against his will. The Humr value the money they obtain by agriculture, and other ancillary economic activities, mainly as a means of accumulating livestock and of meeting commitments which would otherwise entail the selling of animals. They market the surplus of their millet crops[1] and they now grow cotton in the *Bahr* so that they may have money with which to buy more cattle and smallstock.

The urge to accumulate and hold livestock, even though their numbers are greater than the land can safely carry, is common to

---

[1] Cunnison (46) points out that this is usually a spurious surplus, since the sellers have either gone without solid food, living for long periods almost entirely on milk, or have paid out of pocket for grain during the summer months. "Few Baggara can produce a surplus after continuous use of their granaries for a year."

pastoralists of today and of the distant past. There is an early account of overstocking in the Book of Genesis: "And Lot also, which went with Abram, had flocks and herds and tents. And the land was not able to bear them. . . . And there was a strife between the herdsmen of Abram's cattle, and the herdsmen of Lot's cattle."[1]

In explaining the attitude of Africans towards their herds, anthropologists now tend to place less emphasis on the mystical and ritual values attached to cattle and the quasi-religious aspect of the association between man and beast. These values are important, but it seems that the social role of cattle, as a means of "investment in human relationships," is, very often, the main motive behind the urge to acquire animals. "Over much of Africa," says Elizabeth Colson, "cattle are a form of wealth invested in the building up of a varied range of social relationships which give the cattle-owner rights over persons" (39). In an earlier paper she describes how large stock-owners among the Plateau Tonga of Northern Rhodesia herd out their cattle with a number of people who are not their kinsmen. These people become the "clients" of the cattle owner and, in return for the use of the animals, they identify themselves with his interests. Thus the cattle owners forge social bonds which extend beyond their own groups of kin but have the same strength as kinship ties.

Gluckman points out, in his classic analysis of the economy of the Barotse Plain (65) that "in all communities social relationships are the sinews of the economy, and as capital is the chief social relationship in our society which enables a man to control others, so in primitive communities immediate distribution of his plenty enables a man to bind himself to many other people. . . . Control of economic resources [among the Lozi] as elsewhere, gave status and power in the social organisation, but only by making a man head of a dependent group." Cattle were one of the very few forms in which the Lozi could acquire durable goods to invest in "personal social relationships" for most of their other products, such as grain, fish, and meat, were perishable and could not be stored for long "in a hot wet tropical climate, in a country without stone and abounding in destructive rodents and insects."

If livestock play so significant a part in predominantly agricultural societies, their social role is likely to be even more important

[1] Gen. XIII. 5–7.

in pastoral societies, since wandering herdsmen must have even greater difficulty in accumulating any form of property other than cattle. Cunnison (44, 46) has shown that to the Baggara Humr "cattle are not an end in themselves, they are a step up the ladder of ambition." Ownership of many cattle gives a man prestige, social standing, and a position of power. They are a passport to political office, and to fortune in love as well, for the possession of cattle attracts women to a man; and they enable their possessor to exercise the cardinal virtue of generosity. The Humr "value nothing more highly than cattle," says Cunnison, "and they will cling dearly to the nomadic way of life in order to maintain the system of values they have at present." A "man," in the full sense of manliness, is one rich in cattle.

This assessment might be applied to the majority, if not all, of the surviving pastoralists. Among Fulani the status and power of clans, lineage groups, and households is measured largely by the size of their herds. The human group is virtually identified with the herd. Stenning says of the Fulani of western Bornu in Nigeria that "the disposal of stock in any but emergency circumstances is a notion which runs counter to their social experiences, not to say their morality." These attitudes appear to be common, in varying degree, to all pastoralists. For the Somali, camels take the place of cattle and the Somali attitude towards camels has much the same content as that of the herdsmen for their horned-stock; acquisition of these beasts is a major objective. But some change is taking place, however slowly. The Masai of Kenya are not unwilling to sell at least a fraction of the increase of their vast herds.

These attitudes have underlying economic motives, though they are obscured by the accretion of emotional and social values, and the motivating circumstances have changed in recent years. The flocks and herds of nomadic pastoralists were continually menaced, to a much greater extent than is generally the case today, by epidemic disease, drought, and the depredations of human raiders and beasts of prey. There was no absolute security against complete disaster, but relative security lay in the maintenance of large numbers of animals, so that even after heavy loss enough might remain for subsistence and the rebuilding of the herds. But, although epidemics on the grand scale are a thing of the past, disease is still prevalent among nomadic stock. As late as the middle 1930s the cattle population of Acholi in Uganda was decimated by rinderpest epizootics and by trypanosomiasis caused by the advance of tsetse.

Raiding has been reduced to sporadic forays and stock thefts, but drought may kill off 40 per cent or more of local herds in seasons of exceptional severity, and carnivora still take their toll. Of the 8,600 head of cattle owned by the Mambwe, 498 were killed by lions and other predators, and 370 died of disease, age, and debility in a normal year (1952). Catastrophe on the grand scale may be a thing of the past but disease or a combination of disasters can still greatly deplete the family herd or wipe it out altogether.

The herdsman had to think not only of the immediate security of his household but also of its future expansion and prosperity. He expected a high fertility rate of his women and his livestock. "The traditional aim of a Bodaado elder was, and is, to pass on more cattle to more sons than his father was able to do" (158). This was written of a Fulani group in the Bornu Emirate of north-eastern Nigeria but the same might be said of a Masai elder, or, probably, of almost any traditional pastoralist. Among the Masai, rights in livestock begin at birth. Cattle from the household herd are allocated to the new arrival, very commonly a heifer for a girl and two, three, or more heifers for a boy, as the nucleus of future herds. As he grows up, a boy constantly importunes his father for more stock and the father generally gives him a heifer, a bull calf, a sheep, or a goat from time to time. With these additions, and the natural increase, he may build up a sizeable herd. Favourite sons generally come off best in these gift transactions and are at an advantage in herd-building, but there is also a bias in favour of the eldest son of the household.

Women too have rights in livestock. A Masai woman may bring to her marriage the herd founded at her birth, and her husband is expected to add to it. Eight head of cattle is considered a decent gift from a husband to a new wife—though the rich and uxorious may give 20 or even 40 head. Brothers of the groom also bring small gifts of livestock to the bride—a heifer, a sheep, a goat, or a donkey according to their circumstances.

These transfers within the family are not, however, finalised until after the death of its head. The head of the houshold retains a general control of all the livestock during his lifetime. In his later age, when he thinks he is about to die, he will usually allocate any remaining livestock, "or give them to his eldest son if he likes him," according to my Masai informants: but if he dies without making such an allocation the residue of the livestock will be inherited by his eldest son or, if there is no son, by an elder or younger brother. When a woman dies her livestock are divided among her sons, the eldest taking the largest share, or, if she has no son, by the male children of the next wife in the household. A considerable time is allowed to lapse between the death of the head of a household and the administration of his estate; some said that this period should be as long as two years, because it is most unseemly to show any haste or anxiety in the matter.

7. Dynamics of Pastoral Economics

When conditions are favourable and there are no epidemics of the killing diseases, livestock numbers tend to increase fairly rapidly, more rapidly than human populations. There is no knowing with any certainty just how fast flocks and herds can increase under primitive pastoral management when conditions are favourable but some idea of possible increase rates of cattle may be got from available data for African herds under present-day conditions. None of these can be regarded as more than approximations, for there are few accurate statistics of herd composition, calf drop, or mortality rates, and gross statistics of national and regional herds vary in accuracy and completeness. The natural increase rate of African herds in Northern Rhodesia has been estimated at 4 per cent; on the basis of a typical herd containing 45 per cent of breeding cows and heifers, a calf drop of 40 per cent, a calf mortality rate of 33·3 per cent, and a herd mortality rate of 8 per cent per annum.[1] This estimate probably errs on the low side for present-day conditions. The general figures for African-owned cattle in Northern Rhodesia indicate an average net increase rate of about 4·3 per cent per annum over the twenty years period 1937–57, in spite of the fact that significant numbers must have been slaughtered or sold for slaughter. For Uganda it has been estimated that the annual gross increase of cattle throughout the country was about 16 per cent over the period 1945–54, but the slaughter rate was in the neighbourhood of 12 per cent per annum. During the same period the human population appears to have increased at a

[1] Veterinary Department estimate, 1946. Personal communication.

rate approximating to 1·5 per cent per annum. In Kenya, judging by estimates of de-stocking requirements, gross annual rates of livestock increase vary from, perhaps, as much as 20 per cent in Samburu, where disposal is about 10 per cent in terms of livestock units "whereas it should be nearer 20 per cent to keep pace with natural increase," to about 12 per cent for Masai and Mukogodo cattle herds, 7 per cent for the Nandi, and 3 or 4 per cent in South-Baringo (1). Estimates of annual increase rates of Fulani herds in West Africa range from a general figure of 2·2 per cent for Nigeria, arrived at by the Nigerian Livestock Mission, and 9·2 per cent for certain herds in Adamawa Province (158), while a study of a single large herd in Bamenda has indicated an increase rate between 11 and 17 per cent.[1]

It may be fairly assumed that the pastoralist was under a continuous compulsion to increase his herds, and that, while conditions were favourable and there was freedom from epidemics and disastrous droughts, the herds did tend to increase annually at rates varying from about 4 per cent to, perhaps, 10 per cent or more. If the herds increased continuously even at a rate of the lower order the land requirement would grow alarmingly, and as a geometric progression, doubling in less than twenty years. Assuming that the cattle at present owned by the Masai of Kenya require 25,000 square miles of grazeable land and that they increase steadily at the lower rate, then in little more than half a century they would need an area of grazing land equal to the whole of Kenya, and within a century an area greater than that of the three East African territories combined.

This pressure caused by the need for more and more land to maintain the growing herds would not, of course, be exercised uniformly, in all directions. It would be concentrated and directed along the lines of more desirable grazing, avoiding close woodland, bush, and thicket, and regions infested with tsetse fly. Theoretically, the increase of cattle, at a greater rate than the human population, and the pressure thrusts along these lines, might continue until the number of men in relation to cattle declined below the minimum required for herding and protection: in practice outbreaks of cattle disease, drought, or disaster in war, or a combination of catastrophies, usually applied an effective check before this stage was reached. For these reasons the histories of East

[1] Miss J. Carter: personal communication.

African pastoral societies commonly show aggressive expansion phases alternating with periods of quiescence.

When Joseph Thomson visited the Masai in the 1880s he found them in a period of relative quiescence following an aggressive phase of expansion during which they raided and grazed their cattle over a domain extending from Lake Rudolph to Ugogo. This expansive phase seems to have lasted for more than thirty years. From at least 1850 until the early 1880s, says Hollis, the pastoral Masai were a formidable power in East Africa. They asserted themselves against the Arab slave traders, took toll of all who passed through the country they occupied, and treated other races, African or not, with the greatest arrogance. The end of this phase came with the rinderpest epidemic of 1884 when loss of livestock followed by the inevitable famine greatly reduced their fighting strength. But this was only a prelude to more complete disaster. Six years later an even more virulent epidemic of rinderpest swept through Masailand and at the same time smallpox broke out among the people. According to contemporary accounts, three-quarters of the Masai pastoral population died of famine or disease.

They were not the only sufferers. The 1890s must have been a terrible time throughout much of east and south-central Africa. Not only did smallpox decimate the people and rinderpest sweep southward killing cattle, smallstock, and wild game, but a great outbreak of the red locust brought famine to many of the agricultural peoples. More than forty years later, when I was investigating the history of locust outbreaks in Northern Rhodesia, memories and accounts of the years of catastrophe were still vivid among Africans.

With the decline of the Masai, the Turkana to the north of them began a phase of expansion during which, Gulliver says, they spread outwards "pressing back their neighbours on all sides." The reasons for this, he adds, "were first, that they were isolated from the main brunt of the rinderpest epidemic of the end of the 19th century and were thus comparatively stronger; second, that they were most probably forced to expand by the pressure of an increasing population (human and stock) on an increasingly arid country; and, third, they obtained guns and ammunition from Abyssinia, whence they also received encouragement and help in initiating raids." About the same time the Karamojong too were showing signs of expansion. When the British arrived they were pressing upon the Jie, and forcing them to give ground. These expansive phases came to an end with the establishment of British administration; or, rather, with the military occupation that preceded the establishment of civil government. The Turkana were subdued and their lands occupied only after a campaign on a considerable scale.

The pastoral Fulani of West Africa were more fortunate, since, in the vast savannah grasslands of the western Sudan, their expansive phases could take the form of peaceful "migratory drift" into regions undisputed by cultivators or fellow pastoralists. These movements, and migrations for other reasons such as the avoidance of wars or the imposition of tribute, carried them from Senegal across the Sudan plains to French Equatorial Africa in the long space of eight hundred years. In contrast with the east, the establishment of colonial governments stimulated a fresh wave of migration by creating political conditions which allowed Fulani to move into areas, such as the Jos plateau of Nigeria and the British and French Cameroons, previously inaccessible to them. They established themselves in Bamenda only after the First World War, for the Germans had excluded them during their occupation of the Cameroons. The first pioneer groups to enter the country were soon joined by others as news of this fresh grazing for the taking reached herdsmen who were already suffering from shortage and deterioration of their grazing lands.

In regions of poor and uncertain rainfall periodic droughts impose a check on livestock numbers as harshly and dramatically as the epidemic diseases. It has been estimated that losses as high as 45 per cent of all livestock occur in Libya during years when rainfall is much below the annual overall average of 9 inches. Dumont quotes even more startling figures of losses among the flocks of Algerian shepherds (52). "In the course of a single dry year, as in 1920, more than half the sheep and goats may perish, especially if the winter is unusually rigorous as well." It happened in 1945–6 that drought was followed by a winter of exceptional severity, and three million animals died. Losses were highest in the south where in some areas, nine animals out of every ten perished, and flocks of the Ghardaia were reduced from 60,000 to 1,500. During that appalling winter many nomadic families reverted to the age-old way of dealing with famine; they let their young daughters die of starvation to give the rest of the family a chance of survival.

8. Change and Development in Pastoral Societies

The way of life of the traditional pastoralist is, at best, precarious; an alternation of periods of expansion and prosperity and of dearth and disaster. In this lie the seeds of change. The periods of disaster, when the number of animals falls below the "basic" level, impose strains on the food-producing economy which induce change in the direction of crop production. The pastoralist must take to the hoe, if this alternative is open to him—however great his dislike and contempt for this implement—or he must starve. Once this road has been taken there is, generally, no return, for the practice of cultivation allows of population increase well beyond the limit that a simple pastoralism can support. Consequently, wherever conditions are favourable for crop-production agriculture tends to displace pastoralism, either by conversion of the pastoralists or by the encroachment of cultivating peoples on their grazing lands. In this conflict between Cain and Abel, the pastoralist may dominate for a time—Hollis sees as one of the most important features of Masai history in the nineteenth century a conflict between their pastoral and agricultural sections, which ended "in a victory for the former and annihilation of large settlements of the latter"—but, in the long run, time is on the side of the cultivators. The expansive phases of the pastoralists are transient—though they had, when contained, a certain explosive quality—while the pressure exerted by the cultivators, though slower in its effects, is continuous and inexorable. Thus, over the centuries, community after community of Nilotes, Nilo-Hamites, and Fulani have taken to the hoe and exchanged the freedom and austerity of nomadism for the greater security and routine labour of a sedentary or semi-sedentary way of life. Pastoralism, in the sense of complete dependence on flocks and herds, survives in eastern Africa mainly in regions marginal or unsuitable for agriculture, where the conditions that discourage crop production also impose the necessity of nomadism on the pastoralist; and, in the west, in the savannah regions as yet only sparsely occupied by cultivating peoples.

The impact of European economic concepts, administrations, and systems of government has had the effect of supplementing and strengthening forces which have always acted against the herdsman and shepherd. For administrative and economic reasons, suzerain governments have usually regarded pastoralism, especially the more nomadic variants, as an undesirable form of land-use. Wandering peoples are not easy to administer, to "develop," to bring within the orbit of the state as obedient taxpaying citizens, and primitive stock-raising is unquestionably a wasteful form of land use where more intensive forms are possible.

Worse still, the pastoralist has been indicted as a destroyer of land on the grand scale in the drier regions. Herdsmen and shepherds commonly set fire to grass and bush late in the dry season, for a number of very sound practical reasons. The burn gets rid of useless straw, incidentally destroying disease-carrying ticks, and allows the grass rhizomes to push out young shoots which give a green bite for the starving beasts. It also checks woody growth that would otherwise tend to crowd out the grasses. Many people maintain that the damage caused by repeated late burning and other practices of the pastoralists has been very great. Over a large part of Africa, they believe, the hydrologic cycle has been seriously affected; evaporation from the soil surface has increased, with a corresponding fall of the water-table and progressive dessication, especially in areas bordering the Sahara and the deserts of the Sudan and Somaliland. In these marginal zones the grip of soil-holding vegetation is weakest. Here the scavenging flocks and the fire of the nomadic shepherd break this tenuous grip so that the desert spreads over land where there was once at least sparse grass or scrub-bush.

The view is widely held that the desert areas of north and east Africa are expanding at a disquieting rate. The Sahara, the world's largest desert, is said to be advancing on a 2,000 mile front, at a rate of 30 miles a year in places, and there is evidence to suggest that the Lake Chad basin is slowly filling with the drift of wind-blown sand, that desert conditions are moving southward in the Sudan (155), and that Somaliland and large parts of East Africa, particularly pastoral areas such as Turkanaland and Karamojong are becoming more arid. In parts of these regions grass has disappeared and desert succulents have become conspicuous within the memory of the older inhabitants. It has also been suggested that such man-made disasters have happened more than once in the past. Egypt may have been a land of semi-desert until the seventh century when hordes of invading Arabs brought in great herds of goats, sheep, and camels which destroyed the vegetation and reduced the whole country outside the narrow ribbon of the Nile to the stark desert it now is.

There is, however, reason to doubt whether these changes are wholly the work of man and his animals. Ecological evidence, remnants of a former vegetation cover which survive as post-climax relics, indicates that eastern Africa is in a post-pluvial or relatively dry phase which may not yet have reached its peak of aridity, and there is no knowing with any certainty how far the actions of man and natural causes—destruction of vegetation, decreasing rainfall and drift of sand by the harmattan—have contributed to the outward creep of the desert. But there is little reason to doubt that deterioration and destruction of vegetation caused by pastoralism has accentuated and hastened the effects of natural changes, and that the deserts of East Africa are to some extent man-made. Nomadic pastoralism is inherently self-destructive, since systems of management are based on the short-term objective of keeping as many animals as possible alive, without regard to the long-term conservation of land resources. "The general picture," to quote the Director of Veterinary Services in Kenya, "is one of steadily increasing stock numbers on progressively deteriorating land."

Suzerain administrations usually aim at converting their pastoralists into cultivators, where conditions allow of this, or economic producers of livestock and livestock products, and limiting the size of the herds. Their methods are generally less drastic than those applied by the Soviet Russian government to the solution of the Kazak problem—and much less effective. The Kazaka—probably the largest tribal nation in the world—did not fit at all well into the socialist pattern; according to the Kremlin, their pastoral way of life was "demoralising and must be broken up." This meant the total destruction of the tribal organisation and the abrupt conversion of the tent-dwelling Kazaks into settled herdsmen on state ranches, workers on collective farms, and wage-earners in mines and factories, a course which was justified on economic grounds and on the basis of Stalin's dictum that "in a Communist state we do not deal with content or discontent, only with figures."

The economic argument did not appear to the Kazaks, who preferred to remain nomadic pastoralists, and they resisted their conversion to proletariat very bitterly and stubbornly. The *Great*

Soviet Encyclopaedia, with characteristic euphemism, records "most serious deviations from the party line in Kazakhstan, making it easier for the Beys, the Kulaks and the Alash-Orda elements to carry out anti-Soviet and anti-revolutionary activity." These "mistakes" were eventually "put right," a process which, according to Sir Olaf Carol (34) took eleven years and involved the death of one in three of the Kazak population by mass starvation or violence, and the loss of great numbers of livestock. Even Communism is bound by the limitations of environment. Many of the first-formed *kolkhozes* failed because, under the more arid steppe conditions, nomadism is a necessity of livestock management. As the grass dried up and feed failed in the season of heat and drought, the herds died or were slaughtered by the desperate herdsmen. Now, in the new grain lands of the north, all is far from well; in Kazakhstan "things are bad, very bad indeed," or so Comrade Khruschev is reported to have said,[1] while placing the blame squarely, if not altogether fairly, on Comrade Belyayev. Reports on the exploitation of the virgin lands that have come out of Russia give a picture of mismanagement on such a scale as to make our own East African Groundnut Scheme seem by comparison almost a little masterpiece of applied knowledge, planning, and organisation. No doubt the mistakes will be put right.

The policies of the Colonial Powers in Africa—where there can be said to be any definite policy—has been one of gradualness, but so far results have not been conspicuously successful. Many difficulties beset the evolutionary approach to conservative ranching and a money economy, which appears to be the general objective, difficulties which are well illustrated by the history of the Konza scheme in Kenya. This was a small scheme, covering some 23,000 acres and intended originally for ten Masai families: its importance lies not in its size but in the fact that it was at one time regarded as a possible blue print for the whole of Masailand. As an example of land planning the scheme was perfectly sound; it included rotational grazing, adequate water supplies, control of disease, and maintenance of a balance between land and livestock. The whole area was fenced externally against game and encroachment of cattle, with wire inside a triple line of sisal, and divided by internal fencing into four paddocks each of approxi-

[1] Press reports, 29 Dec. 1959.

mately nine square miles, three of which were intended to provide four months grazing in the year while the fourth rested. Three boreholes, a large storage tank and two dams provided adequate water, and a dipping tank was installed together with a hide *banda* and dairy for processing livestock products. The intended livestock limit, close on 2,000 head of cattle, could hardly be considered inadequate for 10 families numbering not more than 90 people; and, apart from exclusive grazing and limitation of livestock numbers, the scheme did not seem to conflict at any point with Masai social custom.

The settlers were required to observe only three conditions: to adhere to the rotational grazing pattern: to dip their cattle weekly and submit them to regular inoculation against disease; and to dispose of surplus stock above the prescribed maximum. There was no stipulation that the surplus stock should be sold for slaughter, since the Masai Administration considered that the land would not have been given or the scheme accepted if this condition had been imposed. The warning signal was there from the beginning.

Early in 1949, after two years of preparation, settlers selected by elders of the Kaputei section moved in with 1,400 of their cattle. Under rotational grazing and at an initial stocking rate of about 15 acres to the beast, the land and the livestock improved rapidly. There was a wave of enthusiasm and the scheme was publicised as a success. I remember listening to a B.B.C. radio feature[1] from which I learned that in two years the demonstration had shown remarkable results, the Masai were asking that the method should be applied throughout their land unit, and the Kenya Government proposed to do so. There was no mention of the very large capital sum or the drastic destocking that the creation of a multiplicity of Konzas would require.

Ten years after its beginning, in the very dry summer of 1959, I saw what was left of the Konza scheme. There was little to see. *Banda*, dairy, and every vestige of fencing had disappeared. One dam was broken, the other water installations showed signs of neglect, and the cattle dip lay empty and unused. The scheme was still, theoretically, in operation; nine families lived there with about 2,200 cattle and 150 sheep and goats, but the grazing rotation had broken down almost completely and on nearly every

[1] Radio Newsreel, 24 Nov. 1950.

horizon one could see other herds—of wildebeeste, zebra, and *kongoni*, for this was the season of mass migration of game through the area. Two of the paddocks had been scorched and denuded by fire; there were no fireguards—and, I was told, no money to pay for the making of them—although the area lies between two railway lines. The land within the scheme was indistinguishable from the surrounding part of Masailand, no better and no worse; it was all one parched and denuded grey plain with a uniformly degraded cover of sparse short *Themeda* and *Pennisetum* and a few stunted *Acacia* remnants.

Why had a scheme that started with so much promise ended in failure so complete? Mainly, I think, because the Masai had not accepted—even if they understood—the new alien values implicit in a transformation from nomadic herding to commercial ranching. The settlers were still nomadic herdsmen, members of and subject to the suasion of the larger community, and they were under the old compulsions to increase their herds. In 1952, when the question of overstocking was becoming critical, the settlers flatly refused to sell for slaughter and resorted to subterfuge in the hope of keeping their beasts. They maintained that they could not sell because of quarantine restrictions and then that disease and drought had prevented any increase. Losses from disease were, in fact, small—the heaviest being the death of 26 head of cattle from black-quarter when the owners refused inoculation—and a surprise count made in 1954 showed a natural increase of no less than 32 per cent over two years, although the first of these years had been one of exceptional drought when cattle died and the herds diminished in neighbouring parts of Masailand. A follow-up count in 1955 showed a natural increase of 20 per cent in a single year. The settlers, relatively poor people "selected by the elders of the Kaputei from among the less wealthy of that section" (1), had been presented with an excellent opportunity of acquiring wealth and prestige in the old terms of cattle, an opportunity they were reluctant to forego. When they were induced to remove cattle from Konza they appear to have done so mainly by transferring them to the already overstocked common grazing. Interest in the scheme evaporated; the fencing—which had proved inadequate to hold back the mass onslaught of migrating game—was removed; fire and game reduced the grazing; and, finally, the Konza idea was "shelved in favour of less radical policies, such as the use of boreholes as centres of controlled grazing and stock limitation, or the Ilkisongo scheme" (1).

It is difficult to see any wide divergence of policy or principle between the Konza and Ilkisongo schemes. The latter, which is on a much larger scale, seeks to achieve by more gradual methods the same aims of conservative land management, limitation of livestock to carrying capacity and eventually a ranching economy. The scheme covers the south-eastern part of Kenya Masailand, with the Chyulu hills in the north and the foothills of Kilimanjaro in the south, an area of about 1,300,000 acres which was traditionally grazed by the clans of the Ilkisongo section. Rainfall in the region varies from ten inches or less to about fifteen inches; and conditions range from near-desert in the central hollow of sparse rainfall, areas almost denuded of ground cover, through thicket and bush-group country of low potential, to relatively good grazing ground with an almost continuous cover of annuals and perennials and colonies of star grass. The area of superior grazing is very limited, but the proportion of wholly useless land—swamp, bare lava flows, and saline lake bed—has been estimated at only one-sixth of the whole.

The scheme has been based, with much care, study and forethought, on the traditional nomadic pattern—which was, in essence, an outward movement in the rains as far as the Chyulu hills and a retreat to the perennial springs at the foot of Mount Kilimanjaro as surface water failed—and on the customary division of water and grazing between clans. The region is divided into grazing blocks, with wet and dry season grazing and additional water supplies from "tank" dams, drinking troughs supplied from the new railway pipe line, and bore holes, allowing of a simple two-way grazing rotation as near as possible to the traditional pattern. Improvement of water supplies enables the dry season areas to be used and the wet season areas rested for longer periods, so that the grazing is much more fully utilised and stock-carrying capacity is increased.

Stock limitation can be imposed under a Masai Land-Use Byelaw, but it was decided that no attempt at general destocking should be made as this would wreck the scheme politically, and it was considered unnecessary "since the pastures can be gradually restored by good management." The intention was to limit the number of stock entering the grazing blocks after water supplies had been installed, leaving the owners at liberty to transfer any additional stock elsewhere.

In 1954, when the scheme started, the number of livestock was estimated at 80,000 stock units, allowing about 16 acres per unit, while the carrying capacity was thought to be about one beast to 30 acres under existing conditions of management and the state of the grazing at that time. Five years later, when I visited the scheme, I was told that there were 120,000 or 125,000 cattle and the effort to limit numbers was evidently meeting with considerable difficulty. In that season of severe drought and poverty of grazing, Masai outside the scheme were pressing for permission to bring in their cattle and make use of the water supplies, a request the Ilkisongo would probably not have refused in the past.

Marketing facilities for surplus cattle are an essential part of the scheme and trade with northern Tanganyika, particularly Chaggaland where there is an effective demand for meat created by wealth from coffee, has been stimulated by the establishment of an auction yard at Lasit on the Tanganyika border. Sales have averaged approximately 16,000 head of Masai cattle annually in recent years, about half of them from the Ilkisongo section, but the natural increase rate is believed to be of the order of 12 per cent per annum. In spite of the take-off, the net cattle increase rate probably exceeds 5 per cent per annum. These Masai appear to be neither unreasonable about prices nor unwilling to sell cattle; indeed they would probably sell more if they could. At the auction sale I attended, nearly half the beasts on offer remained unsold, but bidding was slow on this occasion owing to a temporary shortage of ready money in Chaggaland, and offerings may have been unusually heavy because of the drought. The Ilkisongo have co-operated in the scheme to the extent of taxing themselves surprisingly heavily to pay a large part of the cost, including the recurrent expenses, and this provides an additional incentive to the sale of cattle. They have done so mainly because they place a high value on the new water supplies; the other and more fundamental features of the plan seem to have little appeal or meaning for the great majority.

An event which might well be regarded as of more significance is the decision of the Lodokelani section to set aside 4,000 acres— though only 2,000 acres have been taken—as an individual ranch for the use of one of their members, a progressive and cultured

Masai who served for some time with the Veterinary Department and has since been ordained as a clergyman. The Masai, notwithstanding their preference for the pastoral life, do not lack men of education and technical training, including a fully qualified Veterinary Officer who was for a time in charge of the Konza scheme. Their decision to allocate grazing rights to an individual, however exceptional his attainments, to the exclusion of all other members of the section and the tribe, is significant since it abrogates one of the fundamental principles of a pastoral society. The Lodokelani could hardly have been unaware of the significance of their decision.

Recognition of individual rights must inevitably create a whole crop of new social administrative and economic problems. Among them is the question of whether the individual holder sacrifices his traditional right to unstinted grazing on the common land of the tribe. This pioneer Masai rancher maintained strongly that his traditional rights remained unaffected. When I questioned this he said, by way of proof, that he kept only his best cattle on the ranch; the others ranged with his brothers' herds on the commonage of Lodokelani.

Any local limitation of livestock numbers, however successful, is likely to result in the transfer of animals elsewhere and the placing of a further burden on grazing lands already grossly overstocked. An example of this was noted by members of the East Africa Royal Commission (138) when they visited the tribal ranching scheme of the Samburu on the Leroghi plateau of Kenya, "which is one of the places where first steps are being taken towards rational stock control." The number of cattle on the land within the scheme has been successfully limited to 40,000 head—a stocking rate of one beast to ten acres—but, in relation to population, this number appears to be well below the minimum requirements of a simple pastoral economy. "The Samburu told us that they liked the ranch," says the report of the Royal Commission, "but resented the stock control rules. On further enquiry it appeared that the customary system of communal right of usage made it necessary for everyone in the tribe to get a quota on the ranch. The limitations of stock numbers under the rules, however, meant that each family herd had to be split into some animals in the quota on the ranch and the remainder, which had to find their grazing in distant *wadis*. As a result the herdsmen were separated from their wives and the children from their milk, and very naturally the idea was unpopular."

Opinion on the value of such efforts to adapt and develop pastoral systems varies greatly. The late Clement Gillman, a geographer of Tanganyika and for many years a forthright critic of land-use policy in that territory, could see no merit in them. "Eight per cent of the territory is held by the nomadic Masai and Tago. They will remain stable only so long as the geographer can persuade the administrator to abstain from his futile dreams and efforts to make them sedentary, to divert them from the strict discipline of roaming with the rains by laying on short-lived piped water supplies at an expenditure far beyond economic limits. He must refrain from trying to change our small nomadic populations into sedentary peasants" (62). Negley Farson (57), on the other hand, was impressed by the work in Kenya Masailand. He writes: "I have never seen a more tolerant, well-meaning, even intelligent effort to get a fine race of natives to accept modern times." But he shares a common reluctance to interfere with the way of life of the pastoral peoples. "If it were possible, and I know it is not, I would say leave the Masai and the Somali nomadic camel tribes alone to lead their wandering pastoral life."

The pastoralists are relatively few, because their land and their way of life hold human populations to a low level, but they occupy an enormous area of eastern Africa over which rainfall is too sparse and precarious to allow of tillage. This area covers nearly all the "horn" of Africa, nearly three-quarters of Kenya, a large part of Tanganyika, and a little of Uganda. The much smaller areas favourable to agriculture, highlands, and mountain massifs, rise like islands from the vast expanse of the drought-land. Much of this land, in the north and east, is near-desert and conditions are so difficult that the nomadic camel, sheep, and cattle herdsmen are likely to be left largely to their own devices, at least for many years to come. It is probably best that they should be. But in the better grassland and savannah regions, such as Masailand and Karamoja, development of economic animal husbandry is certainly possible, as far as physical conditions are concerned. Here the desirable pattern for the future is seen—by land-use planners, but not yet by the herdsmen—in terms of ranching, either communally or by the splitting up of the land into family or individual ranches, or a combination of the two. This was the

solution proposed by the East African Royal Commission, with
voluntary communal ranching and experimental family ranches as
a first step. It is, indeed, difficult to think of any other solution
less drastic than the Russian method that will check and reverse
the descent of the land towards desert conditions, but the difficulties in the way of achieving such a solution within reasonable
time are formidable. In most of the pastoral areas many technical
questions remain to be answered, and this will require long periods
of experiment and trial, but the technical questions are likely to be
much less difficult of solution than the human problems. Some of
these problems have been discussed by Harrison (75) and Cunnison (46) for the Baggara, and by Stenning (157) for the Fulani
of Bornu. Harrison concluded that capitalistic ranching would
defeat its purpose, since the available land would be used up for
larger herds requiring little labour, and many Baggara would lose
their means of livelihood. Cunnison points to certain consequences which would arise and processes likely to be set in
motion if ranching were to be based on the present ownership of
animals, with changes involving only matters of husbandry, including stock limitation, and the stabilisation of lineages on different pieces of ranch land. He concludes that the final outcome of
these processes would be to leave each ranch in the hands of one
or two rich cattle owners, employing only a few workers, and to
create a proletariat with no means of subsistence. "This would be
all the more likely to occur," he adds, "if attempts to make the
people more money conscious and less bound by obligations of
society and kinship were successful. The question would then
have to be asked if it was worth while making these changes in
Baggara country before there was enough industrial or other employment to absorb the surplus population the scheme created."

Individual ranching may be easier to achieve than communal
ranching on a voluntary basis, if we go by the analogy of community farming, which has failed, and individual farming which
has succeeded to some extent. Another indication is to be found
in the fact that most pastoral peoples do permit individual use of
tribal land for cultivation where this is possible. In the small part
of Somaliland where tillage is practicable enclosures for cultivation are made by individuals within the area habitually grazed by
the clan and no objection is raised by the group to such enclosure
by one of its members. The cultivator acquires special rights over

the land, by virtue of the labour he has put into it, and these rights persist even if he abandons the plot for a time. Among the Jie of Uganda range land is, similarly, free for any member of the tribe to take up. Even the resistance of the Masai to enclosure of land is breaking down and there are now six areas in Masailand where cropping is attempted, largely as a result of intermarriage of Masai with Chagga and Kikuyu and the infiltration of other tribes.

The problem also has an economic aspect beset with difficulties which are illustrated by the history of meat marketing in Kenya. The first meat packing factory failed because it required but could not get a regular supply of four thousand beasts a month. During the War the needs of the troops in East Africa were met partly by requisitioning cattle, but when requisitioning stopped "the supply of meat to Kenya's markets almost dried up," according to one of Sir Philip Mitchell's dispatches. The wartime organisation was then replaced by a Meat Marketing Board, which operated as a public utility with Government funds and even subsidised prices when necessary. This revived the flow of sales but the Board was, in turn, replaced by a Meat Commission, operating on a strictly commercial basis and burdened with heavy investment of loan capital, a change which, in the words of the report of the Royal Commission, "had a most disastrous effect on the marketing of African stock which appears to have been brought almost to a standstill." More cattle were being offered than the Commission could buy.

There are cash crop areas where an effective demand for meat remains unsatisfied and pastoral areas where the herdsmen would sell more cattle if they could, though it is doubtful if they would sell more than a fraction of the increase of their herds. But the problem of matching supply and demand remains unsolved, and no one has yet calculated how far effective demand and free offerings of cattle correspond with the number that must be absorbed if livestock are to be limited to the carrying capacity of the land.

The human problems present difficulties at least as great as those of environment and economics, for the old values of the pastoralists are highly resistant to change and the majority will cling stubbornly to their right to hold unstinted herds. In the course of its enquiries, the Royal Commission met, as I did five years later, many technical officers "who were sceptical of any adequate response in time and considered that only firm administrative control of stock numbers could save the situation." Such control is probably impracticable on any large scale and the Commission regarded it as "a measure of last resort."

The alternatives for the pastoralists, and for the cultivators who maintain great herds, are succinctly expressed in a dispatch of Sir Philip Mitchell's: "There are only two alternatives for the African people—either they eat their surplus stock or their surplus stock will eat them." This remark recalls the words of another knight of an earlier age[1] who wrote, in bitter denunciation of the sheep-farming enclosures of early sixteenth-century England: "your sheep that were wont to be so meek and tame, and so small eaters, now be become so great devourers and so wild that they eat up and swallow down the very men themselves."

[1] Sir Thomas More: *Utopia*.

PART IV

CHANGE AND DEVELOPMENT

CHAPTER XIX

THE PEACE OF THE SUZERAIN POWERS

1. FOSSILISATION OF POPULATION-LAND PATTERNS, THE MONEY ECONOMY, LOSS OF LAND

Africa today has something in common with Sir Thomas More's England. Land is still the only security for the great majority of people, the only certain means of subsistence and a decent life; and when they are deprived of land, "by one means or by another, either by hook or by crook, they must needs depart away, poor innocent wretched souls . . . small in substance but many in number as husbandry requireth many hands. . . . And when they have wandered abroad till that be spent, what can they else do but steal, and then justly, perhaps, be hanged, or else go about a-begging. And then also they be cast in prison as vagabonds, because they go about and work not, whom no man will set to work though they never so willingly proffer themselves thereto." The job-hunting African is in no danger of being hanged for theft, but he may fall foul of some law such as the Southern Rhodesia Vagrancy Act and find himself classified among the "spivs, loafers, and hoodlums" and treated accordingly.

One of the first effects of the division of Africa among the European administering and colonising powers was to solidify population-land patterns which had previously been, to a considerable extent, fluid. When a community increased until the numbers on the land it occupied exceeded the critical level for the system of land-use, sections hived off and settled elsewhere, or the land area was increased by the occupation of unclaimed tracts, or by peaceful agreement such as the Kikuyu land "purchase" from the Dorobo, or by aggressive expansion. Natural checks, warfare, and customs limiting fertility, probably restricted the general rate of population increase to a relatively low level, and as communities waxed and waned there was a continuous rough-and-ready adjustment between populations and land. The peace of the suzerain powers disrupted this mechanism of adjustment. International boundaries were established, often without regard to tribal distribution or land needs, warfare was proscribed, customs limiting fertility were discouraged, and, in response to new administrative needs, the limits of tribal areas and of chiefdoms and sub-chiefdoms were defined and fixed. Change and adjustment on any considerable scale became difficult or impracticable. Chieftaincies were created as agencies of administration and for tax collection, where none had existed before, and people were registered in the books of the European District Commissioners as belonging to a particular chieftaincy and to a particular area or village. In the countries of European colonisation, land was taken and set aside and populations were transferred, or allowed to transfer themselves as best they might, with little or no thought for the ultimate consequences of these displacements.

Lord Lugard foresaw the danger inherent in this "fossilisation" of the population-land patterns and the need of a substitute for the old mechanism of adjustment: "The larger question of the augmentation of the area held by a tribe, or by an advanced community, whose increasing population has caused acute land hunger, while perhaps a neighbouring tribe has so decreased in number that its lands are in excess of its needs, is one for the Government to deal with. . . .

If the facts are established a transfer of land must be made, but in my own opinion, in no case—whether the country is conquered territory or not—should a rental be demanded from the community which receives the additional land. In days not distant it would have seized the land, and would probably have exterminated its owners as well. The peaceful adjustment of such claims, when proved to be well founded, is the function of the suzerain Government" (104).

He did not say how land needs were to be established, whether on the basis of the requirements of customary forms of land-use, of which practically nothing was known, or on some hypothetical system of "improved farming." In any case, his advice on this point was little heeded.

Other and more profound changes came with the cash economy, the alien standard of money values set before the African by his new rulers. Thoughtful minds are sometimes troubled by the moral implications of this change and find it difficult, as Sir Roy Harrod has put it, "to answer the old philosophical question—are we justified in inflicting our standards of material wealth on primitive tribal people who are, quite possibly, happy without the 'benefits' of our monetary system?" Whatever the answer to this question, it is now much too late to reverse the processes that have been set in train. In any case, some such change would probably have come about in the course of time without the European intervention. Exchange and barter trade, specialised crafts and village industries, and probably some forms of currency, existed in pre-European Africa. In the region of the southern mining cultures, copper bars and H-shaped ingots seem to have been used as currency by the eighteenth century or earlier. But the need of every man to possess money, the minted money of the suzerain powers, was something altogether new and revolutionary. Money was necessary to pay the tax imposed on every able-bodied man, and rigorously collected against threat of fine or imprisonment; and, later, more money was needed for the satisfaction of new wants. It had to be earned by wage labour where work was available, or by the sale of the surplus of subsistence food production where markets offered, or by growing industrial cash crops where these were introduced by the new masters. These changes did not come easily and were at first resisted. In many cases volunteer labour for the new economies had to be supplemented by arbitrary conscription, not only for public works but for mines, plantations, and farms, and there are few areas in Africa where industrial cash crops have been established without some measure of coercion, open or disguised. The ultimate acceptance of this money economy and new standard of values, grafted on to the old forms of social organisation and land rights, was to create unforeseen agrarian problems which have been intensified and rendered almost despairingly difficult by the comparatively recent upward surge of populations.

The period of colonial imperialism in Africa is now quite commonly painted in the deepest black, with no relief of lighter shades. According to this view, it was no more than a greedy grabbing of land and minerals in the interests of capitalist enterprise, a ruthless robbery of the African's most prized possessions which reduced him to peonage and a status bordering on slavery. This picture is no more true than that depicting the European settler as the saviour of the land from wanton destruction by "slash and burn" methods of snatch cropping, and the Administrator as the deliverer of the African from insensate savagery and bestiality. It is easy to present the one case and not too difficult to make the other, by judicious selection of facts. There was selfishness and greed of gain and brutality; there was also devoted, self-sacrificing labour and genuine belief that what was done was done for ultimate and lasting good. We are too close to the events to give an unbiased judgment, or to separate and weigh the good and evil with the precision and detachment of a chemical analysis.

Probably the greatest "sin" of the suzerain powers was the saving of life, the lives of millions of men who under the old conditions would have died in early childhood, or in later life, of famine, disease, and violence. Cattle too were protected against the diseases, the predators, the raiding and pillaging that had held them in check, so that in places they now swarm as destructively as locusts and threaten to "eat up and swallow down the very men themselves.'¿

Over large regions of Africa where the old balances and controls have broken down and the fertility of the land is falling, the reasons are to be looked for in cash cropping and population increase and over-stocking within circumscribed areas, rather than loss of land to Europeans. North of the Zambesi, except in Northern Rhodesia where a great extent of land once reserved for European settlement was restored and resettled, and in the highlands of Kenya where the "white" lands have recently been opened to African farmers, the loss of land was not great, or, generally, of more than local significance in its effects.

"The white man's 'Native problem' in Africa has its origin in his expropriation of the land," says Alphaeus Hunton. "It was this which gave rise to repeated revolts in the Mediterranean colonies, and in Eastern and Southern Africa. It was this that led to the founding of organisations such as the African National Congress in South Africa in 1913 and the Kikuyu Central Association in Kenya in 1922" (89). This may well be true of South Africa and Southern Rhodesia, where only 12 per cent and 44 per cent of the land, respectively, remains available for African use, and of Algeria, Mozambique, and the Kikuyu area of Kenya.

The opposing point of view is that there is no real land shortage, only a relative shortage caused by the wilfully destructive methods of the African. Hunton points out that in Kenya "in 1938, 1,890 Europeans were in possession of 5,053,448 acres of land of which only 546,602 were under cultivation, while some 600,000 or more Kikuyu were crowded into a 'Native Reserve' measuring 3,936,640 acres." Yet, in 1956 when the concentration of men and cattle had grown worse, an official publication of the Government of Kenya deprecated "the obsession with over-population and the imagined need for more land" (1).

The Kikuyu themselves were in no doubt as to their situation. In a memorandum addressed to a Land Commission in the 1930s they said: "Our cultivation does not improve because our system has been overturned by the advent of the Europeans. We would therefore beg members of the Commission that they consider well how they can help us that we may have better gardens producing crops for export and better grazing lands with sheep that produce wool and good cattle producing much milk. That we have not these things is not due to our stupidity, as some think, but to the smallness of our land." At the same time Jomo Kenyatta, then general secretary of the Kikuyu Central Association, expressed his impatience with the many commissions that had looked into the affairs of Kenya: "What Africans want now is not commissions but the restitution of their land." Numerous protests were made by the Kikuyu to other commissions or were sent to London, and in one of these they said: "Had our land been thus robbed by any other native tribes, the Kikuyu would have certainly given their lives for their property, but confronted by a people with the latest and most formidable weapons of precision and destruction such an idea was and is unthinkable."[1] The idea was not to remain unthinkable.

Even where the loss of land was small and of little real signi-ficance in the genesis of agrarian problems, this little loss and fear of great expropriation created resentments and suspicions which were fomented by the propaganda of nationalist organisations and the rhetoric of firebrand politicians. Alienated land, and especially land held in reserve and not yet developed, provides a most con-venient stick for beating governments. Sir Sidney Abrahams' Land Commission noted this resentment in Nyasaland. "I think it convenient to refer here," he says, "to the widespread grievance in the Protectorate which natives claim to feel at the possession of large unused tracts of land by non-natives. There was not a single district which I visited, with the exception of Fort Johnston, where this grievance was not presented to me by deputations of chiefs, by

---

[1] Quoted by Alphaeus Hunton (89), from Martin L. Kilson, "Land and Kikuyu Political Movements," *Journal of Negro History*, April 1955.

the local branch of the African Congress and by other natives. These lands (the Africans maintain) were not acquired lawfully. The chiefs had no intention of making grants in freehold, or had no right to do so."

African fears of a great influx of Europeans and loss of more of their land were not wholly without reason. In 1953 a conference of delegates from Kenya, the Belgian Congo, Northern and Southern Rhodesia, and Portuguese Guinea called for a "considerable increase" in European immigration. They proclaimed "the pre-eminence of the ideas of Western civilisation," declared increased European settlement to be essential for the development of Central Africa, and set up a permanent organisation to further their aims. This conference was held at Bukavu in the Belgian Congo, six years before the first outbreak of violence which the official committee of enquiry attributed to "scorn of Africans by European settlers, unemployment and nationalism fomented from Ghana." And there were those who saw the federation of the Rhodesias and Nyasaland as the first step towards a Central African Dominion dominated, not only politically but also numerically, by Europeans. A statement such as the following, attributed to a British town-planning expert in Lusaka and quoted in a South African paper, could hardly fail to alarm Africans: "In the general plan for the development of Central Africa the decentralisation of an overpopulated Britain is called for. By 1958, 250,000 settlers will have arrived, and by 1975, five millions, so that Europeans will outnumber natives."[1]

The European intervention and the partition of Africa did not, of course, wholly arrest population movement. Changes were, rather, circumscribed and oriented in new directions. Workers had to move, often over great distances, to the new centres of employment, and, though they were expected to return to their places of origin, they sometimes failed to do so. The drift to areas of economic opportunity had begun.

In addition to such transfers of individuals or families, there were occasional infiltrations on a larger scale, particularly across international boundaries. Such immigrations were regarded with tolerance by the suzerain Governments of the receiving areas as evidence of the greater wisdom and benignity of their own form of colonialism. But, as a general rule, these movements were not

[1] "Blueprint for Dream Cities," in *Outspan*, 23 Feb. 1951.

adjustments of population-land balances; quite often, they tended to accentuate pressure of population on the land. The Abrahams Commission noted that population increase in parts of Nyasaland was due not only to natural increase and immigration from other parts of the territory, "but very largely to immigration from Portuguese East Africa."

2. POPULATION GROWTH

Carr-Saunders, who surveyed the available data in the inter-war years (35), concluded that the population of Africa as a whole "is probably not decreasing; it may very likely be about stationary; it is not impossible that it may be increasing, but if so the rate of increase is certainly very slow." He also pointed to evidence that Africans had declined in numbers during the eighteenth and nineteenth centuries, owing to the ravages of the slave trade and its concomitant wars and turmoil, and to the introduction of new diseases and their spread by the opening up of communications. African demographic material is, in general, poor and unreliable and the statistician may affirm that there is no proof of population changes in the past or of more recent increases. Kuczynski (99) took this view: "Practically nothing is known of the population trend in the seven dependencies or in the whole of British East Africa; there is no reason to assume that the total population in 1940 was any larger than in 1895 or that the total population in 1895 was much smaller than in 1875." The present view tends to be less rigidly pedantic. Commenting on Kuczynski's statement, Goldthorpe (68) says: "Such agnosticism may have been exaggerated even at the time, and certainly since Kuczynski's death the weight of evidence for population increase has become more formidable."

It is not difficult to believe that populations declined in the 1890s when, before the turmoils of the slave trade had come fully to an end, great swarms of the Red Locust devastated crops over wide regions, while rinderpest slaughtered cattle and game, and smallpox killed the humans. Recovery from this concatenation of catastrophies may have been slow: but since the early 1920s medical services have been greatly extended, there have been no widespread famines or killing epidemics, and conditions have been favourable to population growth. It is true that there was a very serious outbreak of the Red Locust in the 1930s, and a threat of the spread of rinderpest. Some years of difficulty and hardship followed, but the handling of the situation by the suzerain Governments averted disaster. Disease outbreaks were controlled; hunger was kept at bay by compulsory planting of locust-resistant food crops, by issue of famine relief when necessary, and by direct protection of crops where this was possible. Early in this cycle of activity the areas of outbreak origin were discovered, and, with the control of these areas by an international organisation, it seems probable that the Red Locust will never swarm again.

The sums of the published population figures for East Africa as a whole (Uganda, Kenya, Tanganyika, Ruanda-Urundi, and Zanzibar) show a very great increase of numbers over the last thirty years:

1931	1946	1960
14,600,000	17,153,000	25,989,000

The general increase has certainly not been as great as these figures indicate. Total population in this region of 727,000 square miles is probably of the order of 26 millions, but the two earlier figures are serious underestimates. In 1948, for the first time, a complete census based on house to house visits was made in the three territories of Uganda, Kenya, and Tanganyika. This showed far more human beings than anyone had thought; the census, in fact, revealed more than three million souls in these territories whose existence, it seems, had not been suspected. The error had arisen through previous methods of estimating total populations. Counts were made, usually, for the purpose of tax assessment and the number of tax-paying males was known with fair accuracy, but the factors used in converting these figures to total populations were much too low.

Even when allowance is made for substantial error in the earlier estimates, the figures are not inconsistent with rapid population increase over the last three decades or more, but the rate of increase cannot be measured with any certainty. Goldthorpe (68) concedes that the growth rate may be as high as 2 per cent per annum in the more favourable areas of Kenya, and, though he doubts if this figure is applicable to the colony as a whole, he considers that the general rate is "quite high enough to give rise to pressing social and economic problems." For Tanganyika his "reasoned guess" is an increase rate of about 1·5 per cent per annum, and 1 per cent per annum for Uganda where the birth rate is lower. Increase rates of 2 per cent, 1·5 per cent, and 1 per cent double population numbers in thirty-five, forty-six, and seventy years respectively.

It is not improbable that the rates are higher than these tentative figures indicate. Sample surveys in Southern and Northern Rhodesia to measure vital statistics of African populations have indicated annual increase rates as high as 2·8 per cent in Southern Rhodesia and 2·5 per cent in Northern Rhodesia, while a rate of 2 per cent has been suggested for Nyasaland. It is expected that the African population of the former Federation will double itself in twenty-eight years (147). Clyde Mitchell's study of human fertility in some Yao hamlets in the Liwonde district of Nyasaland supports the supposition of high increase rates. He arrived at an estimate of 2·249 for the net reproduction rate of his population, and, though he thought it possible that he might have underestimated the mortality rate, he found his high figure partly confirmed by the fact that the increase in total population for parts of the Liwonde district, according to official census data, was 2·69 per cent per annum. The net reproduction rate indicates by what percentage a population subject to a certain fertility and a certain mortality, both being constant, will increase or decrease within a generation. But a generation is an indefinite period, and it is not the same everywhere. An annual increase of 2·69 per cent would double population in about 26 years, while a net reproduction rate of 2 means that population would double in one generation, or, say, twenty-five years.

It is supposed that the native population of Southern Rhodesia has increased very rapidly since the beginning of this century. An estimate made as early as 1902 put the African population of the colony at a mere 530,000 people owning only 55,000 head of cattle. By 1926 this population, "sheltered by European government from the attritions of tribal warfare and the worst effects of famine" (182), had risen to 936,000, and by 1944 the figure had reached 1,390,000. Cattle increased even more rapidly: in 1944 they numbered 1,916,000. No doubt cattle numbers were low in 1902, so soon after the great rinderpest epidemic, but it seems not improbable that the usual errors of underestimation entered into the first reckoning of human numbers. Nevertheless, one cannot doubt that the increase has been great. By 1926, very probably, the numbers of humans and cattle had caught up with or exceeded the carrying capacity, for traditional methods of land-use, of the areas set aside for African occupation, though these areas may well have been adequate for the numbers existing at the time they were set aside. Somewhat similar increase rates are claimed for Africans in the Republic of South Africa, while the population of Basutoland is said to have multiplied fourfold over the period 1875–1921.

The population of the Gold Coast, now Ghana, has increased more rapidly than that of Southern Rhodesia, if the published figures are to be taken at their face value. According to the census of 1911 there were 1,500,000 Africans in the Gold Coast. In the next twenty years the population more than doubled, reaching a figure of 3,160,000 by 1931, and it seems to have doubled again within the last thirty years, since the present estimate of the population of Ghana (1960) is 6,691,000. A considerable part of this increase is, however, to be accounted for by an inflow of immigrants attracted by the wealth from cocoa and the ready availability of land in the underpopulated forest region. The net reproduction rate for Africans in Ghana has been estimated by Myburg at 1·5 (147).

Over the great region of the Congo the upsurge of population appears to have developed much more recently, but by the middle 1940s the rate of increase may have been approaching 1·5 per cent per annum and it is not unlikely that it had reached a higher value before the Belgian withdrawal. A visiting writer of the later 1950s, Alan Moorehead, was impressed by the number of babies he saw. "On every woman's back—and the word 'every' is hardly an exaggeration—a baby is riding in a sling of cotton cloth. Even now I find it hard to think of the Congo without conjuring up a vision of innumerable little black cannon-ball heads pressed into the women's shoulders" (120).

But uncertainties and disagreements about African population changes, past and present, remain and are expressed on a scale which reminds one of the great population controversy in England. During the latter part of the eighteenth century one school of thought contended that the English had declined in numbers since the Glorious Revolution while another maintained with equal conviction that there had been a considerable increase. The first complete census in Great Britain was not made until 1801. Such uncertainties must continue until, in some unforeseeable future,

there are adequate census data or vital statistics. It is often remarked with a good deal of justice, that cattle numbers and even
populations of wild elephants are known with greater certainty
than the number of humans.

Like many agricultural workers who were in close contact with
Africans during the 1930s and 1940s I formed the impression that
most of the populations I had occasion to observe were increasing
at a rate which must be taken into account in the assessment of
agricultural problems. This impression was reinforced by comparison of tribal and district counts made at different times by
officers known to me, with whose methods I was familiar, and
counts of smaller populations made by myself and my staff in the
course of agricultural studies. Increase rates of 1·5 per cent per
annum and even more were quite commonly indicated. Kuczynski
was not impressed by such "mere casual observation," and he dis-
approved of the tendency "to brush aside the statistics and continue to accept as finally established facts the impressions of
people who have a long experience of natives." He was, of course,
right to question the statistical validity of these observations and
to point to the error of accepting as generally applicable high
growth rates which might be true for certain restricted areas. But
the existence of a situation is not disproved by the lack of statistic-
ally valid evidence, and general increase rates over vast regions of
desert, semi-desert, Shifting Cultivation, and Permanent Cultivation land are of less significance in the genesis of agricultural
problems than the incidence of population increases. Some peoples, probably few, remained more or less static or even declined
in numbers, while others increased at such a rate as to bring about
the emergence of acute agricultural, social, and economic problems
in a surprisingly short space of time. These pressures developed
most rapidly in the best regions of soil and climate, where humans
and cattle bred and accumulated at too high a rate. The operation
of the system of kinship obligations and, more recently, the attractions of economic opportunity, tended to direct population drift
towards the areas of highest fertility and potential, and to accentuate the effects of natural increase in favourable environments.

This was no new phenomenon. It had happened in India and
elsewhere. Darling, in his work on the Punjab peasant (47), points
to the "unprecedented increase" of the population of the Punjab
in the period 1921-41 and comments: "In India every advantage

of nature is sooner or later neutralised by an increase of population." And he adds: "It might almost be said that the fertility of the land is a measure of the fertility of women."

3. CASH CROPPING

The extraordinary development of the production of cash crops by African cultivators, mainly within the last forty years, is something unprecedented in colonial history. Although the volume of produce that comes out of Africa is now very great, the main export crops are remarkably few: cotton, oil palm products, coffee, groundnuts. Others, such as air-cured and fire-cured tobacco, rubber, coconut palm, cloves, and bananas are of local or minor importance, while flue-cured and Turkish tobacco, pyrethrum, and tea are very recent developments still in an embryonic stage as native-grown crops in parts of the Rhodesias and East Africa.

Cotton, coffee, and groundnuts were known in Africa long before Europeans had penetrated beyond the coastal fringe, and the oil palm is, of course, indigenous to the equatorial forest region. When European traders first reached West Africa they found that textiles were being made there from locally grown cotton and there is a record of the shipment of this cloth from Benin to England as early as 1558. Coffee has been known in Bukoba, where it was first developed as a native-grown cash crop, for several centuries. It is believed to have been brought by Bunyoro conquerors more than three hundred years ago, and it was used as a masticatory, as the Haya still use it, while the beans served also as a form of currency for the purchase of livestock, barkcloth, hoes, and other goods. European travellers who passed through Bukoba in the later nineteenth century remarked on the coffee trees to be seen round most African homesteads. In Chaggaland, on the other hand, coffee is a comparatively recent introduction dating back, probably, no more than fifty or sixty years and first grown by one of the Christian missions. The missions played a very considerable part in the early introduction and spread of cash crops among African peoples.

Some of the nineteenth-century explorers too had a hand in this. Sir Samuel Baker brought Egyptian types of cotton to Uganda in 1872. More rarely, the African people themselves took the initiative. The one outstanding example is the development of the cocoa industry in the Gold Coast, an industry Ghana now proudly claims as "a product of the initiative of Ghana farmers." It seems that cocoa was introduced to Nigeria in 1874 by a local chief who brought pods from the Spanish island of Fernando Po and the first commercial plantation on the Gold Coast, in 1879, is credited to a Fanti blacksmith who also got his seed from Fernando Po, though there is evidence that there were cocoa trees in the country as early as 1815 and the Basel Mission had a plantation at Akropong, grown from Surinam seed, which was bearing in 1866.

In spite of these early introductions the growth of commercial crop production was at first slow. A tiny export of cocoa came from the Gold Coast in 1893 and by the end of the century the output was no more than 360 tons, while cotton production in Uganda grew from very small beginnings in the early 1900s. Before there could be any rapid development of commodity production the peace of the suzerain powers had first to be firmly established and after that the means of marketing, transporting, processing, and handling bulk produce had to be provided. Crop varieties suited to the requirements of overseas markets or to local conditions had often to be found and introduced or, later, produced by plant-breeding techniques. In Uganda the Uganda Company Ltd, which was established in 1903, prepared the way for large-scale cotton growing by pioneering the erection of ginneries with the help of the newly founded British Cotton Growing Association, and by introducing and distributing American Upland varieties. But the great period of expansion of commodity production did not come until after the First World War, when Departments of Agriculture were set up or brought to effective strength in most colonial territories. These departments concentrated their efforts on the development of cash crops, for it was firmly believed at the time that this was the key to the sound evolution and development of African agriculture. The motives were not, of course, entirely altruistic. New sources of raw material were wanted by the industries of Europe, and Britain had long been sensitive to her dependence on American cotton. In his address to Parliament in 1904 Edward VII had said: "The insufficiency of the supply of the raw material upon which the great cotton industry depends has inspired me with deep concern. I trust that the efforts which are being made in various parts of my

Empire to increase the area under cultivation may be attended by a large measure of success."

The efforts were attended with some success, particularly in Uganda—though as events transpired Uganda's cotton was to go mainly to the mills of India and Japan. But still the pace was not fast enough and in 1917 a new organisation, the Empire Cotton Growing Corporation, was set up to provide research and information services and general assistance and encouragement for the development of cotton growing. From 1918 onwards production in Uganda soared, to reach in 1938 a peak which has not been surpassed. Correspondingly, the output of cocoa on the Gold Coast, from its small beginnings of about 360 tons at the turn of the century, reached a figure of 300,000 tons in 1937, before the decline due to swollen-shoot disease set in.

This great growth of production for export was generally seen as a healthy development. The benefits were to be mutual, in accordance with the principle of the double duty of colonial powers to protect and sponsor the development of dependent peoples, and at the same time to make the resources of the colonies available to the world as a whole. This general principle seems to have been tacitly accepted by most of the suzerain Governments before it was explicitly expressed in Lord Lugard's "Dual Mandate," though a few unkindly critics pointed out that the two duties might not be altogether compatible and that the rights of the colonial powers in the matter rested on no better foundations than conquest, occupation, and military strength.

These two major successes of the period of expanding commodity production, cotton in Uganda and cocoa in the Gold Coast, were in a large degree spontaneous developments aided and fostered rather than forced by direct government action. In Uganda many of the chiefs became shareholders in the Uganda Company: they took to cotton growing with enthusiasm and their people followed suit. But the new wealth of the Gold Coast was created by "stranger farmers" rather than by the native Akim people who occupied the south-eastern zone of forest ochrosols in which the cocoa industry first took root and flourished. When it became clear that there was wealth in cocoa, the people of the Cape Coast were in a position to take advantage of the new opportunity. They had economic experience and capital derived from a long period of contact with the commerce of Europe and the export of produce such as palm oil and rubber. In the 1890s the Gold Coast was still the world's third largest rubber producer, and all of it came from wild forest resources. Plantation production killed the trade in wild rubber and, with the coming of the new and greater opportunities offered by cocoa growing, Ga, Krobo, Akwapim, Fanti, and others flocked to the forest lands. There was ample room, for the native Akim population was then far below the point of critical density. Much forest land lay unused and the Akim were as anxious to sell this land as the stranger farmers were to buy.

The success of these two ventures was determined by several factors common to both. Over large areas in southern Ghana and in southern and central Uganda soil and climatic conditions are almost ideally suited to cocoa in the one case and cotton in the other. Production of the crops called for relatively little effort and skill, and no great capital investment was required. The forest ochrosols of Ghana and the cotton lands of Uganda are regions of high human-carrying capacity in which, at the time of development of the industries, population densities, though high by African standards, were generally below or well below the critical levels, and the climates are such that a small cultivated acreage will suffice to ensure the food supply. Under such conditions of ample land, high fertility, and a long growing season a family with only traditional equipment can extend the cultivated acreage to include cash crops without endangering the food supply. In less fortunate regions with a single uncertain cropping season and a short sowing period the cultivator may be hard put to it to get his relatively large area of food crops planted in time. The plough, of course, can break this deadlock, but, with the exception of Teso in Uganda, the two industries were created with the hoe and the equipment of subsistence cultivation. There was cheap labour to be had by those who wished to expand beyond the family capacity, from the starveling north of the Gold Coast and from crowded Ruanda on the borders of Uganda. Finally there had been no large-scale alienation of land to create suspicion and distrust of motives, and in each case there was a native driving force strong enough to overcome initial resistance and inertia and to eliminate or greatly reduce the need for coercive action. It is not improbable that the success of cotton altered the course of Uganda's history, for Sir Harry Johnson and his immediate successors were in favour of developing the country on plantation lines for such products as rubber, coffee, and cocoa, and arguments on the need to alienate land for European use went on into the 1920s when the evident success of cotton as an African crop brought about a change of attitude. Even in these days "groundnut" schemes were not unknown. Watson (180) mentions a co-operative scheme for production of cotton on the grand scale which was started in Teso in 1919. A commercial company undertook to clear and tractor-plough large areas of land on which Africans were to be encouraged to grow cotton in return for a share of the profits. Some development must have taken place for a visitor to Teso in 1920 records having seen a single field of cotton "several miles long." One can imagine the rate of land degeneration and erosion that would take place under such conditions and it is not surprising that the project was short lived.

Production of cotton by Africans in the Congo followed a pattern of rapid expansion similar to that of Uganda, with a lag of more than a decade (see Fig. 10), but here the rapid expansion of production was ensured by a system of compulsory cultivation. Experimental work in the period 1915–20 had shown that cotton could be grown successfully over extensive regions of medium altitude with a sufficiently definite dry season; and, since the country straddles the equator, the inversion of seasons in the north and south adds a considerable economic advantage by assuring continuity of supplies. Compulsory production of the crop was linked with an elaborate system of zoning for ginneries and a complicated marketing organisation in which cotton-buying companies held purchasing monopolies over large areas at controlled prices. This was all part of the Belgian policy of planned development on the grand scale, and of "educative cultivation" designed to advance the agriculture of the African and improve his standard of living. The rapid build-up of cotton growing in the Congo until there were more than 800,000 African growers, willing and unwilling, was claimed by the Belgians as "one of the most brilliant successes" of their agricultural policy.

There were successes also in the French territories, including their great irrigation scheme for cotton and rice on the upper Niger, but there were disappointments and failures as well. Northern Nigeria, of which much had been expected, proved disappointing as a cotton producer. The variety of American Upland so successful in Uganda gave lower yields and poorer lint in the Nigerian environment. The plant changed in character. It became more hairy and therefore more resistant to disease-carrying insects such as jassid, but it produced a weak staple and this was attributed to a short growing season and to fluctuations of soil moisture. Soon it became clear that new varieties would have to be found and that a long period of plant-breeding and experiment would be needed before much progress could be made. During the inter-war period production rose to and fluctuated around a figure of some 20,000 bales, and a considerable part of this crop was used in the local hand-spinning and weaving industry: but after the last War, and following a special survey by the Empire Cotton Growing Corporation, exports of cotton from Nigeria increased very materially.

Neither in West Africa nor elsewhere in East Africa was success repeated on the Uganda scale. Although cotton was established as a cash crop for Africans in parts of Tanganyika, Kenya, and Nyasaland—mainly in Sukumaland, the Nyanza Province, and the lower Shire valley—the combined production of the three territories amounted to only about a fifth of the output of Uganda alone. The main factors limiting expansion were, probably, pressure of human and cattle populations in the areas suited to cotton, consequent shortage of land, and the need to concentrate on a relatively large food-crop area in order to ensure against hunger.[1] It is significant that when, in 1952, Tanganyika produced a remarkable record crop of 75,000 bales this followed on the most unusual coincidence of two near-perfect seasons for cereal crops and the consequent accumulation of a considerable reserve of food. "Such a large cotton crop was only possible," says the East African Year Book, "because the territory had, exceptionally, experienced two good grain harvests in succession and the usual urgent need for maximum food production had vanished."[2]

In Northern Rhodesia failure was complete. There cotton first came into prominence as a possible crop for the small body of European farmers most of whom had settled in the country just after the First World War. A lucky—or, in the event, unlucky—trial season generated so much facile optimism that a considerable acreage was planted in 1924–5. The crop was a total failure. In the following year the farmers tried again with the same result.

[1] See above p. 349.
[2] *Year Book and Guide to East Africa* [1954].

A crop of 202,500 lb of lint was picked from 14,400 acres—an average yield of 14 lb per acre: Following these failures, in the period 1929–38, a good deal of work on cotton was done in Northern Rhodesia with the help of the Empire Cotton Growing Corporation. New, jassid-resistant varieties gave better results but yields of marketable lint were still too low, except on the alluvial soils of Lower Valley regions. The local pest situation was the main reason for this continuing failure. Stainers and bollworms destroyed the earlier crop, and on the plateau the setting of a later crop was prevented by the sharp and sudden onset of low winter temperatures. All that came of the work was a small industry of about a thousand African growers in the Luangwa Valley and lower Petauke district, but even this declined and died in the 1950s through lack of interest. It was not worth the grower's while, at the return he received, to plant the small area of cotton he could manage with the hoe after attending to his food crops.

The Gold Coast story is somewhat similar. The Dagomba still practise their simple but sound traditional agriculture uncomplicated by cash cropping, but this is not because of any failure or neglect on the part of the agents of development. Cotton work was carried out over a long period between 1910 and 1929, to the point of seed distribution and plans for a ginnery at Tamale. All this work ended in failure owing to low yields, high transport costs to railhead at Kumasi, and "the backwardness of local farmers" whose primitive inertia was such that they would not grow the crop for an uncertain pittance.

A high local incidence of pests seems to have been the main reason for the failure of cotton as a commercial crop in the Gold Coast savannah region, and also for the very meagre results achieved south of the Zambesi in spite of strong efforts there by the Empire Cotton Growing Corporation and the incentive of relatively high prices created by the establishment of a manufacturing industry.

This situation may be changed by new insecticides—such as "Endrin," a chlorinated hydrocarbon which has given very promising results against some of the major cotton pests. In Northern Rhodesia, treated plots under experimental conditions on the plateau have given very good yields, commonly of the order of 1,500 lb, and occasionally as high as 3,000 lb, of seed cotton per acre. But it remains to be determined whether this type of insecticidal control can be applied economically and effectively on the large scale to African-produced cotton.

The pattern of cotton production in Uganda and the very similar pattern in the Belgian Congo are illustrated in the accompanying figure (Fig. 10). Both differ very markedly from the pattern typical of "normal surplus" sales of a food crop grown wholly or largely for subsistence (see Fig. 1, p. 41), particularly in the comparatively steady build-up of production and freedom from very extreme fluctuations which have no evident economic cause. The industrial crop pattern conforms more obediently to economic expectation. Uganda's production increased fairly steadily to its pre-war peak, but during the War cotton acreages were reduced in favour of food and other crops—especially coffee, and mainly the robusta coffee of Buganda.

The conditions of the world market, which was dominated by the South and Central American producers, chiefly Brazil, were not such as to encourage any great expansion of coffee as an African crop during the inter-war years. In the Congo, where production—mainly from European-operated estates—was tending to increase, this tendency was deliberately checked by prohibitions on further plantings by Africans and Europeans alike. In Kenya, too, coffee was a European crop, and, though there was no legal prohibition, coffee growing by Africans was not encouraged. There are those who interpret this as an attempt "to guarantee the European farmer's dominance, and more especially to ensure a ready supply of black labour for him" (89): but if one recalls the economic circumstances of the time when Brazil was burning coffee or dumping it in the sea one may find in the attitude of the Kenya Government nothing more sinister than simple prudence. Economic circumstances changed completely with the War. Coffee became a useful dollar-earner, demand and prices were high, and there was a large and sustained increase in production in the sterling area during the post-war years, mainly in East Africa.

The most notable increases in acreage, output, and exports of coffee after the War were in Uganda. These came mainly from the robusta of Buganda where the crop, easily grown as an "understorey" in the banana groves, rapidly replaced cotton as the chief source of wealth: but production of the arabica of Elgon also increased very considerably under the stimulus of demand and high prices. After 1954, as post-war plantings came to full bearing, the increase in output was spectacular (see Fig. 10), and in 1959, when an astonishing record for coffee coincided with the second highest production of cotton, the African producers of Uganda derived more wealth from coffee than from cotton (£11·72m from cotton and £13·72m from coffee, on the basis of prices paid to growers) (20). Immediately before the last War cotton accounted for 80 per cent by value of Uganda's overseas exports of agricultural produce; in 1959 cotton accounted only for

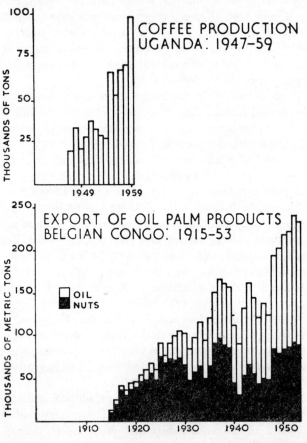

FIG. 10. The Expansio

Sources: *Annual Report of the Department of Agricul* *Uganda*, 1959; *Agriculture congolaises*, Brussels (Mini des Colonies) 1954; *Statistiques: Principales Cult* Leopoldville 1958-9.

41 per cent of the value, and coffee and cotton together for over 90 per cent.

Expansion of arabica coffee in Ruanda-Urundi, almost entirely by Africans, also proceeded at a very high rate in the late 1940s and the 1950s, while production of robusta in the Congo

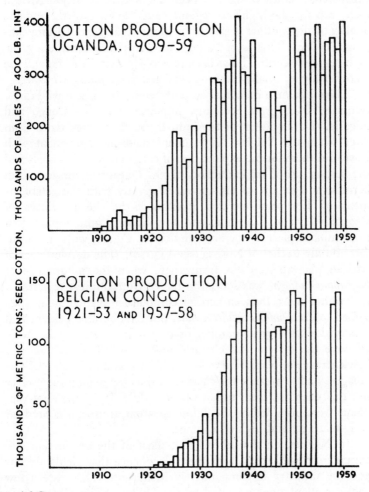

mmercial Crops.

ton = African production only.
   palm products includes production from European
rated estates.
Tee = African peasant production only.

increased considerably. The Ten Year Development Plan for the Congo contained provision for a great expansion of African coffee-growing, partly voluntary but mainly under the "educative" system, which would have raised production much above that of the European sector. In Kenya, though there has been no great expansion, arabica coffee has been adopted as a major African cash crop for the highland regions suited to its growth, and the quality of the product is said to be higher than that of European-grown coffee. This is not altogether surprising considering the high degree of control it has been possible to exercise so far and the fact that higher quality is to be expected from younger bushes.

The oil palm, a perennial crop like coffee but also a wild forest resource, is of great economic importance to the Congo and Nigeria. Development of the industry in the Congo dates from 1911 when the Belgian Government made an agreement with Lever Brothers for the exploitation of certain concession areas and the setting up of oil extraction plant. Output of oil and palm kernels, and export of oil, increased greatly with the establishment of European-operated plantations in the provinces of Leopoldville and Equateur, and the industry grew rapidly to a predominant place in the economy of the Congo, with an output second only to that of Nigeria (see Fig. 10). The development of African plantations dates from 1936, when the programme of *paysannat indigène* was started in the equatorial forest region. At first rather more than an acre of compulsory plantation was assigned to each *homme adulte valide*, but as it became evident that supervision of a great number of tiny units could not be made effective the system was changed and each village was given a block acreage of plantation to be established and maintained. The villagers had to arrange the sharing of the crop among themselves but this does not seem to have been a difficulty (52). First-year plants were provided by the Administration, from stocks bred for early maturity and high oil content.

In Nigeria, on the other hand, most of the production still comes from wild trees, with the consequence that yields are low and the industry is comparatively inefficient. There are a few well-run plantations operated by the United Africa Company in Nigeria itself and in the adjoining Cameroons, but capitalist plantation production has never been encouraged and even the idea of small African plantations was resisted by the chiefs on the grounds that such a development would lead to individual tenure of land and this, in turn, to the collapse of tribal authority. Nevertheless, Nigeria remains the world's largest producer of oil palm products, with the Belgian Congo not far behind at the time of independence, and the countries of what was formerly French West Africa in third place. Sierra Leone also produces a respectable amount of oil, and Ghana a few thousand tons of kernels.

PRODUCTION 1950

(IN THOUSANDS OF LONG TONS)

	KERNELS	OIL
Nigeria	381	160
Belgian Congo	127	178
Fr. W. Africa	130	22
Sierra Leone	—	65
Gold Coast	4	—

The production figure for the Congo is higher than the export figure because a considerable proportion of the output was used in local manufacture of margarine, cooking fat, and soap.

Nigeria's large dependence on the oil palm is a reflexion of soil and climatic conditions, for the soils of much of the forest region are leached, weak, and acid. The oil palm is tolerant of such soils, but they are unsuited to any other product of commercial value. In the western part of the forest zone, the country of the Yoruba, there is cocoa land, but the extent is so limited that production falls far below that of Ghana and the product takes third place in the list of Nigeria's agricultural exports. The second place, in terms of value, is taken by groundnuts from the one-season savannah region of the north.

The groundnut is of major importance as an African cash crop mainly in the countries of the West Coast—Nigeria, Gambia, Senegal—and the trade is of a respectable age. The merchants of the Industrial Revolution looked to the West Coast with its oil palm to meet increasing demands for industrial and illuminating oils, and they found an additional source in the groundnut. Exports of nuts from the Gambia started quite early in the nineteenth century and by the middle of the century the trade was considerable. This was not merely the sale of a subsistence surplus: groundnuts were grown as a cash crop, very often by "stranger farmers" who came from beyond the borders of the territory. Here was a development foreshadowing what was to happen with cocoa on the Gold Coast half a century later, with the difference that the strangers did not have to buy land and settle permanently, since the groundnut is a short-term annual crop. They could come as transients, grow a crop or two and return home with the proceeds. Like cocoa, this development of groundnut cultivation was a product of African initiative and enterprise unassisted in the beginning by any official government action. It has produced an unbalanced system of land-use dependent on a single crop of very variable market value, as have the similar developments in Senegal and parts of Nigeria.

Gambia's export of about 60 thousand tons a year is very great in relation to the size and population of the river-strip colony and protectorate, but small when compared with the output of Senegal and Nigeria. These two main producers greatly increased their output during and just after the War, partly at the expense of food production and at the cost of soil exhaustion. In 1947–8 Nigeria produced 313,000 tons of nuts, compared with about 145,000 tons immediately before the War. This huge crop was more than the available transport could handle. While the East African scheme for mechanised production on the grand scale floundered towards failure, groundnuts accumulated in up-country Nigeria and could not be moved even as far as the coast.

Such are the main African cash crops and the countries in which they are chiefly produced, but there are a number of other crops of local or general importance in individual countries. A notable example is the fire-cured tobacco production of Nyasaland. Early in the 1920s it was realised that soil and climatic conditions over large areas in the central and northern districts of the protectorate were ideal for growing dark-fired, sun-cured, and burley tobacco, types which are used in Great Britain for pipe tobaccos, and that the Nyasaland leaf was an effective and commercially acceptable substitute for the American product of the same type. Encouragement was given to African growers, to whom the crop is well-suited since it does not require the capital equipment, skill, and experience needed for flue-curing, with such effect that Nyasaland has become the United Kingdom's main supplier of the dark fire-cured types, while much smaller but significant quantities of sun-cured and burley are also grown.

Elsewhere tobacco is still of little general importance as an

African cash crop, in spite of efforts over the last ten years and more to push production of Turkish leaf in the Rhodesias. Small quantities of flue-cured and air-cured types are grown in parts of East Africa, mainly for local use, and some efforts are being made to encourage African-grown flue-cured tobacco. This remained for long a European monopoly, partly from fear of competition with European interests and concern for the quality and reputation of the leaf, but also because of the costly capital equipment and the high degree of skill and experience required for flue-curing. As very few Africans can command the equipment and skill required, most of their crop is sold as green leaf to tobacco companies or is cured by co-operative societies.

Other crops new to African cultivators, but grown by Europeans for thirty years or more, are tea and pyrethrum in the highlands of Kenya and Tanganyika. In both these cases, as with arabica coffee in Kenya, the new crop has been introduced with and used as a focus for a new system and standard of husbandry.

This has not been the case in the past. The great development of commodity production during the inter-war period and after the last War had simply been imposed and grafted upon the old systems of land-use and land-holding.

CHAPTER XX

LAND-HOLDING

1. TRADITIONAL AFRICAN LAND TENURE

To analyse land-holding in Africa would take another book, and here I give only enough information to provide a background for an understanding of agricultural changes and developments. On the surface, the indigenous systems of land tenure and the ways in which they have changed appear to have varied very considerably, but both can probably be classified into a number of categories in relation to four different complexes of facts:

(1) the plenitude or scarcity of land of different types, assessed by the factors which measure the Critical Population Density, including land categories, climate, and agricultural systems;

(2) the degree to which a tribe's political structure is developed, and particularly whether or not it had a governmental organisation;

(3) the main source of cash income in the new economy—whether from migration to centres of employment, or from the sale of new industrial crops or staple crops, or from sale of fish;

(4) the period and extent of historical contact with external trading centres.

The simplest situation resulting from the interaction of these complexes of factors is found in South Africa and among many tribes of south-central Africa. Here the situation up to 1943 has been reviewed by Gluckman (66). He examined the tribes organised under chiefs which had been adequately studied, and compared land-tenure systems and developments with his own results from a field study in Barotseland. In all these tribes he found that the chief was regarded as the owner of the land as trustee for his people. Anyone coming on to the land had to pay allegiance to the chief and he in turn was under an obligation to provide all his

subjects with a sufficiency of arable and building land, and to protect them in free access to wild products, public fishing waters,
and pasturage. These systems might be regarded as "pre-feudal,"
since rights to land were an incidence of citizenship. Gluckman
related this situation to the limited amount that a man could produce with simple equipment, to the fact that production was in
simple primary goods which excluded the development of major
differences in standards of living between superiors and sub-
ordinates, and to the accompanying restricted amount of trade.
In these conditions, chiefs used their control over land to enhance
their status by building up their following.

In practice, in all the southern Bantu tribes, and among the
Barotse, Ngoni, Yao, and other central-African peoples, chiefs did
not give the land directly to the subjects who would use it. Land
was generally allocated to sub-chiefs who in turn allotted shares to
village headmen: but sometimes the allotment was directly to
headmen. The number of steps in this hierarchy of land rights
depended on the depth of the political hierarchy. At the village
level, the headman allotted lands to heads of sub-sections or heads
of families, and they distributed land for use to their dependents.
Each of the persons granted land in this way was secure in his
rights and could not be expropriated without fault. He could
transmit his rights to his heirs, but could not transfer them to
anyone else without permission of his seniors. If rights were
vacated they rested in the next senior in the hierarchy.

Hence there existed a series of rights in each piece of land
which paralleled the social hierarchy. Gluckman argues that the
complexes of rights involved throughout this series differ funda-
mentally from "usufruct," from "use," and from "possession,"
which are among the terms commonly used to describe the situation; and he suggests that in order to bring out the connexion
between land rights and status, these rights should be called
"estates of holding," and distinguished as primary, secondary,
tertiary, etc., to show that they occur in a hierarchy. In a later
article (67) he accepted an improvement of this terminology proposed by Sheddick in his study of Basuto land tenure (148). Since
the superior estates consist of rights to control, administer, and
distribute land, Gluckman agrees with Sheddick's implication
(Sheddick does not discuss this point explicitly) that the superior
estates should be called primary, secondary, tertiary, etc. "estates

of administration." These are controlling interests in land which is eventually parcelled out in "estates of cultivation." An individual who works an "estate of cultivation" has an indisputable right to the produce, though he may give a little of it away as tribute to the chief and gifts to other superiors.

It will be apparent, and it is important to note, that a holder of a primary estate of administration will hold a secondary estate within the primary, a tertiary within the secondary, and an estate of cultivation within the tertiary estate of administration, since he too has status in a decreasing series. The essence of this proposed terminology is that it brings out the close association between land-holding and status, and emphasises that while the cultivator is protected in his land, and transmits rights in it to his heir, he cannot give these to strangers without consulting those who hold estates of administration; and these persons have residuary rights in the land if it is vacated.

Gluckman's survey showed that where land is very plentiful this series of estates does not emerge, even among tribes with a governmental organisation such as the Bemba who were studied by Dr Audrey Richards (139). In this case the Paramount Chief allots provinces to subordinate chiefs, but the process goes no further; any subject of a subordinate chief may cultivate anywhere within the province of that chief. One may also see in this an adaptation to the *citemene* system, with its brief cultivation and very long fallow period, practised by the Bemba on their poor, weak woodland soils. It seems possible, however, that where among the Bemba land falls into short supply, the hierarchy of estates might emerge: Dr Richards does not discuss rights in fallows and regenerating woodland which might test this hypothesis. But she makes it clear that something like this hierarchy exists where land is improved, as on old hut sites, and where soils of strong staying power are worked continuously by people who are normally *citemene* cultivators, as in the case of the Bisa on Chiluwe Island (139).

Mitchell (115) adopted the terminology for the Yao, who have small chieftaincies; and the team investigating the Plateau Tonga applied the concept successfully in this case, though the system was developed in terms of different kinds of social status and was not clearly emphasised owing to the lack of governmental organisation. Nevertheless, since the Plateau Tonga had passed out of the phase when land was plentiful, there was a tendency to focus rights in land on headmen and on first settlers in an area. This tendency is well developed among the related Tonga of the Gwembe section of the Zambesi Valley where the restricted alluvial soils are held through membership of segments of matrilineal lineages (39). Evidence on societies without governmental organisation in other regions of Africa, such as the Tallensi of northern Ghana, the Ibo of Nigeria, and, formerly, the Kikuyu and related tribes, suggests that where land is in relatively short supply the land-holding system of this type of society can usually be envisaged as a series of "estates of administration," or "control," vested in the hierarchal segments of clan and lineage. Here again a man could not hand over land of the kinship group to a stranger without the permission of the superior groups' representatives, who had to abandon their rights before the transfer became valid. Estates of this kind, involving residuary rights, can be vested in groups as well as individuals. This seems to be the case among some Northern Rhodesian tribes whose laws are cited briefly by C. M. N. White in his survey of Luvale rural economy (183). He reports the development of "lineage" estates among Luvale and also among the Lungu of the Tanganyika lake shore, to the extent that when individuals clear land their gardens become so involved in lineage relations that transfer outside is difficult or impossible. Among the Luvale resting land is "identified" with the village, and not with the individual who previously cultivated it. Here the lineage or village holds an "estate of control" over the land.

The rule by which an individual can clear and take over unclaimed land freely, but that it then, and particularly when inherited on his death, becomes part of the group's estate is very commonly found throughout Africa. Fortes has described how this tendency operates in the case of cocoa plantations in Ashanti (59). While in principle land is owned by the Stool—or, in effect by the community symbolised by the Stool—cocoa farms are very rarely "lineage" property in the same sense as food gardens for subsistence. In the case of these farms the emphasis is on individual ownership of the farm by the man who established it, and the rules applicable to personally acquired wealth come into play: but, as Fortes points out, cocoa farms may become lineage land by the operation of the customary laws of inheritance. Indeed, he adds: "if the lineage system holds its own in Ashanti for another

fifty years possibly all cocoa farms will be lineage owned." But he
noted contrary tendencies. Inheritance of cocoa farms was becoming restricted to closest kin in the matrilineal succession and
there was a strong desire to leave property to children instead of
nephews and nieces. The most marked tendency was for the line
of inheritance to be limited to the matrilineal issue of the man's
own mother and her sisters. "It is only they," Fortes says, "who
can claim any contingent rights over a person's cocoa farm, if we
go by current practice. Thus there is no difficulty about determining ownership of a cocoa farm. It is essentially owned by an
individual either by right of making the farm, acquiring it by
inheritance, or acquiring it by purchase or mortgage. This explains why alienation and mortgage of cocoa farms is so little
subject to restraint by the lineage. If a man wants to sell or mortgage his cocoa farm he usually has a complete legal liberty to do
so." In all this we may see a confusion and a difficulty created by
the introduction of permanent cash crops, a confusion between
the hierarchical rights vested in groups or individuals, or in this
case the holder of the Stool, and the rights of the individual to the
control of the land he has improved by planting a permanent crop.

So long as a group has certain overriding rights to exclude free
transfer of land by its members to outsiders, and so long as the
group insists that it has power to veto such transfers, and so long
as an individual on leaving the group is considered to abandon
thereby his rights in land, it is profitable to relate land-holding to
the series of statuses which an individual occupies. The hierarchy
of status is paralleled by primary, and frequently by further
grades of estates in land.

Inherent in the system discussed in these terms by Gluckman
and Sheddick, is exclusion of the right to sell land. Lease, mortgage, and pledging of land were also unknown in most if not all of
the customary systems of land-holding. The Southern Bantu
peoples, and most of the central-African tribes within the British
sphere of influence, have resolutely opposed the idea of selling
land, particularly where there are chiefs who insist on their
ultimate rights as owners, with obligation and power to give land
to their subjects.

Gluckman informs me that the Zulu "king" in 1936 fined a
man who had tried to sell his hut, and the man who wanted to buy
it, on the grounds that they were dealing with his property, ad-

hering to his soil. And it was only in 1940 that the Barotse National
Court authorised the sale of doors and windows in huts, though
not of huts themselves. Gluckman's 1943 survey showed that all
these peoples insisted on maintaining ultimate tribal rights in land,
and excluding sale and other transactions involving the land. Indeed, he found a general tendency to emphasise the right of every
tribesman to some land. He describes a series of steps taken by
various southern African chiefs to obtain land for this purpose, as
it became in short supply. In different Tswana tribes chiefs have
claimed the right to take over land allotted to a man, but not yet
in use, and to put a limited period on fallowing so as to get land
for distribution to the landless. (The second step indicates that the
Critical Population Density has been passed.) The climax is the
situation found in Basutoland, where the unmarried are not allowed to have land, and married men are restricted to three fields
of two acres each. Gluckman informs me that in 1947 members of
the newly reconstituted Barotse Katengo Council, who were
elected, pressed for this kind of legislation, and that similar proposals were made in 1942 by the Plateau Tonga Native Authority.

The researches of anthropologists in South and south-central
Africa indicate that this development is associated with a situation
in which the major source of cash income is migration to labour.
They argue[1] that because of the uncertainty of urban employment,
the lack of social security, the inability to acquire land and houses
in the towns, migrant labourers still look for their ultimate security
to the tribal lands. They claim rights to this land as members of
the tribe and members of specific villages or kinship groups; and
in effect their chiefs and seniors keep the land for them in return
for the money which they bring home from the urban centres.
Because cash cropping has not developed in these regions, and
because they lie well south of the area with which Arabs and others
have been trading for centuries, the land-holding systems of these
tribes have been insulated against change. To this has been added

---

[1] Gluckman summarises these studies in his article "Tribalism in Modern
British Central Africa," in *Cahiers d'Etudes Africaines* [1960], and in *Social
Change in Modern Africa*, edited by A. Southall, O.U.P., for the International
African Institute [1961]. See also J. van Velsen, "Labour Migration as a Positive Factor in the Continuity of Tonga Tribal Society," in this volume. Gluckman argued the case in *Essays on Lozi Land and Royal Property* (66), and it has
been forcefully applied to the Mambwe by W. Watson in his *Tribal Cohesion in
a Money Economy*. For the urban situation, see J. C. Mitchell (116), and A. L.
Epstein (54).

the effect of the labour migration as a positive factor inhibiting change. The effect of the dominance of labour migration as a source of money income is illustrated by the way in which the individual plots allotted to men under the Glen Grey Act in the Ciskei have supported far more people than lived off the produce, a development that may well appear, unless it can be forcefully checked, under the new Southern Rhodesia Land Husbandry Act.

It seems that this system of using, in effect, the arable land as a base for subsistence production from which men can migrate to labour-centres to "raid" there for money (to quote Watson) can continue until pressure on the land becomes far too heavy, and the chief is not left with enough land to distribute in any fair way. One report on a Southern Natal tribe, by Jaspan, states that in this situation chiefs and headmen will take all the land they can, and a large number of people will be left without land. These people are then dependent on the urban economy, even though their families are left in the reserves, scratching at a completely degraded soil from which they can produce very little.

Gluckman's concept of a hierarchy of estates is more difficult to apply in East and West Africa, in the modern situation, where cropping for cash is better developed and trade with the outside world has existed longer. Nevertheless, some hierarchy of rights in land seems to have existed in tribes which are now engaged in production of cash crops, and it is still found among many tribes which earn their money by sending men to work elsewhere. The hierarchy of estates was probably marked among the Ganda, though some primary holders of estates of administration were "chiefs" and not lineage heads, until it was overset by the Uganda agreement of 1900 and the creation of the *mailo* estates. Here there was a strong governmental organisation.

Buganda was ruled by a powerful monarch, the Kabaka, who, in addition to appropriating estates of his own, allocated tracts of land to members of his family and to his principal followers as a reward for faithful service. There were also clan lands administered by lineage heads whose status resembled in some respects that of feudal lords. The mass of the people were, in effect, tenants of the landowning princes, the holders of primary estates of administration, fief-holding chiefs, and lineage heads, and they paid rent in the form of labour and tribute for the land they cultivated. But the cultivator had rights over the land allocated to him by his landlord, and these rights were secure beyond question so long as he paid his tribute and performed his labour dues. Furthermore, he was not tied to the land like the serf of medieval Europe; he was perfectly free to move if he wished, and his rights and freedoms were safeguarded by the fact that landlords valued a numerous and contented peasantry. There was then no shortage of rich and fertile land, but there was a shortage of men to till it. The Uganda Agreement of 1900, which was largely the work of the redoubtable Sir Harry Johnston, conferred freehold title on many individuals who ranked as holders of primary estates of administration at that time, in accordance with decisions made by the Buganda Council. The Kabaka, the princes, and the great chiefs received large estates, but the majority were about two square miles in extent. Recipients of these estates were free to sell the land, subject to registration of title and transfers, and they did so to such an extent that most of the original allocations are now split up among many owners, though a number of large estates remain.

The general effect of modern changes, including cash cropping, particularly with permanent crops, and increasing population pressure and land shortage, is to eliminate or hasten the elimination of the holders of estates of administration in hierarchical systems, and the groups' estates of control in lineage systems. Often the Chief retains some claim, even though it may be no more than the right to a small gift to mark his ultimate ownership: but in the end result no one intervenes between chief and individual landholder, and the latter may sell to whom he wishes or mortgage as he pleases.

In some situations this tendency probably developed quite early, where land was becoming short and chiefs continued to build up their followings. This seems to have happened among the Chagga prior to 1926 and before the great development of coffee planting. Gutmann (72) records that there was much bitterness and trouble because chiefs were encroaching upon lineage rights in clan lands. If a man had more than enough land the chief would take some of it away from him to give to a stranger whom he wished to add to his following. By 1926, Gutmann says, clan rights were disappearing, individual rights were being strongly asserted and were supported by the chiefs, and land had become freely saleable. Thus the sale of land, and other cash transactions such as rental and mortgage developed early among the Chagga. A similar development seems to have taken place even earlier under the congested conditions of Ukara Island, where land has long been saleable.

This is now the situation among most of the coffee—and cotton—producing tribes of Uganda, in the cocoa region of Ghana, and in other areas of West Africa where coffee and cocoa are produced. It is to be noted, however, that the process may develop only in relation to one type of land or land-use while the old rules continue to apply to others, as in the case of cocoa plantations and subsistence food-crop lands in West Africa.

If we refer back to the four complexes of factors set out at the beginning of this chapter, we can say that so long as pressure on land is not overwhelming and the main source of cash-earnings is labour migration, the indigenous land-holding system, with its involvement of social status and rights to gardens, is likely to survive. When pressure on land reaches a certain point of excessive severity the system must break down. Even then hidden subdivision goes on and pressure increases, for land-holders share what they have with needy kin, until it is barely usable for agricultural purposes. At the other extreme, where land is used to produce crops for sale, and particularly new permanent crops such as coffee and cocoa, it is probable that the rights of intermediate holders of estates will tend to be eliminated, and only the rights of ruler and cultivator will prevail. But there is still the possibility that land which has been appropriated by an individual may on his death become family property encumbered by rights of kin to prevent the inheritors freely selling, leasing, or mortgaging it, as described by Fortes for Ashanti cocoa gardens. We may observe two processes at work, whose weights it is not easy to determine. The first, outlined above, occurs normally in the indigenous systems as land passes from one generation to the next. The second is a process of change in which individual rights come to exclude group rights altogether. Under the latter process, land will become marketable property which can be sold, leased, mortgaged, and pledged.

The effects of these developments on social organisation falls outside my province. I note only that there are these two major trends which appear in varied patterns of inter-relationship in the different regions and tribes of Africa, and that they may help to explain why land has become freely saleable in some regions while in others this change is absent or resisted.

2. LAND AS A SALEABLE COMMODITY

In South and Central Africa the sale of land has not developed to the extent that it has in many parts of East and West Africa, but even here one may observe a tendency towards cash transactions in land. Even in *citemene* areas, standing crops are sometimes sold for cash. This is not a sale of land in the normal sense, though rights of cultivation for the brief remainder of the cropping cycle may pass with the crop, but in regions of Permanent and Semi-Permanent Cultivation where land has acquired a commercial or scarcity value, or both, transactions difficult to distinguish from sales of land have arisen.

In the maize-growing parts of the southern and central provinces of Northern Rhodesia cash transactions in land have emerged in the form of payments for improvements, a development which appeared first among the Plateau Tonga with their comparatively long history of plough cultivation and maize marketing. Where the plough is used land must be stumped, at much greater labour or cost in wages of labour than in the case of normal hoe cultivation. Stumped land thus acquires a special value, easily assessed in money terms, which is independent of the scarcity or abundance of land in general. Nowadays when land is transferred, payment is commonly asked for the value of stumping and for such other permanent improvements as houses, out-buildings, wells, fencing, and fruit trees. This practice is not confined to the land-hungry Tonga: a very similar pattern of payment for improvements has appeared among the Soli and Sala and other comparative newcomers to the maize market who are not yet short of strong and fertile land. On the other hand, cash transactions in land appear to be unknown in the greatly overcrowded lands of the Ngoni where the plough is not used and land is not stumped.

By this formula of payment for improvements the tradition of inalienable land is reconciled with the requirements of the new economic age, at least to the satisfaction of the Native Authorities who are not yet prepared to recognise outright sales of land. In this they probably have the support of majority public opinion. Yet for all practical purposes these transactions are sales of land, though in theory differences in productive capacity do not affect the price. In practice there probably is a differentiation but the premium on productivity is disguised as payment for the residual value of manure, among the Tonga where cattle manure has acquired a commercial value, or is concealed in inflated values of houses and other fixtures. Among the plough-using Teso of Uganda sales of stumped land also takes place, apparently with much less reticence.

It is, however, in areas where permanent cash crops are grown that the change has come about most completely and to the greatest extent. We have already noted the early appearance of land sales on the Gold Coast and the very rapid extension of the practice with the establishment of cocoa. A similar development has taken place more recently in the coffee-growing regions of East Africa. In Buganda, of course, land became a saleable commodity with the agreement of 1900. Here the original *mailo* estates—which were measured in square miles, and from this the word derives— have become so subdivided by sale that the average owned holding of the present day is probably less than 50 acres. Many peasants own small plots, but the great majority are still tenants of some two to four acres whose security of tenure, and even of inheritance, is guaranteed by law so long as they continue to cultivate and pay a fixed cash rental which is little more than nominal in relation to the economic value of coffee land at recent price levels. But elsewhere the change has come about as a spontaneous process, aided and accelerated by increasing shortage of land. As in the case of stumping for the plough, the planting of a permanent cash crop creates a special value which can be estimated separately but cannot be divorced from the land. Here, however, there is no reticence over land sales and no pretence that only crops or "improvements" are sold. Quite commonly the two values are assessed separately and added to form the purchase price. Chagga informants told me that in some recent sales the land had been valued at £25 to £30 per acre while coffee bushes had been valued separately and individually at half a crown to ten shillings each, according to age and quality, and banana stools at two to three shillings each. Many others told me they had bought bare land at about £25 an acre, and land with coffee at prices ranging from £70 to £200 an acre. One man said he had recently refused an offer of £2,500 for five acres of exceptionally fine coffee, but this price probably included a small house and cattle sheds. Others affirmed that land they had bought before the War for £7 to £10 an acre could now be sold, with bearing coffee on it, for £150 to £170 an acre.

There is intense competition for coffee and banana land, with many potential buyers and few if any willing sellers. Land comes on the market, generally, when a man is forced to sell to pay a judgment summons for debt or to meet some other pressing need, and there is then no lack of bidders to force up the price. The motive behind this competition is not so much the accumulation of personal wealth as provision for the future of sons, a paramount preoccupation of Chagga fathers, and also of eldest and youngest sons, who share the responsibility of providing land. Among this strongly patrilineal people, father to son inheritance of land is the general rule. In theory, inheritance rights might be held to extend in varying degrees of interest throughout the clan group: but in practice they end with the immediate heir. In Rombo the eldest son inherits his father's *kihamba*, while in the other divisions of Chaggaland it is the youngest son who does so, and it is a major responsibility of fathers to provide land for their other married sons. If this responsibility has not been discharged it passes to the heritors. In the past many individuals had considerable holdings, including *marena* or reserve land which was used to provide for sons. One case I investigated, which may be illustrative of the amount of subdivision that has occurred over the last two generations, was that of a group of nine families whose heads were all grandsons of one grandfather in the patrilineal line. Their holdings ranged from an acre and a quarter to three acres in extent and totalled 17 acres. These nine holdings were subdivisions of one large holding of 17 acres which had belonged to the grandfather and comprised his *kihamba* and *marena* lands.

If there were no *marena* and no clan lands remaining for allocation, land was purchased by those who could afford to buy or "begged" from a chief, as my Chagga informants put it. Now there is virtually no means of obtaining additional *kihamba* land except by purchase at prices far beyond the reach of the majority and, in the last resort, the holding may be subdivided even though it is already too small to provide a decent living. There is quite a distinct land-purchasing class, including successful coffee planters and people in well-paid local employment, school teachers, and workers for Government and the co-operative union, who invest savings in land and devote the proceeds of coffee to buying more land. I even came across examples of "hire purchase" of land by Chagga in secure employment who were paying a regular sum from their monthly wages to meet their commitments. But most people who have a responsibility for providing land look to the low-lying *shamba* region for a solution of their problem. When I asked Chagga fathers how they proposed to provide for their sons some said that they had bought or would buy land for them, a few answered that one son would inherit the *kihamba* and the others would have to go out to work, but the reply of the great majority was: "I will beg *shamba* land for them from the chief." Here there is a problem.

The outlook of the cultured and sophisticated Chagga chiefs is quite different from that of the Tonga Native Authorities. It is remarkably modern. They see the mountain lands of the future divided into specialised coffee plantations of viable size, and the lower *shamba* lands developed as comparatively large arable farms supplying food to the planters and producing a surplus for export. The inevitable landless population in excess of local labour requirements will, they hope, be absorbed by a general expansion of Tanganyika's economy. The majority of the people share neither the vision nor the faith in an expanding economy. They want *shamba* land for their own immediate needs and to provide for their sons. To meet this situation, and as a compromise until such time as a general land-use policy can be devised, grants of rights to *shamba* land are made, very freely it seems. I was frequently told that "to get *shamba* land you have only to ask: if the chief refuses you go to your elected Councillor and he sees that you get some land." These grants are, however, made on the condition that they may be revoked at the end of any season. The grantee is entitled to crop the land, but his right is automatically extinguished after harvest and renewed at the next planting season. This innovation is greatly disliked and many of the people question the right of the Chagga Council to institute such a form of tenure. Some maintained that by building a hut on the land, planting a few banana stools, and enclosing the holding they had established *kihamba* rights which could not be disturbed; others simply said they regarded their *shamba* grants as permanent and would not give them up. I was told that grants of *shamba* land had even been "sold," in spite of the conditions of tenure, for as much as

£10 and £15 an acre. So far these rights have not been disturbed in any instance, as far as I could ascertain, and any attempt to do so would almost certainly precipitate a major conflict between the people and the Native Authority. Nor is this the only tension in the situation. As the eyes are picked from the lower region and the water sites occupied, the Masai watch the shrinking of their grazing lands with a rancour that is not lessened by the contrast between their former power and their present impotence.

Purchase is now a common method of acquiring land in many other regions of permanent crops and continuous cultivation. On high Elgon I was told that bare land suitable for coffee was commonly valued at about £25 an acre, but much higher prices are sometimes asked. My Gishu host complained of the high cost of land and by way of illustration showed me a piece he had thought of buying for which the owner was asking £200. It was a tiny plot little more than a tenth of an acre in extent! On further enquiry, I learned that the plot was regarded as a highly desirable store site and the owner, knowing that several traders were in the market for the site, was holding out for the highest price he could get for his plot as building land. In the more prosperous rural areas the question of sites for shops, trading stores, tea rooms, bars, artisans' premises, and the like, and the possibilities for speculation that come with individual tenure and shortage of land, are introducing new problems to agrarian situations that are already complex and confused.

In Buganda a figure around £25 an acre was also commonly mentioned as the value of coffee land, but Kikuyu in Kiambu and Nyeri told me they had paid £75 to £100 an acre for first-class land suitable for coffee or intensive market gardening, while in the high bracken zone of Kikuyuland some land had recently been sold for grazing purposes at a little over £5 an acre.

Although the change has come about mainly in regions of permanent cash crops and where the plough is in general use, there is some tendency for land sales to appear also in subsistence or semi-subsistence areas of hoe cultivation where land is in very short supply and money for its purchase can be obtained from other sources such as wage labour, livestock and fishing. We have already noted an example of this in the case of food-crop land on Ukara Island, which is said to be sold for as much as £50 an acre. A more curious example has been recorded among the subsistence-cultivating Luvale in a remote region on the Kalahari Sands of Northern Rhodesia. Here, in one area of relatively high population, where density is probably greatly in excess of the critical level, cash transactions in land have developed and prices up to £10 an acre are being paid. Yet in other regions of equal or even greater intensity of population pressure on the land, as in the case of the Ngoni areas of Fort Jameson, the selling of land has not yet become an accepted practice. The extent to which the process has taken place varies greatly with circumstances and the attitude of Native Authorities and peoples. In some cases a specific category of land has acquired a special value and become a saleable commodity while ordinary garden land has not. This seems to be the case in parts of the Luapula Valley, where the restricted and highly-prized sites for banana and vegetable gardens are sold, generally when an owner decides to leave the district, while sales of ordinary garden land are rare, if they occur at all.

In general, the main principle holds good: where money income is obtained by labour migration the hierarchical system or some remnant of it survives and the sale of land is resisted; but where cash cropping provides an adequate income the intermediate rights in land are eliminated and sale of land has become, or is in process of becoming, common and generally accepted practice.

CHAPTER XXI

THE CYCLE OF LAND DEGENERATION

1. EFFECTS OF POPULATION PRESSURE

The selling of land is often regarded as a hopeful development indicative of progress towards conservative farming on an individual basis, but this is not necessarily the case. Purchase is simply another means of acquiring land that comes into operation when, because of acute shortage or from some other cause, the traditional machinery fails. It does not follow that there will be any concomitant change of land-use or any lessening of population pressure on the land.

Every African, it has been said, is the centre of a web of kinship relations which carry with them rights and obligations. These rights and obligations are, of course, based on quaint and primitive concepts, such as personal responsibility for kin and neighbours, protection of the individual, concern for the needs of widows and orphans, security for the infirm and unfortunate, and respect for the aged. Since land is the only security and its use the only means of livelihood for most, the holders of land are expected to share with those of their kin who are in need, and refusal to do so would generally be regarded as conduct immoral in the highest extreme. To maintain himself as a farmer, with an acreage much in excess of subsistence needs, a man must cut himself off from his kin and repudiate the values and ethical standards of his people. Usually the strands of the web are too strong to be broken and the individualist finds himself unable to resist the social pressures that support and maintain traditional values. For this reason neither individual tenure of land nor traditional rights over fallow is any certain safeguard against subdivision and fragmentation.

It is not difficult to imagine what can happen in the case of a Shifting Cultivation system where there are no rights over resting land. Consider, as a theoretical example, a small-circle *citemene* system in which the entire food supply is obtained from the burnt gardens and the annual consumption of woodland for all purposes is 4 acres per head of population. Let us also suppose that the minimum period required for tree regeneration to a satisfactory level is twenty-three years and that 60 per cent of the area consists of woodland suitable for this form of *citemene*. Density of population must not exceed 4 to the square mile if the system is to be maintained. The "average" square mile will contain 384 acres of suitable woodland and at a density of 4 per square mile this will be cut through at a rate of 16 acres a year. Now let us suppose that the population density is suddenly increased to 6 per square mile. The newcomers can help themselves to any of the regenerating land and the whole of the increased population will start a cycle of cutting in woodland of twenty-two to twenty-three years' regeneration. The annual rate of consumption will now be 24 acres; the age of the woodland will decrease as cutting progresses, the cut area will be enlarged to compensate for this decrease, and the whole of the available area will be cut over in a matter of fifteen years. The second cycle of cutting must, therefore, begin in woodland of fourteen years' regeneration or less. The rate of cutting will continue to increase and the second cutting cycle may be completed in a matter of eleven years, leaving nothing on the area but scrub and small timber of not more than ten years' regrowth. Thus, in a matter of twenty-five years or so, the woodland may be reduced to scrub, with a consequent breakdown of the system, although there has been no further increase of population and it has remained at the low figure of 6 per square mile—a figure, incidentally, which is comparable with present population densities in the Scottish county of Sutherland and the states of New Mexico and Idaho. Four of the United States have lower or much lower population densities; so, for that matter, have vast regions of Canada, Australia, South America, and other parts of the world.

In the case of Recurrent Cultivation systems of hoe cultivation a similar cycle of degeneration sets in when the Critical Density of population is exceeded, but the effects appear as soil depletion, often followed by erosion, rather than wholesale destruction of woodland cover. Rights over fallows are to a large extent nullified by the need to provide gardens for the surplus families. When no unallocated land remains, the needs of the landless must be met by transfers of land which is under rest from a cropping sequence. Such transfers may take the form of loans rather than outright gifts, the owner retaining his rights in the "resting" land, but social pressure is generally strong enough to prevent refusal of a loan of land to needy kin or termination of a loan. This occupation of the resting land results in reduction of the fallow period, followed by declining yields, and this in turn gives rise to a compensatory tendency to increase the area under crop. Fallow periods are further reduced and an increasingly rapid cycle of land degeneration is set in train.

On strong and erosion-resistant land of the Permanent Cultivation category the results may be delayed, but eventually soil structure breaks down under continuous arable cultivation and the onset of erosion sets in. Where such soils are used for continuous banana culture, as in the Chagga system, there may, however, be no physical deterioration of the land. The symptoms of degeneration appear in the form of land subdivision and fragmentation; acute land shortage develops, and poverty increases, although the fertility and productivity of the soil remains unimpaired.

The growing of an annual cash crop such as cotton accelerates the cycle of degeneration, for the extension of the cultivated area to include the cash crop has much the same effect as an increase of population. When cotton is introduced to an otherwise unaltered system of traditional land-use the system is, in effect, modified to one of lower human carrying-capacity, in a degree which is proportional to the area of the commercial crop.

We have already noted examples of degenerative change, caused by population pressure alone and in combination with cash cropping. Continuation of these processes leads to the creation of what are often called "rural slums." These are areas in which yields have fallen, or productivity in relation to population has declined, to so low a level that the food supply is far below requirements even in a good season and the population can maintain itself only by exporting labour and importing food. The "Ngoni devastated area" in Northern Rhodesia, where old gardens are kept in cultivation although "they only yield a few miserable crops" (132), is now largely in this condition: but the most extensive and impressive examples are to be seen in the Native Reserves of South Africa where land shortage, caused by reservation of land for European farming and accentuated by population increase, has long been acute.

The most recently published estimates of yields of the main grain crops in Bantu areas of the Republic are illuminating (50).

AVERAGE YIELDS OF RAIN-GROWN CROPS
(IN LB PER ACRE)

	MAIZE	SORGHUM
1954–5	198	178
1955–6	132	170
1956–7	268	184

The minimum grain yield required to provide a bare subsistence is something of the order of 400 lb per acre, allowing for seed and normal wastage. It is hardly surprising, therefore, that in the rather poor season 1955–6, when "rainfall was generally less favourable than in other years but did not give cause for concern," the shortage of grain in the Bantu areas was estimated at well over 5 million bags (of 200 lb), against a total production of less than 2¾ million bags of maize, sorghum, and winter cereals. In the following year, in spite of favourable climatic conditions, the Report of the Department of Native Affairs again records a deficit: "Owing to the Bantu's injudicious agricultural methods which, despite all the extension work of the Department, are improving very slowly, the production of cereals in the Bantu areas was again insufficient to meet the requirements." The deficit of that year was estimated at about 2¾ million bags. This situation, it seems, has its bright side, since it enables the African to become a fully economic man by providing the European farmer with labour and a market for his produce. The report continues: "There is, however, no danger of a food shortage or famine since sufficient grain is obtainable from European areas. There also continues to be a large demand for Bantu labour and the income from farming can easily be supplemented." The average European farm in the Republic is some 2,200 acres in extent.

Individual tenure of freehold land did not prevent subdivision or arrest the cycle of land degeneration in these Native Reserves of South Africa. Rhodes' Glen Grey Act of 1894 provided for a gradual change from tribal tenure to individual ownership, but even earlier than this the experiment of settling Xhosa people on freehold land was started at Keiskamahoek. The farms were of a fair size, averaging 40 acres, with additional grazing on village commonage. Today these freehold farms are barely distinguishable from the tribal lands of the Reserve. Population densities are almost equally excessive on freehold and tribal land, and standards of productivity have fallen to much the same wretched level. Some of the farms are still held in the name of a descendant of the original owner, but they have become, in practice if not on paper, intensively subdivided among lineage members, while other land-less families have settled as squatters on the communal grazing land. Other forms of tenure, including quitrent with legal provision for the prevention of subdivision, and modifications of the traditional pattern of land-holding, were tried with no better results. Every area, irrespective of the type of tenure, has become a rural slum in which no family is self-supporting from the land and all depend to a greater or lesser extent on the wages of labour. Four and a half million acres of European farm land bought for African settlement at a cost of £7 million is in no better state.

2. Subdivision and Fragmentation of Land

By "subdivision" is meant the splitting up of the land into holdings too small to provide a reasonable standard of living. Subdivision may be "hidden," in the sense that rights are held in undivided shares and too many people are working on and trying to obtain a living from a single holding, or it may consist in the physical division of the land into separately held parcels of inadequate size. The term "fragmentation" is used to denote the form of parcellation in which the holding consists of a number of separate pieces of land so scattered as to make efficient cultivation and management impracticable. The two forms of land division occur together where the aggregate area of all the parcels comprising a fragmented holding is below the desirable minimum. In the sense in which the terms are used here, "subdivision" indicates a multiplicity of owners, "fragmentation" indicates a multiplicity of parcels comprising a single holding.

In the case of African traditional systems a stage of subdivision may be said to have set in as soon as the Critical Population Density has been exceeded. The amount of available land is then insufficient to allow of the regeneration period required to maintain fertility and the size of the "holding" has fallen below the desirable minimum for the system, even though, at this stage, the cultivated acreage can still be extended at the expense of a further curtailment of the rest period. This process is then likely to continue, as the fallow area is used up, until the stage of acute sub-division and fragmentation of the cultivated land is reached. At this point, with the total collapse of its agrarian foundations, the whole cultural and social structure is likely to crumble, as happened in Kikuyuland, and a completely landless class may emerge.

Fragmentation develops rapidly to a serious degree under conditions of land shortage in the case of permanent systems on land of the Permanent Cultivation category and where, as on Ukara Island, land has come under continuous cultivation. In these circumstances an individual can extend his cultivated acre-age only by acquiring additional scattered parcels of land. Once land shortage has become acute, inheritance rights are claimed even over distant parcels of land, which in easier circumstances would pass to others better situated to make use of them, and the accumulation of fragments that comes about in this way is supple-mented by the scramble to buy land, however small and scattered the parcels that are offered may be.

In Chaggaland, where there is direct father to son inheritance, land purchase is the main cause of fragmentation of *kihamba* land, judging by the small sample of 20 holdings I was able to investi-gate, and the results of enquiry. Inheritance seems to have resulted in subdivision rather than fragmentation, for the inherited holdings, and others acquired by transfers between brothers and other close patrilineal kin, were generally small and in one parcel, or occasion-ally in two and very rarely in three or more parcels. Larger hold-ings acquired mainly by purchase over a long period, and in some cases added to in the past by "begging" land from chiefs, com-monly consisted of 5 to 8 parcels often several miles apart and sometimes in different administrative divisions of Chaggaland. The extreme example I came across was a holding consisting of 14 fragments of which 11 had been acquired by purchase.

The area of the *kihamba* belt of Chaggaland, taken as that part of the Moshi district above the Arusha-Tanga road and excluding the alienated land, is 328 square miles.[1] Estimates of the resident population in this area vary from 266,000 to 310,000, according to varying computations of the absentee population in the township and in employment elsewhere. Population density, therefore, almost certainly exceeds 800, and may have reached or even ex-ceeded 900, to the square mile. Under this degree of pressure the

[1] I am indebted to the District Surveyor, Moshi, for computing this figure.

land has become greatly subdivided. Official estimates, and the Chagga themselves, say that the average family holding of *kihamba* land is still about three acres, the area the Chagga regard as the minimum required for decent living. My impression was that it is now less than this, probably somewhere between 2 and 2·5 acres, and there are certainly a great many families with much less. Behind the façade of Chagga prosperity there is a good deal of poverty—the poverty of the family with an acre of *kihamba* or even less. One such family I visited, a man, his wife, their two children and his mother, lived in a single beehive hut of plantain leaves which they shared with two goats and a calf. His *kihamba* of rather less than an acre could produce, he said, about two-thirds of the family's food requirements and the balance had to be bought. The return from his 200 coffee bushes was just about enough to make good the food deficiency, after he had paid his poll tax, his local government tax, and his co-operative society dues. There would be food enough for the family while it remained small, but nothing more.

On the other hand, the high degree of fragmentation that developed in the more variable environment of the Kikuyu Reserves appears to have come about mainly through inheritance, by the division of holdings among groups of heirs in such a way as to give each heritor shares in different categories and qualities of land. The process was aided also by transmission of land in different lines (for a man might inherit part of his father's holding and a share in his mother's dowry land), and by the long-established custom of redeemable and irredeemable sales of land. Here, as in Chaggaland, some men have accumulated and retained comparatively large holdings, from 20 acres upwards: a few Kikuyu even have more than 100 acres, while the largest *kihamba* holding I heard of in Chaggaland was little more than 30 acres. In Kiambu, for example, about 4 per cent of holdings exceed 20 acres in extent but nearly 50 per cent are less than 4 acres, including uncultivable land, and there is a fairly large landless class, the *Ahoi*. In Chaggaland I also met men who said they had no land, and no hope of acquiring any since they could not save from their wages as labourers, but on further questioning all of them admitted to having rights in *shamba* land.

Cocoa plantations in Ghana are commonly fragmented to some extent, at least among native farmers in the more recently planted regions. Akim farmers I visited generally had 3 to 8 separate parcels of land in cocoa, sometimes a few hundred yards and sometimes several miles apart. Here land is acquired by village members, apparently with little or no formality, by the act of clearing unclaimed neighbourhood forest. A stranger, of course, would have to buy land, but the native farmer simply selects and partially clears a site, leaving what he considers adequate shade. He then plants his cocoa and interplants food crops for a year or two. When the cocoa is established he repeats the process, but as many others are doing the same thing he may have to go some distance to find suitable unclaimed land, and in the course of time he becomes the possessor of a number of generally small and scattered plantations. This, then, is a form of fragmentation resulting from haphazard acquisition of land for a permanent crop, rather than from general land shortage. As yet, under present methods of production, it may be of no great moment, but it is likely to prove a serious handicap to the introduction of higher standards of land-use and management.

In the older and more highly populated parts of the cocoa belt, where land is now limited, holdings are quite commonly acquired by gift. These are absolute transfers and they are mostly made by parents to children or by kinship groups to individual members. I met a considerable number of men who said they had received their land as gifts from their fathers. This, it seems, is a device to evade the normal rules of inheritance among the matrilineal Akim, the group of tribes which occupies most of the cocoa region. There is a strong feeling that matrilineal inheritance should be changed by law, but in the meantime evasion is commonly practised through the system of transfer by gift. Here, too, land is frequently mortgaged as security for credit, legal ownership passing to the creditor while the debtor remains in occupation; or it is "pledged" or "pawned." In the latter form of transaction the creditor occupies and uses the land and the profits he makes cover interest on the debt, while the creditor retains ownership. The land becomes redeemed as soon as the capital debt has been repaid. Here, as in many other rural communities, the ability to mortgage and pledge land has resulted in a heavy burden of indebtedness.

A form of fragmentation has also developed in the North Ghanaian region of concentric ring cultivation. Any land which can be acquired is cultivated, under pressure of the need to compensate for falling yields, even if it is some miles from the homestead. Consequently, there are gardens which are neither bush gardens nor part of the typical "compound" pattern. These extensions are generally cropped in the same way as the semi-compound garden, but they are never manured and rarely if ever rested. One man may own several such extensions, in addition to his compound "farm" and a number of bush plots.

Others in this region have neither extensions nor bush plots. I spent a morning with one family who had only a small homestead garden of about 3·65 acres, divided into 0·15 of an acre of kitchen garden, 1·5 acres of compound garden, and 2 acres of semi-compound garden. They had no other land, they said, and they could not acquire more because every uncultivated area was reserved for livestock: in any case, they added, the grazing was all poor land barely fit for cultivation. They had no cattle, but they owned three goats and about forty poultry. The "garden family" consisted of two brothers with their wives and three children. This pattern is not uncommon among the Kusasi and other peoples of the north. When the head of a family dies, the male survivors inherit the land as tenants in common, the eldest son taking the place of the father, and so hidden subdivision takes place. At the time of my visit in early September, the two families had no food of their own but immature groundnuts which they were lifting as they needed them. The first millet had been reaped and eaten. It was a very poor crop, so they had taken it out early and planted a catch-crop of groundnuts to tide them over. In four weeks or so the sorghum would be ripe and until then they could make out on their groundnuts and small gifts of food from kin and neighbours. The situation was accepted phlegmatically as nothing out of the ordinary. When I asked why they had no cow-peas the brothers explained that during a hunger period of the previous season the women had taken the seed to feed their children and by the time the men discovered this it was too late to get more. Here was the apathy of chronic hunger. Neither of the men, it seemed, had any intention of looking for work. They were too tired, they said; there was no work in the neighbourhood at that time; they had no money and no energy to undertake the long trek to the south.

The family of "bullock farmers" I visited in the afternoon of the same day were rich by comparison: their granary was well filled with early millet. They were not "plough farmers," for they had no plough, but they managed to cultivate a good 12 acres, of which 5 acres were well manured. With two bullocks, four cows, and three calves, the family were also rich in cattle, for few households in this area had more than one or two head of large stock and many had none. At the instigation of the Agricultural Department, they augmented the manure supply from these animals by bedding them down with cut grass. This called for more labour, for they had no cart and the grass had to be transported and the manure carried to the field in head loads. Yet the labour strength of the bullock farming family, in which there were two ageing members, appeared to be less than that of their hungry counterpart. The head of the farming household had died some years previously, his three sons had emigrated to the south, and the garden family as I found it consisted of the widow[1] and brother of the dead man with the brother's son and his wife and two children. The cultivated area amounted to two acres for each member, sufficient to ensure a surplus even at low yield levels, and this enabled the group to command the labour of needy neighbours by offerings of beer and food. In this way they were able to keep the area in production and to maintain a level of fertility much above the average. But the labour was withdrawn from the gardens of the workers at the time it was most needed, and they received little if any reciprocal help since they could make no offerings of beer. Thus, in such circumstances, a limited improvement may be achieved at the expense of much greater areas of garden land.

Much of the grain surplus of this homestead was, in effect, exchanged for labour, but some was sold. Even from this hungry region food is sold, and it seems that some is exported, for Mossi people from the densely populated country of the Upper Volta are said to come down to buy grain. The sellers are not only "bullock farmers" and other comparatively large land-holders. There is what has been described as a "pernicious instinct to market," an urge to offer something on market day however trifling it may be. Food which is in no sense surplus is sold after harvest and this is bought back, if any money remains, in times of shortage when prices are high.

[1] She appeared to be the head of the household, but this may have been a matter of personality rather than tradition. She was a formidable woman.

3. Soil Erosion

The cycle of land degeneration and its association with population densities have been remarked by most writers on the problems of Africa. In his *African Afterthoughts* (118) Sir Philip Mitchell wrote: "As soon as population reaches a certain density in East and Central Africa it destroys the soil with a devastating ruthlessness; and the land problem of the region is just that. . . ." Elspeth Huxley says of northern Ghana: "The land is fertile but very light: to overcultivate without frequent resting tears its heart out. The people multiply and so overcultivating is what it gets" (90). From time to time attention has been concentrated on facets of the problem. There was a period when soil erosion was regarded as the great evil and dire prophecies were made, such as this one by a soil scientist in 1941: "It was stated a few years ago that at the then rate of erosion the United States would be incapable of organised existence by the end of the century. For much of Africa, where erosion is a more rapid process, the end of the century would be an optimistically distant date for the end of human dominion over the land" (92).

The erodibility of a soil is largely determined by its texture and structure and slope. By "texture" is meant the size and distribution of the ultimate particles into which the soil can be broken down. Coarse-textured soils containing a high proportion of large particles allow rainfall to penetrate easily and do not erode readily unless there is an underlying impervious sub-soil. By "structure" is meant the state of aggregation of the ultimate soil particles into water-stable compound particles called soil "crumbs." A good crumb structure is characteristic of fertile and durable soils resistant to erosion under conditions of heavy rainfall. Rainfall, as Ellison has pointed out (53), is water and energy, and the energy developed under conditions of tropical precipitation is enormous. The explosive force of raindrops falling on bare soil breaks the surface crumbs and splashes the fragments, which are then carried away in the run-off. Cultivation also tends to break down the crumb structure and induce erosion, while fallow periods under a suitable natural or established vegetation cover promote its formation. The texture, structure, and organic matter content of soils are closely related factors which determine the rate of erosion of a particular soil on a given slope, but the parent material and the type of weathering it has undergone also appear to influence erodibility.

"For tropical soils, perhaps the most significant criterion is the silica-sesquioxide ratio, soils with low ratios being relatively slightly erodible. It is fortunate that the type of weathering that normally occurs under the conditions of high temperature and high rainfall characteristic of large parts of the tropics tends to produce soils of this type. Were it otherwise, erosion losses would be far more disastrous than they actually are" (163).

The African systems of land-use had their own protective devices against erosion. The chief of these was the fallow. Even soils of high fertility, which might have been cultivated continuously for long periods, were usually rested under a brief grass cover frequently enough to preserve the structure and prevent serious erosion losses. During the cultivation period, mixed cropping with a cover of ground-crops protected the soil. Steeply sloping and readily erodible land was avoided. Although such land is now cultivated, usually with disastrous results, when no alternative remains, it is properly to be regarded as coming within the "uncultivable" sector for most of the traditional systems of land-use. Where the necessity of cultivating steeply sloping land was forced upon a people in the past, as it was in the refuge areas, they evolved devices in no way inferior to our own anti-erosion practices: devices such as the Matengo pit system, the ridging and tie-ridging of the Kara and others, silt-traps and live and dead wash-stops, and elaborate systems of stone-walled terracing. That modern Africans do not react in this way to their more pressing land problems is symptomatic of a loss of group initiative and self-reliance, and of new attitudes, concepts, and values developed under European tutelage and dominance. There was no refuge area safe from the alien conqueror with his incessant and insatiable demands for labour, tax money, and economic crops.

As pressure on the land increased with population growth and the production of cash crops, and the systems degenerated, erosion problems came into prominence. Soil conservation, by the construction of mechanical works and the introduction of anti-erosion practices, became one of the main activities of Departments of Agriculture in many African territories. Indeed, one might say that a soil conservation phase followed upon and overlapped with the phase of concentration on economic crops. The approach was largely empirical, for there was neither the time nor the means for exhaustive investigations and trials, and it was realised that these conservation measures must not be regarded as an end in themselves but as a first step towards new systems of husbandry capable of maintaining and enhancing fertility. A sense of urgency prevailed: "You must first rescue a drowning man before teaching him to swim," wrote one Director of Agriculture who was a master of the felicitous phrase. The drowning man was not at all anxious to be rescued if this meant any additional exertion on his part. Soil conservation measures were usually applied under compulsion and against resistance which did not always come only from the cultivators. Sometimes the administrators could not see the need for these disturbing and unpopular innovations. In the Kondoa-Irangi district of Tanganyika, where advancing erosion caused by increasing numbers of humans and livestock had caused alarm even in German times, two successive Provincial Commissioners of the 1930s roundly declared that the situation had been grossly exaggerated and there was no serious erosion. This dissension between Agriculture and Administration, by no means an isolated example, resulted in the withdrawal of all agricultural staff from the Central Province. There was no satisfactory forum for airing divergent opinions and no effective machinery for decision. By the time agricultural staff returned to Kondoa-Irangi erosion had advanced to the stage of severe gulleying, much fertile top-soil had been lost, and the situation appeared to be little short of hopeless.

One could understand the administrator's difficulty in sharing the agriculturist's viewpoint. He was often well versed in the wonders of science as presented by the "digest" type of literature and he knew that modern knowledge and techniques offered a boundless future of abundance for all mankind. All the agriculturist had to do was to teach good agriculture and the land would be able to support unlimited numbers in prosperity and content. On one occasion, many years ago, I had re-settled an area at a density which I thought to be well below the critical level, but I was afraid that it might become rapidly overpopulated by migration from part of the old Reserve which remained temporarily overcrowded. I pointed out this possibility, suggesting that the situation should be watched and any tendency to large-scale movement checked as far as possible. The District Commissioner commented: "What is the objection to free movement? On the face of it, it is the rapid exhaustion of the soil of the new areas by excessive population. The Reserves, however, with no agricultural work have supported dense populations for 17 years [in this short time they had, in fact, become rapidly-eroding rural slums]. The main deterioration has been caused by erosion. In the new areas there will be no erosion—they will carry their population for longer than 17 years and during that period there will surely be improvements in agricultural methods which will again expand, perhaps limitlessly, the period of occupation. If, however, the new areas do show signs of becoming exhausted then the problem becomes a purely agricultural one." As it happened, I was back in that area some fifteen years later and there were no signs of the improvements in agricultural methods so confidently predicted. But population had remained fairly well-balanced and the land had come to no harm.

In spite of disagreements and difficulties, conservation by compulsion did much to retard the rate of land degeneration in many areas, until the development of political climates which made coercive measures impracticable. A recent report from Tanganyika records regression (18). "Little progress has been made in improving agricultural practices in the Uluguru mountains since legal sanctions were withdrawn. . . . Following the repeal of most of the Sukumaland Agricultural Rules, 1959 has been a year of regression. In many areas tie-ridging was neglected and considerable erosion occurred as a result. Several areas that were previously closed to stock, and where soil conservation works had been constructed, were opened to grazing. . . . People in the Central Province are becoming reluctant to do communal work such as soil conservation measures."

Soil conservation works must be maintained if they are to remain effective, and their maintenance is often a greater problem than their construction. When I re-visited the Tonga country recently the works which had been made in the early 1940s were mostly in a sad state of disrepair. The graded contour banks, or narrow-based terraces, were broken in places by footpaths and cattle trampling, drains were choked by vegetation, and in many places a plough ridge which impeded the entry of run-off water had formed above the lip of the drain. Previously these works had been maintained—reluctantly, it must be admitted, and under a Native Authority Order—by the cultivators whose lands they protected. At one time during the War, when I was concerned with the settlement of refugees from Europe, I found exactly the same dislike of anti-erosion works and reluctance to maintain them among Polish farmers. They even broke the contour banks deliberately, to get water away as quickly as possible and to simplify cultural operations.

4. SUCCESS AND FAILURE

Throughout Africa profound changes appear to have taken place since the beginning of the century, and in many countries the increase of wealth has been remarkable. Uganda is a case in point. In 1904 the total value of domestic exports from that country was a mere £60,000: in 1957 the value of agricultural exports alone was £43 million, of which nearly £41 million was accounted for by cotton and coffee produced almost entirely by Africans. Yet even in fortunate and prosperous Uganda all is not well, although pressure of population on the land is as yet no more than local. Commenting on the great increase in production, the report of the Agricultural Productivity Committee says: "Western civilisation has failed to induce a new outlook towards efficiency and productivity. The changes which have taken place in the last half century, though they appear spectacular in many ways, are only superficial. Traditional attitudes and behaviour in the rural areas are still a major obstacle in the way of technological progress" (3).

The increase of wealth appears less spectacular when it is broken down into family incomes. The average cotton-growing family in Teso probably cultivates about two and a quarter acres of this crop: at 1959 levels of yields and prices this would give a gross cash return, for a family of 5 or 6 people, of about £13. Where labour is employed (and this is often the case) the net return is very small. But a better crop of finger millet is obtained in the year following cotton, probably because of the deep-rooted habit of this crop, and an additional profit is sometimes obtained by making and selling beer. Yields of cotton are now low, averaging only about 280 lb of seed cotton per acre for Uganda as a whole, and preference in cultivation is given to the main food crop rather than the cash crop. In Teso, cotton tends to be regarded as a preparatory crop for finger millet.

It seems that the output of cotton has reached its limits in the main producing countries, at least for present methods of production. In the Congo, where production increased spectacularly in the period 1920–40 and then flattened out, the conclusion had been reached by 1954 that no further increase could be expected without the large-scale use of chemical fertiliser (2). Uganda's peak production came in 1938 and the same level has never since been reached. Indeed, it may be that commodity production in general is on the decline. This view was expressed by Sir Philip Mitchell in one of his dispatches on land problems in East Africa: "Thirty years ago it seemed to us that the introduction of economic crops to be grown by African peasants afforded the opportunity of effective and permanent improvement in the standard of living and the production of wealth without a radical change in the methods of agriculture. Now I believe firmly that research will disclose that primary production by African peasants in the manner in which it has been hitherto developed is already on the decline, and that in fact, far from there being any possibility of its substantial increase, populations working under this system are going to find increasing difficulty in supporting themselves even at the present level." Lord Hailey, in his monumental *African Survey*, also notes the signs of land degeneration and their implications: "A rising standard of living cannot be built on a falling level of soil fertility."

The fact has to be faced that in the main problem areas of Africa—and these are, in general, the areas of highest fertility and most favourable climate—the land is not enough to support the present numbers of humans and livestock, nor can the existing land be improved sufficiently to support such numbers. This is recognised in the Report of the East Africa Royal Commission, where it is pointed out (p. 422) that "in crowded areas the introduction of a more efficient system of production will cause a general problem of displacement." Yet, the Commissioners add, "it is essential to avoid the creation of a landless and homeless proletariat which cannot find employment in the towns . . ." and (p. 292) "as this surplus population cannot be absorbed in non-agricultural pursuits, new land has to be found for it."

To anyone familiar with population distribution patterns in Africa, but unfamiliar with the technical, economic, and human problems involved in the re-distribution and re-settlement of peoples, this might seem a task of no great difficulty. There are great areas which are very sparsely inhabited or even in parts uninhabited, but these are mainly the droughtlands and the swamp regions, where reclamation calls for very heavy and in most cases uneconomic capital expenditure, or the vast areas of poor weak soils such as those associated with the *miombo* plateau woodland. The technical problems of the miserably poor soils so common in Africa have received little attention, and it is improbable that any economic system capable of maintaining considerable population densities can be devised for them. When development and working capital has to be employed economic barriers as rigid as any of the physical barriers that nature has erected are soon encountered. We often overlook the fact that our own system of land-use is highly selective of soils, and we use intensive methods only on land that will give an economic return (with the assistance of subsidies). One does not find intensive farming or high rural population densities on the bracken and heather hills of Scotland—where one is more likely to find a grazing regime of one sheep to three acres—or on the heathlands and peats of desolate Dartmoor.

For these reasons, and also because of insistence on "development" and the common belief that if Africans are given more land they will at once proceed to destroy it, planned redistribution of population has never been carried out on a scale sufficient to have a significant effect in the problem areas, though there have been a great many resettlement schemes of varying magnitude and in a variety of forms.

By the end of the first fifty years of agricultural effort, standards of African land-use showed a general decline and fertility was falling. An advanced state of decay, with increasing soil loss by erosion, had been reached in the overcrowded regions where the traditional systems had collapsed and been replaced by continuous cultivation. Elsewhere a slower rate of degeneration had been set in train by labour migration and withdrawal of the most active section of the labour force from rural areas, the weakening of traditional restraints on harmful land-use, and a general loss of self-reliance and sense of responsibility for the land under European domination. Latent resentment of external interference and domination in African affairs was finding expression in non-co-operation in measures originating from Europeans, including land improvement, and the atmosphere was one of growing suspicion and prejudice. These were all the portents of the gathering storm that was soon to burst in the violence of Mau Mau and the cataclysm of the Congo.

CHAPTER XXII

THE NEW FARMERS

1. THE REHABILITATION OF THE KIKUYU LANDS

Nowhere else in Africa has there been any general programme of agricultural improvement so complete, and
initially so successful, as the rehabilitation of the Kikuyu
lands following the Mau Mau emergency. This was a continuation and a breakthrough rather than something altogether new and
revolutionary. Work on similar lines, with limited resources and
against growing opposition, had been going on for some years
before the storm broke in 1952. There were areas where fragmented holdings had been consolidated and enclosed, much anti-
erosion work had been done, particularly on the steep ridges of the
Fort Hall district, coffee and pyrethrum were already being grown
to some extent, and a handful of African farmers had achieved a
high standard of land-use, including the skilful management of
grassland and cattle. By 1948 a programme of "district betterment" had been launched in Nyeri, with the ambitious objective
of raising the general standard of land-use to the optimum level of
intensive mixed farming. But African political leaders openly
advocated non-co-operation and the old story that it was all a trick
of the Europeans to get possession of the land was going the
rounds. Progress was despairingly slow.

The situation at this time is recalled by a correspondent in the
Daily Telegraph. He had shown Jomo Kenyatta round the
Makueni settlement, just before the father of Kenya nationalism
was due to address a meeting called for the purpose of urging non-
co-operation. Kenyatta is reported to have approved the agricultural work and to have said: "If we were governing our own
affairs not only would we support technical advice on land usage
and enforce strict compliance, but we would also ensure that our
advisers were adequately rewarded and respected." But, he added,
"he felt obliged to oppose regulations on land usage which involved

supporting what in his view was external interference and domination in African affairs."[1] This was in 1949.

Agricultural work, already bedevilled by the political situation, was thrown into confusion by the outbreak of Mau Mau violence, the murder of Agricultural Instructors and loyal Kikuyu, who were often the most progressive farmers, and the concentration of the whole population in great villages. But, "When the issues were clarified," to use a euphemism from an official publication, "the gains from the emergency outweighed the disadvantages." Opposition to the consolidation of holdings collapsed, and the Kikuyu, who understand as clearly as anyone else the evils of fragmentation, readily accepted what they had previously rejected. As Kikuyu were "repatriated" from other parts of Kenya and prisoners poured in, a huge labour force appeared for which it was imperative to find work—and what better work could be found for them than soil-conservation and land rehabilitation? Staff and money were provided on a scale which seems lavish in comparison with the past. In 1954, a five-year "Plan for the Intensification of African Agriculture in Kenya" replaced the old and much more parsimonious Development Plan. This new programme envisaged an expenditure of £8½ million, of which £5 million came as a grant from the British Government, and its ultimate aims were to bring about a tenfold increase of the income derived from cash crops by African families in the areas of high agricultural potential, and a similar increase in the value of cattle sold from the African lands. The admirable Kikuyu environment, with its excellent Permanent Cultivation soils and climate conducive to grass growth of high feed value, posed no very difficult technical problems: experience gained in temperate regions was more readily applicable here than elsewhere in Africa, and there was the large body of knowledge accumulated by European farming in the same environment. Another enormous advantage was the possibility of growing high-value cash crops (so long as demand and prices remain high): arabica coffee, and tea and pyrethrum at higher altitudes. Thus, a comparatively small acreage would suffice to provide the minimum desirable standard of living for a family, which was taken to be self-sufficiency in food and a cash profit of £100 a year. In addition to all this, there were the powers given to Government by the emergency regulations, and

[1] George S. Cowley, *Daily Telegraph*, 26 Jan. 1961.

the fact that the Kikuyu social and agrarian system was in chaos and they themselves were looking for new foundations and a new order.

To say that conditions favoured a dramatic change, and that the means of initiating and directing such change were available, is in no way to disparage the splendid work that has been done in the Kikuyu lands: but it would be a grave error to assume that this work can be used as a blue-print for an agrarian revolution in Africa, or throughout East Africa, and it is too early to assess the permanence of the gains that have been made.

Land consolidation—the gathering of each family's scattered fragments into a single holding—progressed rapidly. When I visited Kiambu in 1959 the work was practically completed there, though it had got off to a good start only about four years before, and the other districts were not far behind (see Plate 8). The whole programme was reported as having been completed early in 1961. Details of procedure varied in the different districts, for they were left a good deal of latitude in working out their own problems. But there was one universal rule: consolidation was never imposed by compulsion. As soon as the people of an area had declared for consolidation by a large majority the process went ahead in five main stages: (1) survey based on aerial photography, (2) measurement and recording of all fragmented holdings and drawing up of the consolidation plan, (3) the hearing of complaints by committees of clan elders, (4) demarcation and enclosure of consolidated holdings, (5) registration of the holdings and issue of title in the form of registration certificates. In one operation consolidation was achieved, and the establishment of unquestionable individual ownership, with an immediate ending of the almost universal, long-drawn-out and wasteful legal disputes over land ownership and rights. No doubt there was some discontent, but I do not think it amounted to very much: my impression was that the process was proceeding with remarkably little friction. This was probably due largely to the co-operation of the tribal elders and other men of influence, and to the generally high quality and uniformity of the land. Consolidation is a much more difficult process where great inequalities in land values exist and compensating adjustments of acreage have to be made. Furthermore, the process had not advanced to the extreme stage found in some of the old countries of peasant agriculture. In

Cyprus, for example, the average holding in the Mesaoria, the central plain, is some 18 acres divided into 13 fragments so scattered that the farmer would have to walk about 20 miles to visit every one of them; and these fragments, though farmed as a single holding, often have a multiplicity of owners. Water rights and economic trees are also fantastically "fragmented," to the extent that one carob tree may have twenty owners. Even more fantastic fragmentation, reaching 30 fragments to the holding, has been recorded in parts of India and elsewhere. In Kikuyuland the average number of fragments was some six or seven, and the smallest "fragment" recorded was a single banana plant.

The process of consolidation did not, of course, cure subdivision. Each land-holder got much the same acreage as he had had before—perhaps, on the whole, a little more. Areas were set aside, on the recommendation of committees of clan elders and officials of Government for necessary public purposes such as townships, schools, hospitals, churches, and roads, and a proportionate deduction was made from the holding of each land-holder. On the other hand, some "uncultivable" land and former common grazing was absorbed in the new holdings.

The consolidated holding was placed, as far as possible, where the major portion of the fragmented holding had been, and care was taken to ensure that each had a service road and access to water. Enclosure was regarded as essential and in this climate it is entirely practicable, for hedges of various materials can be established rapidly and with little difficulty: the materials used include, from higher to lower altitudes, bramble, coleus, euphorbia, Mauritius thorn, and sisal. As soon as demarcation had been completed labour gangs came in to trench the boundary lines in preparation for the planting of live hedges.

By 1959 the legal instruments too had been consolidated in a lengthy and complex bill "to provide for the ascertainment of rights and interests in, and for the consolidation of, land in the native lands; for the registration of title to, and the transactions and devolutions affecting, such land; and for purposes connected therewith and incidental thereto" (123). Another bill provided for the setting up of Provincial and Divisional Native Land Control Boards, to regulate and control the sale, lease, partition, and subdivision of the consolidated land (100).

This process of consolidation was, of course, regarded not as an end in itself but as an essential preliminary to better land-use, which was to be brought about by grass-arable rotations—in effect a reversion to the old fallow break—the use of manure to build up the fertility of the reduced arable acreage, soil conservation practices, and the planting of cash crops. In addition, only level and moderately sloping land (0–20 per cent slope) was to be used for the arable grass rotation, steepish land (20–35 per cent) was to be used for permanent cash crops and mulch, with suitable soil conservation works, while steep slopes (over 35 per cent) were to be kept under permanent grass or trees. People who showed an aptitude for progressive farming, by successful practice of the more elementary principles of good land-use, became eligible for assistance in the form of farm lay-outs and, if they survived this "apprenticeship" stage, farm planning.

The acreage which could be regarded as constituting an economic family holding, or the area below which subdivision should not be permitted, did not appear to have been clearly decided. This decision, I was told, was to be left to the Provincial Land Boards. Agricultural opinion was, however, fairly unanimous: the minimum should not be less than 6 acres (some said 7) in the central zone, 12 acres in the high altitude zone, and 14 acres (some said 18) in the lower zone. Administrative officers, more acutely conscious of the problems likely to be created by large-scale displacement, seemed generally to favour a lower minimum of about 3 acres, below which subdivision would not be permitted. The question is not one which can be decided easily or on the basis of irrefutable argument. Even when the minimum desirable standard of living—subsistence plus £100 per annum, or whatever it may be—and the systems of farming have been agreed, the acreage required in a given environment to produce this standard depends on a number of variable factors such as the amount of labour the family is able and willing to provide, the availability and cost of hired labour, and, most imponderable of all, producer prices for cash crops and livestock products.

It is not difficult to demonstrate, on a basis of coffee (at high price levels) and very intensive mixed farming with highly productive milk cows, that a holding of about three acres could provide subsistence for a small family and an income of £100 a year or more; provided, of course, that the holding consisted entirely of first-class and wholly cultivable land. But the agricultural economist is apt to upset the calculation by estimating the labour requirement and pointing out that such a holding could not be worked at the required level of intensity by family labour alone— except on the assumption that men and women are perfect labour machines, capable of high and sustained output, that women have no household and family duties to divert their labour from the farm, that seasons are always favourable, and that sickness and misfortune never strike. The very small mixed farm offers little scope for economic employment of paid labour, mechanisation, or even the use of ox power. Work oxen would have to be kept on and fed from the holding, and they would displace the income-earning milk cows. Specialisation in coffee might well be a more economic proposition for the smallholder, if he could rely on stable prices, but it is an essential feature of the scheme that the farmer must not have all his eggs in the same basket.

We have noted that in Chaggaland three acres of *kihamba* is regarded as just sufficient to provide a decent standard of living for a small family, but here the situation is different. The Chagga are, in effect, coffee specialists rather than mixed farmers, and in their region of permanent banana culture the same land yields both food and cash crops for an input of labour which is not excessive, apart from the new need to carry cut grass over long distances. Furthermore, the Chagga assume that the family will have an additional acre or two of *shamba* to augment the food supply, and access to natural grassland sufficient to provide fodder and litter. The livestock are not fed from the holding. For mixed farming in the best areas of Kenya, with livestock fed entirely from the holding, an estimate of six acres as the minimum desirable family holding does not seem excessive. The successful farmers are, in general, those with larger acreages.

In farm planning, as it is practised in the Kikuyu areas and elsewhere in Kenya, the flatter land on the holding is divided into a number of fields of equal size for the grass-arable rotation. There may be 8 fields, with 4 in temporary grass and 4 in crop (see Fig. 11), or 7 fields with 3 in grass and 4 in arable, or, if livestock is to be the main economic activity, a 6 grass–2 crop rotation may be followed. The number of fields and the proportion of temporary grass to annual crop land is determined by the size and nature of the holding and the economic basis of the plan. Fertility is built up and maintained by the alternation of grass and arable cultivation, and the application of farmyard manure to each field at least once during the cycle of rotation. Crop rotations commonly include maize, vegetables, beans, potatoes, and sweet potatoes, and manure is often applied to the opening potato crop and the final cereal crop with which the grass is established. But no hard and fast cropping rules are imposed, for "it is considered better to drive home the rotation of grassland with arable and leave free choice as to the crops planted in the arable years to the farmer. He can then alter his planting programme year by year, according to the price situation, the state of readiness of his fields, the disease situation, and the suitability of the various crops which could be planted on his holding" (78).

In designing this part of the farm the fields are made long and narrow, as far as possible, to allow of long ploughing sweeps, with a view to future mechanisation. The internal field boundaries, which are on the contour (Fig. 11), are generally planted with thatching grass, to act as live wash-stops and to provide thatching and additional mulch for permanent crops, but other materials may be used for internal field boundaries if the farmer wishes and the planning officer approves.

The area for permanent cash crops (coffee and tea in the middle and higher zones respectively) is sited on the steeper land of the holding with slopes up to 35 per cent. In general, these crops occupy a fifth to a quarter of the holding, including the area of grass which must be grown close to the permanent crop to provide mulch (see Fig. 11), but the farmer may elect to have less cash crop and more arable or grazing. The permanent cash crops may be grown only under licence and stringent conditions are attached to the grant of a licence. In the case of coffee, which is restricted to the central zone below 6,000 feet, the grower must satisfy the department that he can maintain the area allocated to him; he must plant an area of mulch material in accordance with the Department's directions, grow only an approved variety of one type, obtain his planting material from official nurseries, and follow strictly all instructions regarding soil conservation, planting, cultivation, pruning, manuring, and the processing and disposal of the crop. He must also become a member of the local coffee co-operative society. This stringent control, amounting almost to directed cultivation, is intended to ensure high quality and a sound reputation for the native product, while the limitation on acreage is designed to serve the same end and to prevent economic dependence on a single crop. So far, the degree of success has been remarkable, but enforcement of the regulation depends on individual attention to growers and this becomes more and more difficult as the acreage increases.

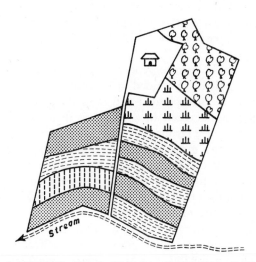

LAYOUT OF A SMALL KIKUYU FARM

🏠	HOMESTEAD, WITH BANANAS & FAMINE CROP	0·75 AC.
	COFFEE	1·00AC.
	NAPIER GRASS	1·00AC.

ARABLE GRASS ROTATION

	ARABLE, 4 PLOTS OF 0·5AC.	2·00AC.
	TEMPORARY GRASS, 4 PLOTS OF 0·5 AC.	2·00AC.
	PERMANENT GRASS	0·50 AC.

FIG. 11. The Layout of a small Kikuyu Farm.

The farm homestead is placed on a site which allows of ready access to every field, and an area around the homestead or close to it is set aside for household and reserve or "famine" crops, such as bananas, vegetables, sugarcane, and cassava (see Fig. 11). This completes the lay-out except for any remaining areas unsuitable for arable cultivation or permanent crops (over 35 per cent slope). Such land is put down to permanent grass, for grazing (see Fig. 11), or used for small tree plantations which provide building material and firewood.

Farm lay-outs conform in general to this type of design, but the plan is not rigid: it is intended to be flexible, so that later improvements may be incorporated and the balance between stock and arable may be adjusted in accordance with market trends. The basis was to be ley farming, or alternate husbandry, with full economic use of the grassland. This implies that the land is cropped and then laid down to temporary pasture (the ley) for a number of years before being broken up and cropped again, much as Permanent Cultivation land is used in the traditional African systems. But in ley farming the grass is established—by seeding Rhodes grass at higher altitudes in Kikuyuland, and by the laborious hand-planting of star grass in the central zone—and there is a profound difference in the management of the ley. It must be skilfully managed and neither over-grazed nor under-grazed. In most parts of Africa natural grass fallows are common grazing and they are almost invariably grossly overgrazed where cattle are numerous, and undergrazed elsewhere. Thus, the improvement of soil structure and the increase of fertility are greater and more rapid under the established and managed ley. In England the increase of fertility under a ley is very largely associated with the presence of wild white clover and its proper management, and it may well be that the success of the ley in the Kenya highlands is due at least partly to the fact that clovers can be grown with the grasses in this warm-temperate climate. In the main vegetational region of higher rainfall, concentration of animals and accumulation of manure or clearance of herbage by ploughing results in a highly productive natural sward of Kikuyu grass (*Pennisetum clandestinum*) and Kenya clover (*Trifolium johnstonii*), which can be maintained under intensive grazing management.

The problem of suitable livestock for the improved farms was not an easy one, despite the excellence of the grazing and the com-

parative ease with which it could be established. It was obvious
that high-yielding stock would be required to make full use of such
grazing and to ensure an economic return from the grassland, and
there were many reasons why a single breed should be used.
Finally, it was decided to introduce grade Guernseys in the areas
of high potential. The "golden breed," as it is called in its home
island, was chosen because of the high butterfat content of the
milk (with an eye to the future when the market for whole-milk
would be saturated) and also because of the high insemination rate
of the cows, for artificial insemination was to be the basis of breeding. This decision was not unheroic, and there were many who
had misgivings. The animals to be issued were no culls from
European herds but potential 600-gallon cows of good constitution,
and great care was taken to ensure that they came from disease-
free herds. Such high-grade cattle are, however, very susceptible
to the tick-borne diseases so prevalent in Africa, and to internal
parasites which might build up in formidable concentrations on
small intensively grazed paddocks. The decision was, in a sense,
a declaration of confidence in the latent farming ability of the
African, for without unremitting care on the part of the farmer,
and skilful management of cattle and grassland, the experiment
could end only in loss and failure. Few could be expected to reach
the standard required, at least in the beginning, and high-grade
cattle were sold only to farmers with suitable holdings where they
had a reasonable chance of doing well. The holding must have a
cattle-proof fence and water within its boundaries: there must be
on it at least an acre and a half of good grass, and it must be capable
of producing enough fodder and bedding for the stock. The
farmer must erect suitable housing for his cows and their progeny,
and he must have a cattle crush, a spray gun and spray fluid for the
protection of his stock from disease. In addition he must spend
some time at one of the new Farm Institutes, which act as collecting and breeding centres for the Guernsey cattle, and at pedigree
bull stations supplying semen for the artificial insemination service. There he becomes acquainted with his animals before they
are moved to the farm and he learns to appreciate the finer points
of management.

In 1959, at the time of my visit to Kikuyuland there were
several hundred mature Guernsey cows on planned farms and all
that I saw, both cows and calves, were a credit to their owners and

to the management of the scheme. All the owners of high-grade stock had wire fencing, or post-and-rail, and well-designed timber cattle sheds. The cattle were healthy and tick free, and the grazing was well managed. The best example I saw was a farm of over 22 acres carrying 9 grade Guernseys. Here, an excellent Rhodes grass ley of 8 acres was being grazed on a strip system controlled by electric fencing, with a daily change of the strip. More usually the ley was divided into four paddocks, with movable wire fencing, for rotational grazing. Hay was generally being made in one of the paddocks, by hand cutting and drying on timber tripods. It seemed that milk outputs of some 400 or 500 gallons per acre, including the fodder acreage, were being obtained, but quite a number of farmers had lower yields because they persisted in keeping one or two native cows. When I asked one farmer why he kept a worthless-looking little black cow with his three splendid Guernseys he gave me a very human explanation: "It's my wife's; the cow is useless but she loves it; I daren't part with it."

Most, but not all, of the planned farms conform to this general pattern of the arable-ley rotation with a permanent cash crop and mulch, and most have subsidiary livestock ventures. These include pigs for pork, sheep for wool and mutton, and poultry. Sometimes the pattern is complicated by the inclusion of a parallel rotation, such as vegetables, sweet potatoes to provide fodder tops for cattle and tubers for pigs, and Napier grass; or the household crop area may be rotated with the mulch. Some of the farm plans, particularly the earlier ones, give the impression of being too complex and labour-consuming. Again, since the object is to obtain maximum returns for minimum capital investment, within the limitations of the rule of economic diversity, the basic plan may be altered in certain circumstances. I saw in Kiambu a holding of 13 acres which had been admirably developed as an intensive market garden, to take advantage of its proximity to Nairobi and the profitable market for European vegetables and flowers. There was even a sort of do-it-yourself overhead irrigation system which was reasonably effective. Vegetables occupied most of the bench-terraced land, but, in order to diversify the economy, there was also a small area of coffee and a deep-litter house for 300 laying birds stocked with White Leghorns. The owner complained that he had not enough land. There was plenty of labour, he said, and it could be had for as little as fifteen pence a day. He already employed five full-time workers and occasional casual labour. With more land he could do very well: but land was not to be had.

The successful farmers I visited were nearly all owners of relatively large acreages. The planned farms ranged from 22·5 acres (omitting one exceptional example of 151 acres) to 6·3 acres, and averaged 12·3 acres, while the lay-out farms were generally smaller: they ranged from 11 to 4 acres and averaged 7·36 acres. But I visited only twenty farms. The general average, I was told, was then (1959) 11·1 acres for planned farms and 6·2 acres for the lower standard lay-out farms. The larger land owners graduated more readily, it seemed, from the latter class to the former.

At recent price levels for cash crops and livestock products, a mixed holding of 10 or 12 acres can give a good living. The more efficient farmers with fully developed holdings in this category appeared to be making net incomes of £400 to £600 a year, in addition to producing the family food requirements. An economic study of one example, a planned farm of 11·9 acres, showed the net income to be £64 per acre. This high figure was, however, due partly to an unusually good coffee yield of 20 cwt of parchment per acre. At the more usual yield level of 10 cwt per acre the net profit from the holding would have been reduced to £47 an acre. The activities on this farm included coffee as the main cash crop, arable and grass, pineapples and orchard crops, cattle, pigs, sheep, and poultry, and the usual range of household crops. Although an ox-drawn plough was used in the preparation of the arable land, the labour requirement of these multifarious activities was such that the holding could not be run with less than four full-time workers, assuming efficient organisation and management of labour. In fact, six full-time labourers were employed, in addition to casual labour at harvest and other peak periods. The farmer himself did no manual work (he was fairly fully occupied with supervisory duties) and the children of the family were all at school or in employment. On many farms, however, the family makes a significant contribution to the labour requirement, particularly in the case of polygynous households and families with grown children, but I did not see a farm on which less than two full-time labourers were employed. The permanent labour force on six holdings where I enquired into the situation consisted of 19 full-time employed workers and 11 family workers for an area of 68·6 acres, and in every case the farmer said that he also employed casual labour from time to time. These holdings ranged from 8·5 acres to 12·1 acres, and the number of full-time workers varied from two to six in accordance with the size of the farm, the range of activities, and the amount of family labour available.

These advanced farmers, with their impressive standards of land-use, form a small proportion of the cultivating population. "In the districts of Nyeri, Fort Hall and Kiambu," says Elspeth Huxley (91), "every square foot of land claimed by an owner has been brought together into compact holdings and each landowner has his valid title. Over a million acres have been dealt with and some 200,000 holdings registered." By 1959 there were, I was told, about 1,600 planned farms totalling 18,000 acres in the Central Province, while simpler farm lay-outs covered about 25,000 acres divided into some 4,000 holdings.

Of those who set out to become advanced farmers, some fall by the wayside. One Agricultural Officer estimated that half his lay-out farmers would fail in reaching and maintaining the moderate standards expected of them, and that only about one in twenty would qualify for the more exacting stage of planned farming. Even among the planned farmers, a failure rate of about 25 per cent was expected, with 50 per cent just succeeding and only some 15 per cent reaching a really high standard of good and profitable land-use. Africans are no different from others in this respect. It is not to be expected of any people in the world that more than a moderate proportion possess the combination of interests, temperament, and business ability required to make a good and successful commercial farmer.

In Kikuyuland, with its swarming population, a great many—probably the great majority of cultivators—are debarred from entry to the farming class by lack of sufficient land, and by the inadequacy of available capital and resources for training and supervision. "It has been estimated," says Swynnerton, "that one farm planning team in Central Province would take 2,000 years to farm-plan the 200,000 potential holdings, and even though noughts are added to the teams and deducted from the years, a vast proportion of the farmers would receive very little attention for a very long time" (161). Indeed, I could see little evidence of any significant improvement of the general standard of land-use following consolidation. Continuous cultivation of food crops was still common practice, anti-erosion works were often neglected and in disrepair, and gardens hung precariously on steep and eroding slopes. The minimum requirements of stable husbandry—adequate soil conservation works, half the land resting in "tumbledown" grass fallow, use of all available manure, and grassing down of slopes over 35 per cent—were generally disregarded, in spite of the endless efforts of the agricultural staff. Improvement by compulsion just would not work, they said, because it was unpopular both with the people and the Administration. The African District Administrations would not prosecute for breach of agricultural rules, or if they did they imposed fines so small as to be no deterrent. Enforcement of the coffee rules was becoming more difficult. The intensity of supervision was diminishing as acreage increased, and some growers, having discovered that nothing very unpleasant was likely to happen to them, openly ignored the rules. The problem of the displaced scrub cattle had not yet been solved. Thousands of these scraggy beasts grazed in herds by paths and roadsides, or wherever a bite of grazing could be had on unoccupied land. Against this background, the planned farms and the best of the lay-out farms, the trim fields of clean, healthy crops and the sleek Guernseys, made a startling contrast.

The successful men are becoming conscious that they belong to a new and distinct middle class. They are capitalist farmers, employing labour on a significant scale, rather than peasant cultivators farming family holdings. If they are to endure, they must exchange the standards and values of their ancestors for those of the European, and they may be expected to form a politically stable and conservative group resistant to rapid change. It is no coincidence that many of the best farmers were numbered among the Kikuyu loyalists. Governments of countries with large peasant populations on a near-subsistence level have from time to time sought to create such a class as a stabilising influence. Tsarist Governments did so in Russia, inspired by the model of the English yeoman farmer, and their policies gave rise to a class of relatively prosperous middle-class farmers, the Kulaks, who were later to be stigmatised as enemies of the revolution and the people. Solid, property-owning farmers are unlikely to favour dramatic change; but a *bourgeoisie* of poorly-paid clerks, school teachers, and urban workers may well form the spearhead of revolt, as the *évolué* did in the Congo.

The African farmers of Kenya owe their origin to the policy

of land development, rather than to Machiavellian statescraft. No one with any feeling for the land could disapprove of this new factor in the agrarian situation. But the rise of the farmers poses imponderable social and economic problems, and the future is dark with uncertainty. It will be difficult, and may well prove impossible, to prevent re-fragmentation of the great mass of small-holdings and the development of further subdivision, open or concealed. Some of the farmers will be brought to failure by the burden of kinship obligations. It is a rule of planned farming that only the immediate family of the owner may live on the holding, but a number of farmers maintain dependent kin who live in nearby villages. In effect, the farm is supporting an extended family and there is hidden subdivision. Others seem to be free of this incubus, either by fortunate chance or by change of residence, or because they have repudiated their obligations. Among them are men determined to hold what they have made, to acquire more land if they can, and to hand on the farm as an intact unit to one of their sons. My impression was that, short of some political or economic catastrophe, the farmers as a class will survive and increase. Many agriculturists concerned with the problem believe that they will eventually take over the land, as the smallholdings become so exhausted or subdivided as to be not worth cultivating. Such an outcome, and the social and economic consequences which must arise from it, is not improbable. There may yet be a long struggle between the old order, with its recognition of general rights in land, and the new.

2. Planned Farming in Uganda and Tanganyika

In Uganda and Tanganyika the approach to African farming is more cautious and exploratory. Uganda's Agricultural Productivity Committee (1954), while strongly in favour of providing opportunities "for the enterprising and progressive farmer to acquire large units of land if he has the human and capital resources necessary to do so," pointed out that very little work has been done on African farm management, economics, and layouts. They recommended attention to these matters with a view to the development of mixed farming. This need was met by forming a farm planning unit which started work in 1957, but it was not intended that there should be any rapid expansion of farming until adequate data and experience had been obtained from a limited number of planned farms, and it was necessary that the pioneers should be men of sufficient education to keep reasonably reliable farm books and accounts. The situation differed greatly from that in the highlands of Kenya: there was not the same sense of urgency, for no land had been lost and the traditional systems and agrarian structures had not collapsed completely under overwhelming population pressure. On the other hand, there was no body of practical knowledge built up from the accumulated experience of European farming. The number of planned farms is therefore limited to a few in each district which can be supervised closely enough to ensure that the data obtained from them are reasonably reliable. Since labour is less abundant and the supply depends largely on immigrants, more attention is given to labour-saving devices. The object is to get away from the hoe and to substitute ox cultivation, where this is possible, and the use of small implements such as hand-operated row planters. Land is relatively abundant throughout most of Uganda and the return from the main cash crops, robusta coffee, and cotton is less than in Kikuyuland; the Uganda farms are therefore of larger size. A holding of less than 15 acres is usually considered too small to be worth planning, but occasional exceptions to this rule are made in special circumstances. The farms I saw ranged from 12 to 40 acres and averaged a little over 22 acres, but I was told that there were a good many larger planned holdings, including one of 680 acres.

In Tanganyika too the approach to farm planning is exploratory, for it is doubted if such a revolutionary advance in agricultural thinking can be imposed from the top, and there seems little prospect of material progress until the aspiring farmer can obtain title to the land—in the European sense. For this there is as yet little if any demand. Even the Chagga, who might be expected to welcome such a change, are opposed to cadastral survey and registration of holdings. The small men fear the cost, the larger land-owners fear the disclosure of the extent of their holdings, and both fear what they imagine to be the implications of registration. "If we accept this title to our land," they say, "we admit that it is not ours but that it belongs ultimately to those from whom we receive the title." Meanwhile the endless disputes over ownership continue to clog the courts with a backlog of land cases.

The idea of farm planning has, however, been fostered in

parts of Tanganyika and cultivators have been taken to see the planned farms of Kenya. Some individuals have asked for assistance in planning better lay-outs for their holdings and an African officer has been specially trained to advise and guide them. But the main initial experience in African farming is likely to come from the areas of the former Groundnut Scheme, now in the charge of the Tanganyika Agricultural Corporation. African tenant farming schemes have been developed at Urambo and Nachingwea, and also at Kongwa, in spite of the hazardous seasons experienced there in the past. In this area of erratic climate and extreme dry season, the annual rainfall has varied from 6 inches to 25 inches during the period of the Corporation's activities, but experience has indicated good prospects for beef production on a ranch scale. Boran and Zebu cattle have been used, at an initial stocking rate of one beast to 15 acres. Flue-cured tobacco has done well on the poor *miombo* soils of Urambo, but the dark fire-cured type suited to the heavier and more fertile soils of Nachingwea has been less successful owing to low prices for the product. Cotton also has proved disappointing at Nachingwea because of a high incidence of pests, particularly red bollworm, and farm revenue is derived mainly from oil seeds and surplus food crops.

These tenant farms vary in size, but are generally in the range 11 to 40 acres, as they are intended to provide information on the optimum size of holding for a peasant family assisted by a limited amount of mechanisation, sufficient to break the restricting factor of the hoe. When the scheme started there was no knowledge on which to base the selection of farm size and experience has shown that the earlier farms were too small. At Nachingwea, the first farms, which were established in 1952–3, averaged 11·3 acres but by 1956–7 this had been increased to 23·6 acres. Mechanisation must be kept as low as possible because of its high cost in relation to the low value of most of the cash crops and the large element of subsistence cropping. The land is ploughed and ridged mechanically by the Corporation and for this the tenant pays, but he is expected to carry out all other farm operations with his own resources.

The basis of fertility maintenance is a short period of arable cultivation, on a rotation of (1) miscellaneous crops, (2) leguminous crops, (3) cereal crops, followed by a rest period of equal duration under natural grass fallow. Tobacco, cotton, sunflower, sesame, and chillies are grown as miscellaneous crops, or have been tried, in different localities; the leguminous crops include ground-nuts, soya beans, velvet beans, pigeon pea, and green gram, and the cereals are sorghum, maize, and upland rice. A vigorous grass growth follows the short cultivation period on the undepleted and undamaged soils, but there are as yet no data to show whether the brief fallow period alone is sufficient to maintain fertility. This, however, is merely the initial rotation, and it is not intended to rely on natural fallow only. Tenants are encouraged to bring livestock into the scheme and farmers of some experience may hire cattle from the Corporation, retaining the progeny as their own and thus building up small herds. The aspiring mixed farmer must construct suitable sheds for the animals and tether his cattle on his own land, to reduce the danger of trypanosomiasis.

Essential features of the scheme are a very high degree of supervision, amounting to direction, and the insistence that the farms shall be fully economic. Great care has been taken to eliminate any form of hidden subsidy as far as possible. In prac-tice it is impossible to do so completely during the early years of development, for, unless prohibitively heavy charges are made, capital and administrative costs cannot be recouped until the scheme is fully developed, and an element of subsidy, or at least under-recovery, remains. Some loss arises from low recovery rates and the failure of a minority of farmers to meet their commitments, and there have also been losses on crop sales. The rental is calcu-lated to cover amortisation of capital expended on buildings and on land clearing, preparation and conservation, while the cost of all subsequent services and materials provided by the Corporation, such as food during the period of settlement, the use of mechanical equipment, and the provision of tools, seed, fertiliser, and market-ing services, are debited to the tenant. In order to ensure the collection of these debts, tenants are required to market their produce through the Corporation.

So far the scheme has had a limited success, which is attributed mainly to good management. The turnover of farmers is still high, in spite of careful selection of entrants, but the loss is decreasing. Tenants are under no compulsion to remain. Each entrant to the scheme receives a "farming licence" which grants him the use of the land, and he undertakes to observe the minimum requirements of good husbandry as laid down in the Corporation's farm regulations. He may elect to take a licence for a period of one year only, with certain security of tenure for that period, or he may take a licence which contains no provision for termination by natural effluxion of time, in which case he enjoys security of tenure so long as he continues to comply with the farm regulations, but he may be ejected as a last resort if he fails to do so. Modifications are continually being made in the endeavour to make the scheme more attractive.

Losses are easily replaced, for there is no shortage of applicants anxious to enter the scheme, and over the first five-year period, 1953–8, the number of farms increased from 39 to 251, although no great profit is to be expected from small-scale farming in these regions of long dry season and relatively low potential. Results over the seasons 1952–3 to 1956–7 show average farm profits ranging from £14 to £121 per annum according to the nature of the season, the district, and the stage of development of the farm— but it was expected that the more able and industrious would become farmers of greater acreages on their own account. Two farmer tenants in the settlement scheme now farm holdings of 200 acres each, with half of the land in crop, but the emergence of the "yeoman" has proved to be a slower process than was at first hoped. Attempts to establish farms of 50–100 acres at Nachingwea and Urambo gave disappointing results. A few candidates were selected at Urambo, but at Nachingwea, according to report, "the most enthusiastic search did not produce anyone of sufficient calibre to be entrusted even with a 30-acre farm." A review of the tenant farming scheme as it has operated at Nachingwea (38) concludes that the largest remaining problem is in the socio-economic sphere. The original intention of a plural society, with farmers of different tribes working within the scheme, is said to have added much to the social difficulties encountered and the reviewers suggest that future schemes should be operated on a tribal basis. They also point out that the association between the farmer and the Corporation tends to take the form of an employee-employer rather than a tenant-landlord relationship, a situation which is likely to arise in any closely supervised and directed scheme. The farmer, having received advances and being obliged to sell his crop to or through the Corporation, regards the final pay-out as a bonus rather than a farm profit. Measures are being taken to correct this attitude in the hope of establishing the relationship necessary for long-term success, and it is made clear to the farmer that he need sell through the Corporation only while he is receiving financial assistance. If he pays for services as he receives them he may sell his crops as he wishes.

So far, the indications from this careful and well-conceived experiment are that many Africans, including the pastoral Gogo, are capable of profiting by the scheme and acquiring proficiency in farming, given adequate supervision and direction from the start, but the evolution of the yeoman farmer who can handle a relatively large acreage, organise his resources efficiently and make the most of mechanisation with little or no supervision is likely to be a slow process. It is thought that the aspiring farmer must first serve an apprenticeship period on a smallholding in a tenant settlement scheme and then graduate to a larger farm unit before finally becoming eligible for a leasehold farm of his own after he has accumulated sufficient capital to establish himself with the assistance of loan institutions.

Experience of African farming and the difficulties which impede its development go back a good many years. I remember visiting one of the earlier schemes, at Kingolwira in Tanganyika, a year or two after its establishment in 1935, when hopes were high and a promising beginning had been made. The main technical problem at that time was seen as the elimination of persistent riverine pockets of tsetse in the neighbourhood. The farmers were released prisoners, accustomed to discipline and regular labour, and their participation was entirely voluntary, but otherwise the pattern was essentially similar to many of the farming settlement schemes of today. Land was cleared and prepared for the farmers, they were helped to build brick houses, they received easy loans for oxen, trek gear, ploughs, cultivators, and hand implements; and water supplies were provided. The land was held on a "cultivation tenure," subject to effective use and good husbandry practices, and it was expected that many of the tenants would eventually return to their homes as experienced farmers with some capital and set up farms there. With cotton and groundnuts as cash crops, the scheme seemed to rest on reasonably sound technical and economic foundations, although there was a considerable element of hidden subsidy mainly in the form of free prison labour, overheads, and costs of supervision. But when I revisited the area some twenty years later I found that Kingolwira had long been abandoned. It was difficult to find out just why a scheme so promising in the beginning had collapsed in final failure, but the labour of farming and the strength of kinship ties seem to have been important factors. After the first flush of enthusiasm, labour input fell and standards of husbandry degenerated. Farming involved too much work, too much sustained and dreary individual drudgery, for a people accustomed to carrying out the heavier agricultural operations in neighbourhood groups enlivened by the prospect of the following beer party. Many of the wives and families refused to join their men on the farming settlement, preferring to remain in the established security of home among kin and neighbours.

There are now many settlement and farming schemes throughout Africa and the results of most if not all of them have fallen far below expectation, notwithstanding the incentive of cleared land and the gifts of what Elspeth Huxley calls the "Santa Claus state."

Some of these settlements are irrigated, but irrigation is in its infancy in inter-tropical Africa and there is still much to learn. Most progress has been made in Kenya, with projects such as the large and impressive Mwea-Tebere irrigation scheme, as another fortuitous outcome of the Mau Mau emergency which enabled previous difficulties in the way of acquiring land to be overcome and at the same time provided abundant labour from the detention camps. The excellent Uru-Chini scheme in the lower Chagga areas of Tanganyika was lying fallow when I saw it because of lack of settlers. The productivity of these lower lands of Kilimanjaro and Meru largely depends on irrigation, and the potential productivity is strikingly demonstrated by the experimental holding run by the Agricultural Department: but the scheme had been held up "by the failure of the Chagga Council to reach any decision on the practical recommendations of the sub-committee which was appointed in 1958 to report on the scheme."[1] Africans are not accustomed to the idea of paying rental for land, particularly the relatively high charges which amortisation of capital invested in irrigation works requires.

Irrigation presents technical as well as human problems. Relative scarcity of water where it is most needed limits development, and even where it can be economically provided difficulties

[1] *Ann. Rept. Dept. Agric. 1959.* Min. of Nat. Resources, Dar-es-Salaam [1960].

are apt to arise. To quote from a Tanganyika report: "the provision of water does not solve all the problems of the arid areas and indeed it has increased certain problems. For example, game and vermin concentrate on these areas, salinity is often evident and many crops will not grow well out of season despite ample water."[1]

3. AFRICAN FARMING IN NORTHERN RHODESIA

The emergence of the Tonga maize farmers in Northern Rhodesia was largely an unaided process which derived from the example of European farming. The first successful Tonga farmers were, usually, men of a high standard of education for that time who had acquired knowledge and experience and accumulated some capital by working on European farms. The circumstances and conditions which led to the emergence of this small minority group, and their position in the community as it was in 1945, are described in the work already referred to (10). Following one of the recommendations made in this work, an "African Farming Improvement Scheme" was begun in the 1946–7 season, using differential maize prices to stimulate the adoption of improved methods of farming, a form of incentive which was later changed to an acreage bonus payment for administrative reasons. The development of the scheme and its effects over the following decade have been described by Johnson (94), while Rees (136) has analysed a mass of physical and economic data relating to farmers who have participated in the scheme.

Rees concluded that in some respects the scheme had not been as successful as had been hoped, particularly in regard to the number of participants and the yield levels attained. In the season to which his figures relate (the harvest of 1955) the average yield of maize for improved farms of the higher grade was 3·1 bags per acre, compared with 1·1 bags per acre for unimproved "private gardens" belonging to the improved farmers. For the two grades of improved farmers together the average yield was only 2·8 bags of maize per acre from improved land, compared with one bag per acre from their unimproved gardens. It must be explained that the improved farmer often has more than one "garden," and only a part, though generally the larger part, of his total land-holding is improved. The available labour is concentrated on the improved

---

[1] *Ann. Rept. Dept. Agric. 1959.* Min. of Nat. Resources, Dar-es-Salaam [1960].

part of the holding and the "private gardens" tend to be neglected: consequently, the yields from these gardens are probably lower than those obtained by ordinary unimproved cultivators. The few data available suggest that some fifteen to twenty years ago, when the plough was already in common use and the process of degeneration had set in, Tonga maize yields in the normal season were of the order of 3 to 3·5 bags per acre. The first sampling surveys indicated average maize yields of 3·5 bags per acre in 1937 and 2·75 bags in the much less favourable 1943 season, while yields from improved holdings averaged 5·25 bags of maize per acre in the latter year. Data collected in the course of the Tonga survey (10) suggested that the overall yield in 1944 was between 3·5 and 3 bags per acre. Later surveys by Johnson indicated average yields from unimproved gardens of 3·3 bags per acre in 1953 and 3 bags in 1954—with corresponding yields of 6·4 and 5 bags respectively from improved gardens. Rees's survey was made in a year of rather poor conditions and it is likely that Tonga yields were well below average, although surveys conducted on 31 European farms in the same season, 1954–5, indicated an overall average maize yield of 7 bags per acre for these farms. My own impression, on revisiting the Tonga country in 1959, was that the general condition of the land was rather better than it had been fifteen years earlier. This seemed to be due to a number of general improvements rather than to any marked advance in the standard of individual farming. In spite of neglect of banks and drains, the contour ridging of arable land had held erosion in check. A programme of dam construction and improvement of water supplies had resulted in more even distribution of cattle and less concentrated over-grazing, with partial recovery of areas I remembered as having been practically bare. Wheeled carts, sold at heavily subsidised rates, had largely replaced the ox-drawn sleighs made from heavy forked tree trunks which were formerly used for transport, and there was a marked diminution in the number of sunken and eroding sleigh tracks that had scarred the countryside. Manure was in general use by all who could obtain any, and farm implements had increased greatly in number and range. But neglected implements still lay rusting in the fields and about the homesteads, and carts creaked and groaned on greaseless axles. There was little evidence of any significant general improvement of yields from the arable land: the process of degeneration, it seemed, had been halted rather than reversed, in spite of the large amount of agricultural effort that had been put into the area over the previous twenty years.

Even when allowance is made for the effects of a poor season the conclusions reached by Rees still carry much weight. He concluded that yields from the improved land are far from satisfactory considering the good husbandry practices adopted by members of the scheme, although they are considerably higher than yields from the unimproved private gardens; that "the scheme has been adopted by only a small handful of farmers and administratively it is expensive in terms of technical manpower for supervision," as any closely supervised improvement scheme must be; and that, without the payment of incentive bonus, "there would be little desire on the part of the majority of farmers to remain in the scheme," although "a minority would probably still continue to put into effect some of the good husbandry practices advocated." Johnson points out, in commenting on the number of improved farmers registered in the 1954–5 season, that "the proportion in the Southern Province [mainly the Tonga] seems to have stuck at a little under 4 per cent [of the estimated total number of families on the land] over the last four years," and Rees observes that although the improved farming scheme offers a definite financial incentive to its members, and would continue to do so even if the acreage bonus were withdrawn, it may be that "the disadvantages of regimentation implied by membership of the scheme have outweighed the financial advantages accruing from membership." This period of stagnation was, however, followed by a revival of interest and the number of improved Tonga farmers increased from 732 in 1955 to 1,331 in 1958, while in 1959 there was a marked increase of applications for entry to the scheme following the very poor harvest of the previous season when only improved farmers reaped reasonable yields.

The present standard system for the higher grade of improved farmer is a simple four-course rotation: (1) maize, with an application of farmyard manure, (2) sunn-hemp or velvet beans for green manure, (3) maize, with an application of fertiliser in the form of sulphate of ammonia and superphosphate, (4) a leguminous crop, generally groundnuts, velvet beans for seed, or cowpeas.

Recent fertiliser work has shown that the nutrient most generally limiting the productivity of these soils is nitrogen and

that economic responses may be expected from side-dressing maize
with 200 lb of sulphate of ammonia per acre, preferably about six
weeks after sowing. Phosphate deficiency is not so general nor is
it as widespread as was formerly believed, though considerable
responses are obtained in some areas and are probably associated
with certain soil types (126).

On Agricultural Stations, the use of this system, with fairly
heavy applications of well-made manure, has enhanced fertility
and given high and consistent maize yields. For example, the
following yields of maize were recorded from a demonstration
holding on the Kanchomba Station in the Tonga country over the
eight harvest years 1952–9.

MAIZE YIELDS
IN BAGS (OF 200 LB GRAIN)
PER ACRE

	MANURED	FERTILISED	MANURED AND FERTILISED
1952	15·5	11·5	—
1953	16·5	14·5	—
1954	16·0	17·5	—
1955	—	22·5	20·0
1956	—	18·0	21·6
1957	—	26·0	26·0
1958	—	19·6	12·7
1959	—	24·6	27·0

The rate of manure application was probably of the order of
10 to 15 tons per acre while fertiliser dressings averaged approximately 150 lb superphosphates and 250 lb sulphate of ammonia
per acre. In the last five seasons fertiliser was applied also to the
manured plots and it is probable that the treatment of the demonstration area was overdone, in an effort to show the level of fertility
to which the soils can be raised. The contrast between the yields
obtained by improved farmers and those from the demonstration
holding is, however, very striking. In the harvest year 1955 when
the average yield of the higher grade of improved farmers was 3·1
bags per acre, according to Rees's survey, the demonstration holding gave an overall yield of over 21 bags per acre, and even in the

very poor 1958 harvest year the yield was still maintained at over 16 bags.

In the case of the improved farmers the application of farm-yard manure, which the land receives once in four years, probably does not exceed three tons per acre on the average, though the best farmers may apply 10 or 12 tons. Cattle still range at large on common grazing; the manure supply is therefore limited to night droppings and the quantity cannot be greatly augmented because of scarcity of litter and the labour involved in cutting grass and carting it to the kraals. The quantity of manure obtained per animal is probably less than three-quarters of a ton per annum, and few if any farmers exceed a production of two tons per beast. Furthermore, the distribution of cattle is very uneven and avail-ability of manure follows a similar pattern, since cattle owners now tend to keep the manure for their own use and it is rarely given to others or sold. The rate of application of fertiliser also varies con-siderably. In 1958, 1,331 Tonga farmers cultivated a total of 22,662 acres of improved land and sales of fertiliser to African farmers in the area totalled about 225 tons of superphosphate and 200 tons of sulphate of ammonia in that year. Assuming that 61 per cent of the improved land was under maize (as indicated by Rees's data) and that half of this was fertilised, it would seem that the average application amounted to some 73 lb of superphosphate and 65 lb of sulphate of ammonia per acre. This also assumes that all the fertiliser was used by the farmers on their improved land, which was probably not the case, and average applications may have been lower than these figures indicate. On the other hand, data for 45 farmers in the Demu area indicate average applications of about 93 lb of superphosphates and as much as 180 lb of sul-phate of ammonia per acre. No doubt the rates of application vary very greatly. The best farmers apply over 100 lb of superphosphate and 150 to 200 lb of sulphate of ammonia per acre, and such men, who also apply heavier dressings of manure, probably achieve average yields of 10 or 12 bags of maize per acre. The majority may reap only some 4 to 6 bags per acre in the normal season, and some are said to be "improved farmers only in name."

The acreage bonus system has the disadvantage, as compared with differential prices, that there is no premium on yield: the poorest improved farmer who just manages to qualify for the higher grade gets the same bonus and the same bag price as the best. The differential price policy was changed because of the need to estimate individual yields, in order to prevent the inclusion of large quantities of maize from unimproved land, but the acreage bonus method also calls for close supervision to ensure that the minimum requirements have been met, and it is not always possible to be certain on this score. When it is clear that a cultivator has not fulfilled the obligations that the scheme imposes on him he loses part or all of the bonus, but he may remain on the list of improved farmers until he becomes a persistent offender.

The justification for the initial introduction of the scheme in the Tonga area was the urgency of the need to check and reverse the process of land degeneration. Later (in the 1951–2 season) the Improved Farming Scheme was extended to the new areas of commercial maize production by Africans in the Central Province to the north. Here pressure of population is still slight and there is a relative abundance of fertile land. An economic survey conducted by Rees and Howard (137) among the Sala of Mumbwa district, within this area, revealed the paradox that the ordinary cultivator was obtaining higher maize yields than the improved farmer. Many of these farmers were, of course, very recent entrants to the scheme and there had been little time for improved methods of husbandry to show their effects, but the main reason for the paradoxical situation appeared to arise from the fact it was mainly holders of large acreages who had entered the scheme. Holdings in the improved group were approximately double the size of those in the unimproved group, and these comparatively large-scale farmers were attempting to cultivate too large an acreage of maize in relation to their resources. Failure to carry out farming operations at the right time resulted in depressed yields, in spite of the adoption of improved practices, for in this climatic region a delay of no more than a few days in planting or weeding may have an effect much greater than can be offset by manure or fertiliser. The improved farmers were, nevertheless, in a more favourable financial position, mainly because of the acreage bonus they received. "Without the receipt of bonus payments," Rees and Howard conclude, "there would have been little difference between the average farm income of improved and unimproved farms." This observation points to another possible disadvantage of the acreage bonus incentive, in that it may encourage the cultivation of excessive acreages in regions where there is still ample land: unless, as Rees and Howard suggested, a maximum acreage is prescribed for each African farmer in receipt of an Improved Farming Bonus.

The attractions of the scheme are reduced by the fact that groundnuts, beans, and cowpeas do not do well under the climatic and soil conditions of the area in which it operates for reasons which are not yet clear, and no satisfactory seed legume has yet been found. Yields are usually poor and the return uneconomic. Yet the farmer must have his legume plot if he is to qualify for the bonus, even if it is no more than almost bare ground with a stand of plants so poor that they can be of little value from the point of view either of yield or of soil improvement. By contrast, groundnuts generally yield well in the Katete and Petauke areas of the Eastern Province and this, together with the availability of high-quality soils giving good returns of maize, may have been a factor in the comparative success and rapid development of the Peasant Farming Scheme in this region. The Eastern Province scheme is similar to the African Improved Farming Scheme of the railway line, but is financed from different sources. It too depends upon incentive awards, in the form of bonus payments, on a sliding scale, which range from ten shillings to forty shillings per acre cultivated, and on subsidised equipment, long-term loans, and close supervision. Here, however, transport costs rule out the use of artificial fertiliser on all crops except tobacco, which is very little grown, and the maintenance and enhancement of fertility depends mainly on the application of cattle manure and green manuring in a standard five-course rotation: (1) maize (or Burley tobacco on heavy soils), (2) groundnuts, (3) maize (with kraal manure), (4) legume: which may be soya beans, sunn-hemp for seed, groundnuts, sugar bean; or, alternatively, grass fallow with a small proportion of Turkish tobacco, (5) green manure crop.

The basis of the scheme and its progress from 26 assisted farms in 1950-1 to over 1,300 (throughout the whole Eastern Province) in 1957-8 has been described by Coster (41).

The caution which marks the approach to African commercial farming in East Africa is less evident in Northern Rhodesia, where "peasant farming" tends to be regarded as a panacea for all land-use ills. Acreage bonuses are paid only in the maize-growing area of the railway line, where the Grain Marketing Board operates, and in the Eastern Province, but elsewhere selected farmers are

A.H.—28

eligible for establishment loans to cover the cost of stumping and the provision of equipment, some of which is subsidised, and of trained oxen and breeding stock. The basis of farming is, usually, a simple rotation of two cereal crops with a leguminous and a green manure crop, and the application of cattle manure to at least one of the cereal plots. Fertiliser is also used where transport costs do not make it too expensive, and a rest period of three or four years under Rhodes grass, pigeon pea, or natural fallow is sometimes, but not generally, incorporated. The pattern is rather rigid, considering the wide variation of conditions and the great range of soils of which the capabilities are still little known, and in many areas the soundness of the farming projects, both from the economic and the land-use points of view, are debatable.

The entrant to farming may gain his experience on one of a block of farms laid out and supervised by the Agricultural Department, or he may start farming on his own land. In either case he must obtain the approval of and enter into an agreement with the Native Authority, by which he undertakes to follow the prescribed farming pattern and to observe the rules of good husbandry. In addition to "block farmers" and "individual farmers" there are "individual settlers" who have received permission to live away from their village and a grant of land, generally 20 or 30 acres, from the Native Authority. These "settlers" do not receive loans or other financial assistance, but they also enter into agreement with the Native Authority and undertake to observe certain "requirements of good husbandry," such as contour ridging and rotation of crops. Few of them can be called farmers: they are mostly content with low standards of cultivation and small returns, and it is doubtful if the good husbandry clause of their agreement serves any useful purpose. As far as I could ascertain, no Native Authority had ever dispossessed a settler or ordered him to return to the village for failing to carry out the terms of the agreement.

Although there are some thousands of farmers, many of whom have had no more than a few years' experience, and of individual settlers, they are still a very small proportion of the cultivating population; their effects on land-use and productivity are not yet significant and it is difficult to foresee what the final effects of encouragement to break away from the discipline of village life and the codes of traditional land-use are likely to be. These customary restraints are in process of decay, but there is danger in undue acceleration of the process, unless adequate control can be exercised and land-use regulations effectively applied. In his essay on the Eastern Province Scheme, Coster emphasises the need for continuing supervision. "By the nature of the scheme the amount of supervision required by established farmers should diminish each year but in practice this is not the case. A few farmers (probably less than 10 per cent) require little supervision. At the other end of the scale, a second small group of farmers (again about 10 per cent) prove awkward either through lack of interest or more usually laziness and have to be replaced. The majority of the farmers seem to follow a pattern of behaviour based on the premise that as soon as they take peasant farms they will become wealthy overnight. At the first opportunity they pay someone else to do the work and so mismanage their affairs that they get little income from their farms. Most of these farmers develop at a later stage into an average type farmer who usually knows what to do but has to be prodded into doing it."

Almost certainly, a nucleus of good farmers will be created on the better soils, but probably at the cost of many failures such as have already occurred on the poor lands of Serenje, where farm blocks have had to be abandoned and a high proportion of debts written off. Indeed, it might be said that the success of the farmer is, in a very large degree, a measure of the intrinsic strength and fertility of the soil he farms, and in many districts the first farms have been sited on specially selected land of relatively high fertility which is far from typical of the great range of weak and infertile soils.

Neither in Tongaland nor elsewhere has the introduction of farming led to the development of a system of alternate husbandry comparable with that practised by the new Kikuyu farmers. Grazing land remains communal and for this reason there has been no integration of grassland and livestock into the farming system. Tonga practice has undergone some minor change. Arable lands are quite often fenced and the crop refuse, which was traditionally common grazing, is conserved for the use of the farmer's own stock —though the main object of fencing is usually to prevent damage to crops by free range cattle—and some farmers have enclosed small paddocks planted with Napier grass for the use of calves and for oxen in the working season. But the persistence of common rights over grazing land, the attitude to and pattern of ownership of cattle, marketing difficulties and other factors, combine to prevent a break-through to a system of true mixed husbandry. As we have seen, in Kikuyuland this break-through was achieved only in conditions of emergency following the cataclysmic collapse of the whole social and agrarian system.

The main role of cattle in the farming system is therefore limited to the provision of draught and manure, yet the supply of manure is very small in relation to the number of cattle and the land area required for its production is very great. This limits the human carrying capacity of the system. If we assume that an annual dressing of kraal manure applied to one-quarter of the arable land is the minimum which will maintain permanent fertility and that the average production is one ton per beast, then the number of cattle required must be equal to the cultivated acreage and the additional land requirement will be determined by the cattle capacity of the range grazing. If we suppose this carrying capacity to be 7 acres to the beast, the total land requirement of a family farming 12 acres of arable may, in effect, amount to 100 acres or more, when allowance is made for building sites, roads, paths, bare outcrops, and other wholly useless areas. It is therefore to be doubted whether a system based on manure from range-grazed animals can support population numbers much greater than the Critical Densities of the unimpaired traditional systems of cultivation and fallow as they were practised on the stronger soils, even though the farming systems create a minor labour market and some other opportunities for secondary employment. Over-stocking of the range land will, of course, augment the manure supply and decrease the total land requirement for a time: but the ultimate effect must be a transference of fertility from the grazing land to the arable, a process which seems to have been an important factor in the degeneration of the much more intensive indigenous system of the Kara.

4. FARMERS OF NYASALAND AND SOUTHERN RHODESIA: THE LAND HUSBANDRY ACT OF SOUTHERN RHODESIA

In Nyasaland too the ultimate goal is the individual yeoman farmer with secure but negotiable title to his land. "It is Government's aim," says Kettlewell (97), "to create a class of full-time professional farmers with sufficient land to provide a reasonable standard of living and, as a corollary, gradually to squeeze the subsistence cultivator off the land into full-time alternative employment. . . . The Master Farmers Scheme was designed to create and develop such farmers."

The first scheme, which offered no inducement except a badge and a certificate, was a failure. The second scheme offered a cash bonus of £2 and £1 per acre respectively for first- and second-class farmers, but payment continued for only three years, "a period considered sufficient to help the farmer into his new stride." The qualifying conditions for second-class farmers were simple: retirement of a certain proportion of the arable land for a rest period, use of a crop rotation appropriate to the region, observance of all the soil conservation requirements of the Natural Resources Ordinance, and the employment of all locally sound and proven agricultural practices. First-class farmers were required in addition to keep livestock in accordance with reasonable standards of animal husbandry and to practise integrated husbandry. All Master Farmers' holdings were planned, an operation which limited the number of entrants, fairly high standards were insisted upon, and by the end of four years only 282 Master Farmers had qualified. Again, the scheme resulted in the emergence of a few very good farmers, but it is claimed that "the influence they had upon agricultural practices in their neighbourhoods was out of all proportion to the direct value of their own individual benefit."

In 1957 the scheme was modified by two important changes: the bonus may now be spent only on approved developments to the farm, and natural or "tumbledown" fallow no longer qualifies for payment, but only land under a grass ley or a restorative crop.

The evolution of the yeoman is likely to be a slow process and it will be long before he can squeeze the subsistence cultivator off the land. In the meantime two other lines of policy are pursued. One is to raise the general standard of the great mass of cultivators "step by simple step," and the other is to persuade more progressive communities to make a corporate effort towards better land use. The Village Lands Improvement Scheme is designed "to substitute over a larger area than the individual holding a simple but orderly system of land use for the present disordered and destructive practices." Here too, on the fertile soils of Nyasaland, a great growth of population has disrupted the traditional systems of land-use and they have collapsed in disorder and decay, while a balanced and still stable husbandry of alternate cropping and fallow survives in some of the less fertile regions. And here too agricultural improvement by regulation and compulsion is becoming increasingly difficult. It is not long since police reinforcements were drafted to Port Herald in southern Nyasaland following a deterioration of law and order in that area. "The trouble started," says the press reports, "when the Native Authority arrested a number of people for contravening agricultural regulations. Angry tribesmen marched to Chief Tengani's court and freed the prisoners."[1]

The Land Husbandry Act of Southern Rhodesia seeks to bring about a more complete agrarian revolution by the rapid substitution of peasant farming for tribal agriculture and stock-raising throughout the African Reserves, where the problem of establishing and maintaining a balance between men, land, and cattle has become acute. It is designed "to provide for the control of the utilisation and allocation of land occupied by natives and to ensure its efficient use for agricultural purposes; to require natives to perform labour for conserving natural resources and for promoting good husbandry; and for matters connected with the foregoing (122). The Act, which became law in 1951, contains four principles of major importance: (1) the enforcement of good farming practices by regulation, (2) the grant of grazing rights for limited numbers of livestock to persons defined as elegible to receive them, (3) the grant of farming rights over limited areas to persons defined as eligible to receive them, (4) provision for the establishment of rural townships and business centres in which those who have no rights in land will eventually be obliged to live.

The standard arable holding for a monogamous household is normally 8 acres in the regions with rainfall over 24 inches and 13 acres where rainfall is between 20 and 24 inches, but this may be altered by the application of what is called the "tight formula" where land is insufficient to allow of the allocation of a standard holding to every eligible household. The intention is to offer cultivators a chance of a reasonable living by farming "economic units," but the size of the unit is also governed by the estimate of the arable land available in each area. Allowances for other eligible classes, polygamous households, widows, widowers, and the like, are related to the standard formula. Grazing rights are determined by assessing the stock-carrying capacity of each re-

[1] Press report, Salisbury, S. Rhodesia, 16 Sep. 1960.

serve and granting permits to eligible farmers on the basis of a standard number of cattle for each grazier, within the limit of the total carrying capacity—5 head of smallstock being counted as the equivalent of one head of large stock. Thus, in Chinamora Reserve near Salisbury, where the provisions of the Act had been fully implemented by the time of my visit in 1959, the standard arable holding is 6 acres of dry land (one acre of moist fertile *vlei* land suitable for vegetable growing counting as the equivalent of two acres of dry land), and the standard grazing right is 6 head of cattle. The additional allowance for polygamous households is 2 acres for each wife after the first, up to a limit of three times the standard holding, and eligible single persons also receive 2 acres, or more in the case of widows with dependent children.

The upper limit of three times the standard holding is applied generally. Both arable and grazing rights may be sold, and I was told that arable rights sometimes change hands at £10 per acre and grazing permits at a rate of £5 for the right to graze one beast: but no one may legally hold or acquire more than the limit of three times the standard arable or grazing right. This limitation posed an unusual problem for one exceptional individual who had twenty-five wives. I was told, though I cannot vouch for the story, that he solved his problem simply and effectively by divorcing eighteen of them so that they might become eligible for land grants as unattached women.

The Land Husbandry Act implies a revolutionary change in African attitudes to and rights in land. It substitutes for the tribal concept, with its implicit recognition of the right of every family to hold land and cattle, a sort of hybrid tenure with individual occupation of arable land on conditional freehold and restricted communal grazing. The great bulk of the land continues to support livestock of very low productivity—the average annual value of crop output from the arable land has been estimated at £4 per acre while the livestock output from common grazing has been reckoned at the astonishingly low figure of 3s. per acre—and this persistence of commonage is a barrier to intensive development based on alternate husbandry, although the act provides for pasture improvement and management and the growing of fodder crops. To quote a Government publication (182): "there are insuperable practical difficulties to the allotment of clear individual title to self-contained farming units at this stage, but implementa-

tion of the Act marks the first and most important step in the
movement from communal land-holding to a complete system of
individual tenure, and in the transition from what is predominantly
a 'squatter' system at bare subsistence level to a peasant farming
structure operating in a market economy." Most critics, however,
tend to take the view that the Act goes too far and too fast, rather
than that it does not go far enough: yet, as Floyd (58) concludes
from his practical experience of the working of the Act, given the
existing conditions of man and land, it is hard to conceive of any
working alternative that might have better faced the issues at stake.

Inevitably, a host of new and profoundly difficult problems are
created by large-scale change. One major difficulty is the shortage
of land. In many reserves it is impossible to grant the standard
holding, or any area large enough for successful farming or a decent
living standard, to all who have a claim. In an address to the
Southern Rhodesian Parliament in 1959, the Parliamentary
Secretary to the Ministry of Native Affairs pointed out that "there
were more than 500,000 Africans in Southern Rhodesia who were
entitled to land under the Land Husbandry Act but had no land
available to them under the present method of assessment." He
gave the following figures: "the number of people entitled to land
had been established at 307,000 families (a family being regarded
as 5 or 6 people). However, arising out of the assessment of the
land available it was found that only 205,000 families could receive
a standard holding, leaving 102,000 entitled to land and yet having no land available for them under the present method of
assessment."[1] Since no such numbers of unskilled workers can be
rapidly absorbed by the non-agricultural sector of the economy
and provided with housing, employment, and a reasonable standard
of life and social security, the land must continue to support excessive populations for an indefinite and wholly unpredictable
period of time. This uncertainty is increased by the great upsurge
of the African population; as Floyd points out, if the present rate
of increase continues the average standard holding will be down
to 4 acres in ten years.

There is little reason to suppose, and no experience to suggest,
that the principles of farming can be imposed upon a society of
semi-subsistence cultivators by government order, and it is unlikely that legislation can destroy the kinship system and remove

[1] *Rhodesia Herald*, 21 Oct. 1959.

the burden it places on successful members of the group. Land-holders already allow lackland kin to share their land or to till part of it, a practice which, if it continues, can only lead to the growth of hidden subdivision and further fractioning of the land, while the sale and purchase of arable rights may give rise to in-creasing fragmentation despite regulations for its prevention. The lessons of Keiskammahoek are all too clear. Efforts to arrest these tendencies and to impose the good husbandry regulations against a prevalent apathy and some degree of hostility, and at the same time to maintain the records of a constantly changing population-land pattern, may well create an insupportable administrative burden. Remarkable progress has been made in the initial survey work and the process of land allocation, which would, it was hoped, be largely completed by 1963, but it is far from certain that the end result will be the establishment of a viable and stable rural society.

Again, there will probably be an increase in the nucleus of successful farmers, a nucleus which had already been created by many years of agricultural work in the reserves and the example of European farming. Some of the Master Farmers of Southern Rhodesia reach a standard which, considering their far less favour-able environment, is in no way inferior to that of the best of the Kikuyu. But here too the good farmers are a small minority and the main problem is that of raising the standard of the great mass of cultivators, whose attitude is generally one of apathy rather than hostility to the changes the Act seeks to impose, in spite of the bitter opposition and virulent propaganda of the African National Congress and the natural resentment of those who lose land or cattle in the process of re-allocation.

Rather more than 55 per cent of the land of Southern Rhodesia is set aside for European occupation and for forestry and game reserves and national parks. The Native Reserves and Special Native Areas total nearly 34 million acres, or about 35 per cent of the country, and in addition there are over 8 million acres of Native Purchase Area in which Africans may buy farms.

Farms in the Native Purchase Areas vary from 50 to 1,000 acres, according to the rainfall of the region, and probably average about 240 acres. The applicant for one of these farms is required to enter into a tenancy agreement for a probationary period, and to carry out *bona fide* farming operations to the satisfaction of the

Native Land Board and observe the good husbandry clauses of the agreement, before he can purchase the land on freehold tenure or enter into an agreement to purchase by annual instalments. Established farmers relinquish their rights to cultivate and depasture cattle in the reserves. The result of this essay in the establishment of a class of detribalised farmers operating on a fairly large scale has been disappointing. Standards of husbandry vary greatly, from well-integrated and skilfully managed farming to what is little better than shifting cultivation with the plough.

Of the farms I saw in several of the Native Purchase Areas, not one in ten could be described as reaching a really satisfactory standard. Entrants generally work reasonably well during the probationary period, or so I was told by officers in charge of areas, but when they feel secure they often "just squat and become useless." Leisure is valued more highly than the profit and satisfaction to be derived from a well-managed farm. The ejection of unsatisfactory occupiers has proved to be difficult; the procedure is cumbersome and time-consuming, the able and devoted supervisory staff find it difficult and distasteful to combine the duties of extension agents and policemen, and those who are ultimately responsible are said to be slow and reluctant to take action in cases calling for ejection. There is also a shortage of supervisory staff, owing to the great man-power demand created by the implementation of the Land Husbandry Act. Consequently, the good husbandry requirements are often flagrantly ignored and standards of land-use and management are generally poor, though there are outstanding exceptions. Another reason for this lies in the fact that many of the original entrants were unskilled and uninterested in farming. Entry is now limited to candidates of some technical proficiency and aptitude who have qualified as Master Farmers in the reserves or studied at an agricultural training centre, and this measure will certainly increase the crop of successful farmers. In spite of the limitations on entry, the flow of applicants continues to be greater than the staff can cope with.

5. Mixed Farming in Northern Nigeria

The story of the many and continuing attempts to improve and develop African land-use is by no means one of unrelieved failure but rather of partial and limited success which is disappointing in relation to the effort, the early hopes and expectations, and the

magnitude of the problems. In Northern Nigeria long and persistent effort extending over more than thirty years has resulted in a
not inconsiderable development of what is called "mixed farming."
Here the situation is the reverse of one we have noted in northern
Ghana. The large cattle population is owned mainly by Fulani
herdsmen and there is a long-established "symbiotic" relationship
between herdsmen and cultivators. The herds are folded on the
arable land during the dry season, to feed on crop residues, and
the cultivators, who value the manure that is added to their land,
make token payment to the herdsmen or provide them with subsistence rations. Early investigational work, started in 1922,
showed that quite small applications of manure were sufficient to
maintain yields in many areas of this region of light soils and flat
topography. Penning with bedding doubled the value of the
manure produced, as compared with that from kraals, and manure
from covered pens was shown to be much superior to the product
of open pens. Quantities of two to three tons of farmyard manure
per beast per annum were produced in the covered pens. Further
investigations were made in regard to the use of implements, cattle
capabilities and management, and systems of cropping, and on the
basis of this work an extension programme in mixed farming was
started in 1931. Approved applicants for entry to the scheme were
supplied with work cattle and simple implements, a plough, a
cultivator and yoke and, later, carts also were included; these remained the property of the Native Administrations until the cost
and the "hiring charges" had been entirely paid off by the farmer.

Trypanosomiasis caused cattle losses in some areas and a pre-
war technical commission commented on the scheme with qualified
approval. "We have nothing against the efforts which are being
made by the Department of Agriculture to establish mixed farming in areas where cattle can exist. Indeed this seems to be the
best solution to meet the problem of increasing pressure on the
land in such areas, but in areas where cattle can only exist precariously the introduction of mixed farming methods seems to us
to be Utopian. Agriculture in such areas must in our opinion be
dependent on the maintenance of tree growth" (145).

Later, in the 1940s, a northward spread of tsetse severely
affected mixed farming in some parts, particularly Zaria Province,
and treatment resulted in the development of drug-resistant
strains of trypanosome: but the project appealed to cultivators and

made fair progress where animal health conditions were favourable.

By 1940, 2,652 farmers had entered the scheme, 832 had failed, and 1,820 were still farming. The shortages of the War period inevitably retarded progress, but rapid recovery and expansion followed and over ten years of the post-war period the average intake was 1,900 a year, with an average of 567 failures in each year. By 1958 there were over 15,000 assisted mixed farmers, but many others who had received no financial assistance were including stock in their farming systems (37).

The comparative success of this project—with a failure rate of only about 30 per cent—may be attributable to the fact that it did not ask a great deal of the farmer. It might be regarded as the adaptation of a traditional system which already recognised the value and made use of cattle manure, and its effects on land-use, yields, and productivity were limited. A small survey made by Crosby in 1940 indicated that mixed farming families cultivated more than twice the acreage of those dependent on the hoe, but their crop yields were only slightly better. He concludes: "In general, while the survey was not extensive enough in scope to permit far-reaching conclusions regarding the standard of living of mixed farmers, the findings show that mixed farmers are able to grow more food to eat and more produce to sell and at the same time have been relieved of much drudgery, and this gain has apparently not been made at the expense of soil fertility."[1]

Emphasis is now being placed on the feeding of livestock from the farm, instead of their use as "fertility vectors," the consolidation of holdings and their increase to a satisfactory size—20 acres is regarded as a minimum and 40 acres as desirable—and the possibilities of alternate husbandry. The mixed farmers remain a small proportion of the great body of cultivators, and the incidence of failures may be expected to increase with more exacting standards, in proportion to the standard which is set.

6. The Failure of Group Farming

One apparent lesson of this not inconsiderable body of experience is that only a small proportion of any large cultivating population can be expected to emerge as successful individual farmers from any scheme, however well conceived, whether it is based on incentive or legislative compulsion. Even in a small and carefully

[1] Quoted by Chambers (37).

selected section of the population the incidence of failure is likely to be high, and preliminary technical training is no guarantee of success. It has been reported from the Bukura Farm Institute in Kenya that "under 50 per cent of the trainees from the institute have made good" (1), in spite of the exceptionally favourable natural conditions in Kenya's high-potential area.

This is no reflexion on the ability of the African. In our society few are put to the test of farming. If all of us were put to the test how many would succeed? It would probably be fallacious to assume of any population in the world that all, or any high proportion, possess the combination of interests, instincts, and abilities, of farming awareness and business acumen, required for successful commercial farming under conditions of conservative land-use. For a population largely bound by traditional standards and values, with a high incidence of illiteracy, the proportion must be lower still.

At the time of the 1945 Tonga survey we were impressed by this aspect of the problem. It seemed to us that poverty, apathy, the attitudes created by loss of land, the kinship system and other factors inherent in the social and economic situation, must limit the emergence of the farmers and inhibit the general development of higher standards of land-use. We therefore proposed the institution of a form of co-operative land-use based on what we called "social-agricultural" units, a concept which derived more from the old three-field system of England than from the modern "collective," together with the encouragement of individual farming by those equipped for such an undertaking. The view on which this proposition was based was criticised by Colson (42) and Johnson (94) on the ground that it had been unduly influenced by the conditions existing at the end of the War, such as shortage of implements and incentive goods and lack of fertiliser; and Johnson adds: "there is no doubt, in the light of the subsequent development of Tonga maize farming, that the survey underestimated the response of the people to the opportunities of economic development open to them." The criticism seems to involve some confusion between response to economic opportunity in the form of increased maize acreage—which we did not deny or fail to anticipate—and response in the form of a material improvement in the standard of land usage. It appears to be true that the process of land degeneration has been checked over much, though not all, of the Tonga country, but the productivity of the land as measured by the general yield per acre is not, so far as one may judge, higher than it was twenty years ago. Johnson himself says: "the continuance of extensive methods is producing land deterioration and is retarding the increase in productivity that is required in the interests both of the land and of the people. The official 'improved farmers' who have adopted the prescribed system of arable husbandry number no more than a fraction of the people on the land."

We had hoped for a greater advance in general standards through some form of assisted co-operative or group farming, incorporating individual holdings within the group. Floyd suggests a somewhat similar solution for the dilemmas he sees in the Southern Rhodesian situation. He points out that individual holding is not incompatible with co-operative methods and that group farming might be regarded as a modern version of much that is inherent in the traditional systems of land usage. But he has doubts as to the entrepreneural faculty of the Shona and Ndebele and their ability to respond to the problems of strong management which group farming requires. These doubts appear to be well founded. The fact is that where group farming has been tried in Africa it has failed. Johnson records the outcome of a trial effort in the Tonga country. "To test the feasibility of co-operative or group farming an experiment was begun on a 2,000-acre block of Native Trust Land on the Chalimbana Pan near Magoye, but the settlers displayed an obvious preference for farming their holdings individually. The Tonga do co-operate among themselves in their traditional agricultural operations, but they do this within the framework of individual occupation of the arable holdings. The experiment was abandoned as a venture in co-operative farming, possibly after insufficient trial."

The failure of this experiment, which seems to have been based on collective rather than group farming, can hardly be regarded as decisive, but a more serious effort which was made in the Nyanza Province of Kenya met with no greater success. The Kenya system depended on agreement between neighbouring families within a drainage area to combine in farming their lands as a single unit. This entailed the lay-out of a planned system of contour strips running from one drainage way to the next across all the holdings, and similar use of each contour strip by all

members of the group. The use of each strip was decided primarily by soil and topography, one strip being chosen for housing,
buildings, and cattle yards, and others for bananas or other fruit
trees, fuel or timber plantations, and permanent grazing, according
to slope and soil, while the flatter land was reserved for alternate
husbandry with a regular rotation of arable cropping and grass
leys. The method was very similar to that used for the planning of
individual farms. There was no interference with the individual's
tenure of his holding but he had to farm his land in accordance
with the decisions of the group, as represented by an elected committee which directed the operation of the composite farm. In
addition to the private land there was usually a grazing common,
paddocked and managed by the committee, and communal timber
and fuel plantations, within the area occupied by the co-operating
group.

It was commonly thought at this time that development of
individual smallholdings for mixed farming was not a practical
proposition, "in the face of all the difficulties presented by
questions of economics and efficient usage, and the existing systems
of land tenure," and it was felt that "the evolution of large farms
with employed labour would in general be too gradual a process
and open to ethical doubts, particularly as sufficient industrial
development to absorb the surplus population is most unlikely."
Collective farming was considered and discarded because it
seemed "to be too dependent on drastic coercion of the sluggard ...
and from many points of view the idea would be abhorrent to the
African" (36).

The co-operative approach therefore seemed best suited to the
circumstances. Progress could be made even without a large-scale
initial programme of land consolidation, for individuals with
scattered holdings could be members of more than one group, and
it was intended to encourage a gradual process of consolidation by
exchange of land fragments. Mechanisation would be possible;
for the groups, or associations of groups, would be able to afford a
pool of tractors and farming equipment. Groups could combine
together to form marketing unions and co-operative societies for
better farming, to obtain loans, acquire implements, improve
livestock and pasturage, market produce, and provide and control
individual credit. Specialisation would develop through the
eventual need for stockmen, dairymen, tractor drivers and

mechanics, clerks and book-keepers, and other skilled men. A controlling Land Authority would, it was hoped, grow from the group farm committees. The possibilities seemed limitless.

This idea of group farming aroused a good deal of enthusiasm during the later 1940s, and in 1947 the Agricultural Officers of Kenya met in conference and passed a resolution urging its general adoption: "The policy of the Department for the Native Lands shall in general be based on encouraging co-operative effort and organisation rather than individual holdings. It is considered that only by co-operative action can the land be properly utilised, and the living standard of the people and the productivity of the land be raised and preserved. While this involves a change from the modern trend towards individualism, it is in accord with former indigenous methods of land usage and social custom." This view received a wider endorsement from the Cambridge Conference of 1949. "There is no doubt," wrote one commentator, with particular reference to the reserves of Southern Rhodesia, "that some form of group farming, as it is called, will be the best way to tackle many problems including maintenance of soil fertility and soil conservation" (29). This was the common view of the time.

In the meantime, the first group farm had been started in the Nyanza Province in 1947, and by the end of 1948 there were 27 such farms covering 8,700 acres. It was reported in the following year that Africans were showing great interest. The Nilotic Luo had formed 24 groups with 540 members and made a good start with preparing drainage ways and terraces, applying manure, planting grass, and closing grazing areas for recovery. The first formed group was ready to sign an agreed set of rules, and to pledge unlimited security for a development loan. Land exchanges were taking place and all members were using manure. People with no livestock obtained manure from neighbours in return for fodder and assistance in making the manure. In Kericho, the Nilo-Hamitic Kipsigis had formed 4 groups with 75 members and were using two mechanical units, each with two tractors and implements, provided by their Local Native Council. Other groups were developing among the Bantu peoples of the Nyanza Province. Trial and demonstration groups had also been established at the Agricultural Department's station at Bukura, for the study of social, economic, and agronomic problems, for testing mechanical equipment, and for training specialists to serve the established farms. It was realised that the social and economic aspects of the system required study, and that success depended on the willing acceptance of the idea by Africans and mutual trust between members of the group: difficulties were foreseen, "in particular the rampant individualism that has developed in recent years," but enthusiasm and hope were at their height.

The battle was short and it seems to have been an easy victory for "rampant individualism." Within a few years nothing was left and the idea of group farming had been abandoned. Some reasons for this dramatic collapse are indicated in the publication *African Land Development in Kenya* (1). The early progress, it is said, "was partly due to the mistaken impression of the farmers that group farming included continuous free assistance, and therefore less work by themselves. When in 1949 free assistance was withdrawn, most of the group farms petered out, and by 1953 only two were surviving. In December 1954 every group farm started in Nyanza Province was moribund as such. . . . By this time the group farm idea was dead. It had been found impracticable to run a group farm effectively even under the close control and discipline of Bukura."

The analysis continues: "Another factor which undermined the Group Farm principle was the progressive diminution, in the views of the experts, of the minimum economic holding. . . . How far this is due to the present high prices for cash crops remains to be seen." The decision to base African farming on crops such as coffee, tea, pyrethrum, and pineapples, and their high income yield in recent years, altered the context in which the group-farming idea developed in Kenya, and, together with the changes that became possible in the aftermath of the Mau Mau emergency, induced a shift of opinion and policy. It is difficult to disentangle the effects of this shift, and of the abrupt discontinuance of free assistance, from other factors contributing to the collapse. Would failure have been inevitable in any case, simply because Africans are no less self-centred, quarrelsome, distrustful, and intolerant of restraints than other people? Much stress was put by the advocates of group farming on the co-operative effort inherent in customary land-use, but it is to be noted that both the Tonga and the Kenya experiments were made where the traditional systems were already in advanced decay and the lessons of the acquisitive society had been learned. An entry in the Kenya Agricultural Department

Report for 1951 seems to indicate a failure of co-operation and mutual trust, or growing distrust of the scheme itself: "The object of second-phase group farming in Nyanza was to achieve consolidation of holdings by reallocation within a kinship group, which would have led to enclosure. Unfortunately so much suspicion has been caused by group farming that little progress has been made." No doubt the African politicians presented the scheme to their credulous followers as no more than another plot by the evil and greedy Europeans to gain possession of their land.

To quote again from *African Land Development in Kenya*: "seldom has a principle been so widely accepted and so quickly discarded as that of Group Farming."

This experience was not confined to Africa. In Cyprus, for example, a number of group farms and collectives were started voluntarily after the War, mainly by returned servicemen. By the time I went to the island in 1954 they had been given up or were in process of dissolution and division into individually farmed holdings, except one collective which struggled on with a remnant of its original membership. There was also a large group-farming settlement established by Government and operated on a long-term tenancy basis, but the tenants could not agree on any practicable scheme for running the enterprise themselves and it was held together by what amounted to direct departmental management.

Arthur Koestler has this to say of the collectives in "the diligent, drab and industrious state of Israel": "The most remarkable thing about the Kvutsa is that it has survived." But, he continues, "it would be a mistake to overestimate the social significance of these new communities or to use them as models for social experiment on a mass scale. The members of the collective settlements are an élite; the rigours of their existence are self-imposed. It would be impossible to build any similar society by compulsion, just as it would be impossible to compel any large section of the population to take monastic vows."

It seems that even the milder disciplines of group farming are unacceptable to the great majority of people.

CHAPTER XXIII

REMOULDING THE OLD SYSTEMS

1. PAYSANNATS AND FERMETTES IN THE CONGO

The Belgians took a somewhat different approach to their land-use problems in the Congo. It was based on a frank admission of the inadequacy of European knowledge and experience to cope with the agricultural problems of tropical Africa, and an equally frank acceptance of the essential soundness of traditional practices. The lessons of early failure were noted. At first it was thought that mechanisation and fertilisers could revolutionise African agriculture, until experience brought disillusionment and it was learned that mechanisation could be considered as a practical proposition only in some parts of this vast territory and that, apart from the problem of transport costs which were often prohibitive, the general use of fertiliser must await the outcome of a long and costly programme of experiment. European methods, the practices used on the rich and intensively cultivated fields of Belgium—deep ploughing, clean weeding, thorough cultivation, cover and green manure crops—failed disastrously. Existing knowledge, it seemed, allowed of development only on the safe basis of traditional practices, extensive though these might be, for any scheme of radical change encountered far too many unknown factors. Others might ignore the unknown factors, take a chance, pretend to a knowledge they did not possess: but not the Belgians. They were conscious, too, of the scale of the problems. To work on the basis of the individual was considered too slow a process, because of the magnitude of the task in relation to the poverty of means, the difficulties arising from the systems of land tenure, and the dangers inherent in arresting and "fossilising" an agricultural economy in process of evolution. Political considerations were also involved. The conflict between the policy of preserving the power and prerogatives of Chiefs and Native Authorities on the one hand, and of inculcating European economic and social concepts on the other, and the effects on African life and society which even minor change in the agrarian structure might bring, were clearly realised. The inevitability of change was less clearly foreseen.

The answer to these problems was seen to lie in "rationalising," rather than profoundly altering, the indigenous systems, and adapting them to meet the needs of the new economic situation. In other words, the African was to be required to work harder and to cultivate more land in order to produce industrial crops and a larger surplus of food for sale, while at the same time preserving the balance of cultivation and fallow. And he was to do this with his traditional resources. The Belgian approach was logical and practical enough in the situation of the Congo with its relative abundance of land, generally of poor quality, sparsity of population, and lack of livestock in the equatorial zone. It was less relevant to the circumstances of the Trust Territories of Ruanda-Urundi which, as we have seen, form part of the over-populated and over-stocked East African region of high potential with its altogether different and more difficult set of problems.

The system known as *paysannat dirigé*, and later as *paysannat indigène*, was devised by the research organisation, L'Institut National pour l'Étude Agronomique du Congo Belge (INEAC). The first *paysannat* was established in 1936 at the Gandajika experimental station and there was some small development on a voluntary basis in this neighbourhood. Then, in 1940-2, INEAC set up others near the great central research station at Yangambi, in equatorial forest, and carried out investigations into rates of recovery under forest fallow and problems of lay-out, cultural methods, and management. The "corridor system," which came to be used as a standard lay-out in high forest country, derives from this work.

The area selected for cultivation is demarcated and laid off in long parallel strips each 100 metres (approximately 110 yards) wide, running east and west. Width and orientation are important: if the strips are too wide regrowth is slow in the centre and uneven, and if they are too narrow the crops may be damaged by overshading and border effects; the east-west orientation ensures a sufficiency of sunlight at the optimum width. Each strip is cultivated in turn and abandoned for regeneration after the normal period of cultivation. Thus, in the case of the Kumu system, which has been described (pp. 219-23), there would be three strips in cultivation at any time; a first-year strip planted with the opening cereal crops, maize and rice, a second-year strip carrying maturing crops of banana and cassava, and a third-year strip with mature crops of banana and cassava. In the following year this last strip would be abandoned and a new one cleared and opened for cultivation. One strip is abandoned and one opened in each year, and the total number of strips is so calculated that by the time the last has to be abandoned the one which was first cultivated has completed a rest period under forest fallow, generally of the order of fifteen years but sometimes as long as twenty years, sufficient to restore the fertility of the soil. Thus, in the case of a system such as that of the Kumu, if the cultivation and rest periods are three and fifteen years respectively, the number of "garden areas" required is six and, since each of these areas consists of three strips, 18 strips in all will be required. In such a case cultivated land would move over a distance of about a mile, a degree of shift which does not, of course, necessitate movement of the village.

Distribution of land within the "corridors" or strips followed the customary patterns: it was allocated to family heads or larger family groups, or, very commonly, to clans, for clan loyalties are generally strong and clan rights in land jealously guarded among the forest peoples. The individual's rights extended only over the area he cultivated, which might be as large as he wished and could manage with family labour, and fallow land reverted to the common pool.

In the region of high forest the cash crop is usually oil palm or, much more rarely, another permanent crop—coffee or rubber—which is cultivated separately and does not enter into the sequence of arable cropping. In savannah regions and transitional zones where cotton is universally grown, suitable sequences or rotations were devised for use on the *paysannats*. For example, the following 12-year sequence of cropping and fallow was adopted at

YEAR	SEASON	
	1st	2nd
1st		Cotton
2nd	Maize	Cotton
3rd	Groundnuts	Cassava
4th	Cassava	
5th–12th	Fallow	

Gandajika in Kasai Province on savannah soils of good to moderate strength and fertility (21). Here the climate allows of two cropping seasons in the year.

Similar sequences were used elsewhere, with modifications to suit local climates and conditions and adjustments of the cropping and fallow periods in accordance with what was known of the capabilities of the soils. On weaker savannah soils the cultivation period might be reduced and the rest period increased by a year, as in the following example.

YEAR	SEASON	
	1st	2nd
1st		Cotton or beans
2nd	Groundnuts	Cassava, interplanted with maize or millet
3rd		Cassava
4th–12th		Fallow

In savannah country, where conditions do not require the long corridors of the high forest system, block lay-outs were commonly used and the blocks were often subdivided into individual family holdings—or *fermettes*—each large enough to allow of the predetermined sequence of cropping and fallow. In contrast with the Yangambi system, the holder of a *fermette* possessed indisputable rights over his allocation, including fallow; but land sales were not encouraged. The holding was heritable but not negotiable. Dumont (52) has described the operation of such a system at Bambesa, where *fermettes* were first established in 1942 in the neighbourhood of the agricultural station—primarily to create a barrier against the spread of cotton wilt. This is a marginal forest zone, some 200 miles north of Stanleyville, where the association of cereals with bananas and cassava persists but the dry season is sufficiently marked to allow of the ripening of cotton. A four-year cropping cycle incorporating two crops of cotton was introduced.

Each holding consisted of a strip some 25 acres in extent of which approximately 22·5 acres was cultivated in the main crop cycle, the remainder being hut sites, kitchen garden, space for the

| YEAR | SEASON | |
	1st	2nd
1st	Maize	Cotton
2nd	Groundnuts	Cotton
3rd	Bananas and cassava (maturing)	
4th	Bananas and cassava (matured)	
5th–18th	Fallow	

storage and drying of crops, paths and waste. The cultivation strip was divided into 9 rectangular fields, each of about 2·5 acres, of which two only carried crops at any one time. An extension of half a field, or approximately 1·25 acres, was cleared each year for the first-year crops of maize and cotton, while an equivalent area was abandoned after the final harvest of bananas.

A variation of this sequence, with a single crop of cotton and rice as a main cereal, was used in the marginal forest zone of Nord-Sankuru, where the forest borders the great savannah region of the Kasai. Here the sequence was (1) clearing: rice, (2) rice: cassava, (3) cassava, (4) groundnuts or millet, (5) cassava: fallow, followed by a long duration of fallow (30).

The allocation of a fixed area for each family has the disadvantage, as compared with the Yangambi system, that it makes no allowance for the great variation in size and labour power. Small families may be quite unable to cope with the work expected of them, while large and energetic groups may need or be able to manage more land. The answer to the labour problem was, of course, seen in the provision of mechanical equipment and services, to be hired by the peasant, and a start in this direction had been made in some of the savannah areas. The main purpose was to increase the acreage of cotton, which must bear the cost of the services (127).

Indeed, the development of the *paysannats* was very largely due to the insistence of the cotton companies, who, alarmed by the decreasing number of planters, declining fertility, and falling yields, urged the administration to extend this new form of rural planning. The Congo's post-war Ten Year Development Plan included provision for the establishment of *paysannats* for 385,000 families, and in 1951 the target was raised to half a million. By the end of 1954 no less than 166,228 *fermettes* had been established over an area of about 4 million acres. When independence and the following chaos came to the Congo, the target of half a million of *paysannat* families was within sight of achievement.

The purpose of this policy was: "to replace unorganised extensive agriculture, which often entails the irremediable destruction of natural wealth, by an agriculture which will become progressively intensive, at the same time assuring the continuing fertility of the soil" (79). The first requirement was the stabilisation of populations in the regions of "voluntary shifting cultivation," or agricultural nomadism. Once this had been achieved the regions could be provided with more adequate economic equipment—roads, water supplies, marketing and processing facilities—and social services. The establishment of the *paysannats* was not regarded as an end in itself or as a panacea but as a means towards a gradual intensification of agriculture and increase of productivity. In the first place, cultivators in the controlled and stabilised settlements could be provided with better seed and planting material from the Stations d'Adaptation Locale and instructed in general improvements of technique, while labour requirements could be reduced by offering the means of obtaining suitable hand equipment such as carts or barrows, groundnut decorticators, rice threshers, winnowers, and mills for cereals and roots. Plant sanitation measures and action against major plant pests and diseases could be carried out effectively. The general development of intensive agriculture—or "farming," in the sense in which I have used the term—was generally regarded as a future possibility which must await the solution of many problems, especially the problems of animal husbandry and the cattle complex. But INEAC was giving attention to these matters and the programme of research included the adaptation of breeds and methods to the special conditions of the equatorial forest region. In the meantime the best men from the *paysannats* could go forward to become farmers and planters—*colons indigènes*—practising intensive methods and having full title to their land.

There were, of course, initial difficulties. Early failures made it apparent that a careful vegetation-soil survey and study of customary practice must precede the lay-out of *paysannats*, in order to select the land for cultivation and to decide on a suitable system of cropping and fallow, in accordance with land capability, traditional land-use, and economic requirements. It was thought that success would also depend on a proper appreciation of social factors and the role of the traditional authorities. Political, social, and land tenure studies were therefore made—though generally by administrators rather than trained sociologists and anthropologists—and the data from these surveys were used in deciding upon the method of parcellation and the form of land holding—whether on the basis of the family, the clan, or the individual *fermette*.

Even with the most careful preliminary study, success must obviously depend on the existence of adequate areas of reasonably fertile and uniform land, with a reserve to allow for population increase. As Dumont points out, "the result of the rigid geometrical pattern is that poorer land cannot be avoided," even though "in practice, no attempt is made to utilize steep-sided valleys, marshy bottoms or areas of infertile soils." This effect is less obvious on the seemingly more uniform soils of the forest zone, though it is a uniformity of poverty, than in the savannah regions. In the forest corridors, where a degree of selection within the strips is possible, outcrops, wet depressions, and other unsuitable areas simply remain uncultivated. Dumont clearly perceives the importance of the "cultivable percentage" and of population pressure on the land. With reference to the Bambesa system of *fermettes*, he says: "the exact proportion of poorer land which has to be used depends on the population density, which is thirty to sixty-five per square mile. Reckoned on a basis of four persons per family and holdings of 25 acres, 22 of which are cultivated, the theoretical upper limit of density is 100 to the square mile. In practice this means that in areas with thirty per square mile the poorest two-thirds of the area can be ignored, but where the density rises to sixty-five, even land of mediocre quality has to be cultivated." Here too, "the rigid pattern of rectangular fields makes it impossible to allow for irregularities of terrain, and simple soil conservation techniques like contour ploughing and avoidance of steep slopes cannot be put into effect," but this is not a matter of paramount importance while cultivation periods remain short and rest periods long.

The *paysannat* method is applicable only under conditions of abundant land, where population densities are well below the critical level for the customary systems of land-use on which the method was based. It is not, as has been claimed—but not by the Belgians—"A striking improvement on the African's shifting cultivation" (29), though it is a great improvement on the prolonged cultivation that was becoming the rule in many of the cotton-growing areas, as a reaction to increasing labour demands on the cultivators. The *paysannats* were designed to tide over the long transitional period which must precede the establishment of systems of intensive and continuous cultivation, and to allow of some general advance in cultivation practices and standards of living while preserving the fertility of the soil. Contrary to opinion in many territories under British administration, it was held that "the traditional system is a better guarantee of security for the worker on the land than private ownership can ever be," and that "far from acting as a stimulus, the immediate introduction of private property in a native community would be an obstacle to progress in agriculture," for "it would be accompanied by usury and debt, and would lead the peasant into a condition of slavery" (79). Within its limitations, and in the circumstances which obtained over much of the Congo, the *paysannat* system was a logical and realistic approach to a vast complex of problems for which there is no quick and facile solution. Of course, it imposed more work on the African, and there was more than an element of "educative" compulsion. He had to grow commercial crops or an area of food crops greater than he might need or wish to do and at the same time revert to the old system of annual clearing of new land, a great labour in high forest country with its appallingly enervating climate. "One would hesitate," says Dumont, "to impose such a burden even on those Europeans who sit in their air-conditioned offices and accuse the Negro of laziness on the slightest pretext."

At the time of my last visit to the Congo some eight months before the coming of independence and the accompanying disruption, the *paysannats* still seemed to be operating effectively. Compulsion had been given up in favour of "extension" methods two years earlier and Belgian Officers maintained that this had already resulted in a lowering of standards and decline of production. No one could foresee the shape which events were to take, but there was much speculation as to whether the *paysannats* would survive the withdrawal of European influence and supervision and a prevalent opinion that they would not, unless this influence continued for another decade. There was then only one African Agricultural Officer in the whole of the Congo.

The work of INEAC continued and already it was pointing the way to the more intensive agriculture which might develop from the *paysannats*. On one experiment at Yangambi fertility had been maintained for ten years, at a level of 15 bags of maize per acre, under continuous cultivation to the following rotation, with appropriate applications of fertiliser.

YEAR	SEASON	
	1st	2nd
1st	Groundnuts	Rice
2nd	Groundnuts	Soya bean

Nitrogen, phosphate, and magnesium had been found to be essential. Ammonium nitrate or sulphate of ammonia were applied as side-dressings to the cereals, phosphates to maize and groundnuts, and magnesium to the maize and to the following rice crop also if symptoms of deficiency persisted. But transport made the cost of these fertiliser applications exceedingly high, if not prohibitively so, and in a parallel trial the same cropping was followed by grass leys (of *Setaria sphacelata*) to ascertain how far fertiliser applications and costs could be reduced. There was still a long way to go, not only in the application of results but also in finding out the most effective and economic combinations of fertiliser and ley or fallow, particularly for the great regions of weak and readily exhausted forest soils, and in devising and testing complete systems of husbandry balanced by the integration of livestock.

The disruption of the work of INEAC and Yangambi, and the probable decline and collapse of the *paysannats*, are unrecorded aspects of events in the Congo which may well have disastrous consequences for the future of the land. It no longer seems likely that the development of the *paysannats* will "go down in Africa's history as the greatest event of the century," as de Schlippe thought it might (146).

2. RESETTLEMENT WORK IN NORTHERN RHODESIA

The Zande Scheme in the southern Sudan, started in 1946, was similar in concept to the *fermettes* of the Congo, though the idea originated from local work at the Yambio station. The land for settlement was laid out in long bands of individual holdings, averaging about 33 acres, across which a strip-cropping rotation based on appropriate cultivation and fallow periods was to be practised. But no detailed survey preceded resettlement and no rotation was imposed on the cultivators. It was believed that, confined to a single holding and having had the advantages of strip-cropping and annual extensions explained to him, each cultivator would evolve a rotation of his own. "This hope was not realised," says de Schlippe (146). The fact that the lay-out of holdings did not allow of reversion to the traditional system of the Zande, with its selection of restricted sites, the imposition of cotton as a cash crop, and preoccupation with hunting and fishing, all contributed to this failure, the reasons for which have been discussed in detail by de Schlippe. The balance of cultivation and fallow was not preserved, land was over-cultivated in spite of the adequacy of the holdings in terms of area, and "homesteads established in 1946–7 had reached a stage of premature senility in 1952–3."

The earlier *Citemene* Control Scheme in Northern Rhodesia was also similar in concept and it too originated independently. But this was a stop-gap device to stave off land degeneration under conditions of population pressure, while the work in the Sudan, where land was ample, aimed at "the complete social emergence and economic stability of the Zande people."

The same principle of "rationalising" and building upon the foundation of the traditional systems also lay behind the large-scale resettlement work carried out in Northern Rhodesia in the 1940s. The background of this operation has already been explained; the overcrowding and destruction of Native Reserves often surrounded by great areas of unused land which was degenerating under the effects of uncontrolled bush fires, and the return of a large proportion of this land for the use of the African peoples.

The problem then resolved itself into making the best use of the additional land so as to restore the population-land balance as far as possible. Surveys and assessments of population carrying-capacities and land requirements were made in the vacant land and the overcrowded regions of the reserves by the methods which have been described, and once these had been completed the planning of population movements became, in theory, simple. In practice, of course, it was far from simple. The area concerned, reserves and land available for resettlement, amounted to about 33,800 square miles—4,000 square miles more than the whole land area of Scotland—with a population, in round figures, of 290,000 (Fig. 12). To make the best use of the additional land, in such a way as to relieve pressure within the reserves completely and to restore an enduring population-land balance, would have required the transfer of over 160,000 people, of whom 130,000 were Ngoni, Chewa, and Senga in the Eastern Province. But physical, eco-logical, social, and political factors all restricted the programme of resettlement. Fifty miles was taken as the maximum practical move for any village, since in most cases movements had to be made on foot and goods and food-stocks had to be carried. It was also accepted that people could not be moved to a new and un-known environment unsuited to their traditional crops and methods of production and that cattle-owners would not willingly migrate to tsetse-infested country leaving their herds behind. Tribal boundaries and the original ownership of the land had to be taken into consideration but these were not regarded as sacrosanct and, in fact, large areas were resettled by peoples who had had no previous claim to them.

Thus, in the case of the Ngoni, and to a lesser extent the Chewa, the land which could in practice be used was insufficient to allow of the restoration of a population-land balance. Two alternatives were possible: to re-distribute the Ngoni-Chewa populations more or less evenly over the new land and the reserves, in which case both would be over-populated in relation to their carrying-capacities, or to establish balanced settlement in the new land leaving the reserves still over-populated. The latter course was adopted for a number of reasons, including the fact that much of the "new" land was then tsetse infested and the keeping of cattle and development of mixed farming would not be possible for a considerable time. On the other hand, it was thought that the reserves might be made to support their populations, somewhat reduced by resettlement, on a basis of mixed husbandry, provided

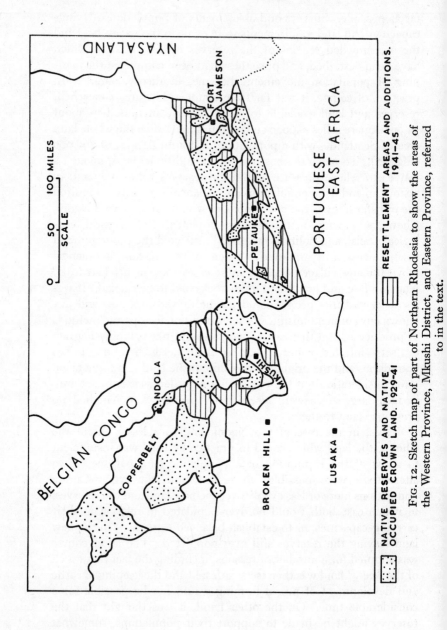

FIG. 12. Sketch map of part of Northern Rhodesia to show the areas of the Western Province, Mkushi District, and Eastern Province, referred to in the text.

that agricultural effort was concentrated on these areas. In the event, this rather optimistic expectation was not fulfilled. The same method of resettlement was, in general, applied throughout. Extension areas were allocated to each tribe and chieftaincy in accordance with the general plan to restore the population-land balance as far as possible. Movement into these areas was largely voluntary, but in many cases a good deal of discussion and persuasion was needed to obtain the necessary numbers, since most villages preferred that their neighbours should do the moving and that they should take over the vacated land.

Headmen and other representatives of the villages who had finally elected to move then toured the areas allocated to them and selected sites for their new villages. The selected sites were then marked on the vegetation-soil map and blocks of land having an estimated carrying-capacity approximating to each village population, allowing for temporary absentees, were demarcated around the selected sites, using roads, streams, hills, and cut or blazed lines as boundaries. The single village was the usual unit of settlement, but in some cases modifications were made. A large area of escarpment hill country in the Eastern Province, much of it inaccessible and uninhabitable except for small pockets of fertile soil, was opened to unrestricted settlement by Ambo and Senga-Kunda people, and other areas of poor soils and low carrying-capacities in Fort Jameson district were also opened to free settlement up to a population total determined by the estimate of carrying capacity. In Ndola district an area was demarcated and opened to immediate unrestricted settlement as an emergency measure to relieve acute land shortage and actual famine conditions in one section of the reserve. A later modification introduced in parts of the Petauke district, where dams had to be constructed to provide domestic water, was to use three or four related villages as a population unit settled in a single large "parish" block centred on the watering point. This was, primarily, to allow of economy in the distribution of watering points, but it was hoped that it would also reduce the effects of inter-village movements and lead to larger administrative units.

Simple improvements and elementary measures of agricultural control were introduced at the same time in most of the resettlement areas. These included anti-erosion practices appropriate to the varying environments and systems of cultivation, planting of fruit trees, use of improved seed, reservation of hill, watershed, and streamside protection areas and timber reserves, early burning of grass and bush, and improvements in the lay-out and construction of villages. Most of these measures were not popular and insistence on their acceptance as a condition of settlement was a deterrent to movement. Few of them, with a notable exception in the case of the system of contour ridge cultivation introduced in the Eastern Province, survived the withdrawal of close supervision.

The resettlement scheme also included construction of roads in the new areas, provision of water supplies, control of game and tsetse, the establishment of schools, clinics, and other social services, and the programme as a whole amounted to a combined operation on a considerable scale by most of the service departments of Government.

Most of the work was done in the period 1941–7, and though the original scheme was not wholly completed the movements which were carried out resulted in a substantial alteration of the population-land balance. The results which were thought to have been achieved are illustrated in the accompanying diagrams (Fig. 13). The region had originally been occupied by ten tribes (see Fig. 13. A) so distributed that each had a plenitude of land except the Ngoni and some of the Chewa in the east, where the incursion of immigrant Ngoni in the later nineteenth century had created an area of over-population. The setting aside of large land areas for alienation and European settlement, and the movement of peoples into Native Reserves, created a secondary population-land pattern containing much larger areas of concentration characterised by rapid land degeneration and failure of the food supplies (see Fig. 13. B). Planned resettlement resulted in a tertiary pattern, with restoration of the balance over most of the region, but the Ngoni problem, which had been intensified by the alienation of the Fort Jameson tobacco farms, remained unresolved, and there was also an area of much less serious over-population in the southern Chewa country (see Fig. 13. C). The area set aside for each village or population group in the settlements was intended to be such as would allow of normal land selection and the continuation of the traditional systems, with some modification, at least for a further generation. This was not regarded as an ideal or permanent solution, or as a substitute for agricultural and economic development, but as a land-saving operation and means of reducing the great

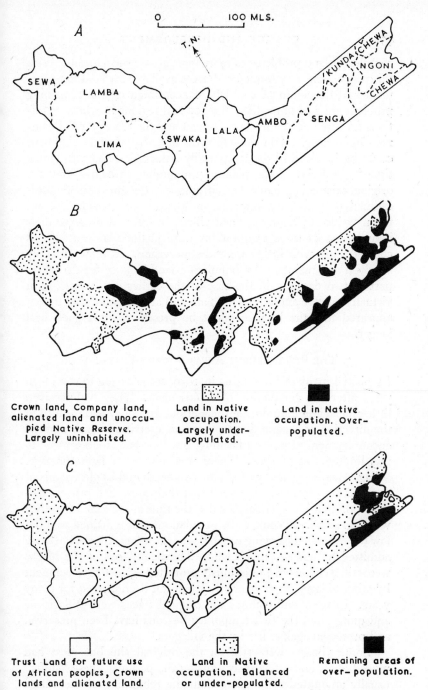

FIG. 13. Sketch map of part of Northern Rhodesia to show the population-land patterns referred to in the text.

complex of land problems to more manageable proportions. With this respite, the very limited resources available for land improvement and development could be concentrated on the remaining problem areas of immediate urgency and regions in which conditions favoured economic development and the emergence of commercial farming. At the same time the line of gradual development could be followed in the temporarily balanced areas, with ample time for experiment and planning: assuming, of course, that the original calculations had not erred, at least in the direction of underestimation of land requirements, and that the people would accept the new idea of clearly defined village blocks and preserve their boundaries. If these assumptions were justified the settlements could endure with little care and supervision. In the event they survived and maintained a population-land balance for the better part of two decades, in the case of the earlier settlements, with virtually no care and attention at all, and at the end of that time it appeared that the balance might be preserved for a good deal longer.

3. THE RESETTLEMENT AREAS FIFTEEN YEARS LATER

I revisited many of these areas in 1959, some fifteen to seventeen years after the completion of resettlement. They had received little official attention during this period, for policy had evolved in the direction of general development on a territorial basis and the encouragement of peasant farming, but they had stood up well to this limited test of time. There was no talk of land shortage. Village Headmen, many of whom I remembered as old friends of the resettlement days, all agreed that their areas had proved adequate, though some had objected at the time and insisted that they were too small. In some cases populations had remained well below the estimated carrying capacities of the village blocks but none admitted he had too much land. The boundaries of the blocks were still well known and jealously protected against encroachment by other villages, even where they had not been cleared for many years. In woodland country the original traces were still visible and quite often the first temporary beacons have been preserved and protected against fire by the villagers.

Some villages were still on the original site but most had moved once, and a few twice, during the period. These "shifts" usually amounted to no more than the rebuilding of the village alongside the original site or within a few hundred yards of it, and the longest move I came across was one of less than a mile from one side of a block to the other. It was intended that villages should be free to move at will within their own areas, since this degree of movement could not hamper the development of social, marketing, or administrative services. But an attempt had been made at the time of resettlement to encourage permanency by assisting the building of villages in brick or sun-dried brick. This could not be accounted a success. The houses had often been abandoned after falling into disrepair or becoming vermin infested and some had been burned on the death of the owner; nearly all were dilapidated and unsightly. Villages rebuilt in the traditional manner looked altogether more pleasant and healthy places of habitation for people who spend most of their time out of doors. The importance of African rural housing is commonly over-emphasised: a dwelling hut is a place to sleep in, to store one's possessions, to shelter from the rain in the wet season, and there is still no general desire that it should be more than this. Urban housing is quite another matter.

The programme of orchard establishment had also failed, even more completely. When resettlement was carried out, incoming villagers had been induced, with some coercion but little difficulty, to plant fruit trees such as mango, pawpaw, lemon, guava, and banana with material supplied from nurseries established by the Agricultural Department. Of these village orchards nothing remained but a few scorched and scrofulous plants barely surviving in a tangle of weed and undergrowth. I did not come across a single individual who had thought it worth while to maintain and protect the trees, probably because the bush provided what was regarded as an adequate supply of wild fruit and green relish.

But the main objectives, relief of population pressure in the old Reserves and the establishment and maintenance of a population-land balance, had been largely achieved.

In the Eastern Province the populations of resettlement villages had generally increased, most markedly in the case of villages with a high proportion of fertile soil and close to main roads, produce-buying centres, and settlements: but the poorer and remoter blocks tended to remain underpopulated. The normal drift of population to the more prosperous villages and areas of economic opportunity had probably been accentuated by the development of the groundnut industry and the buying of maize. There was also a tendency to prolonged cultivation of the stronger soils, where shorter periods of cultivation and fallow would have been preferable, and the cultivated area had been increased somewhat, mainly for the production of a larger saleable surplus of groundnuts. But these changes did not then seem to have reached a rate which would result in rapid disruption of the balance, and they were being offset to some extent by the growth of peasant farming. In these areas of fertile soils and favourable economic circumstances the transition to farming is a logical and hopeful development.

The state to which much of the land of the Reserves would have degenerated if there had been no relief of population pressure was strikingly illustrated by conditions in part of the Ngoni country, where resettlement work had not been carried out because of lack of land and an outbreak of human trypanosomiasis in one of the receiving areas. Here population densities remained at three times, or more than three times, the estimated critical levels, and there were also three or four times as many cattle as the grazing could carry on existing systems of management. Land degeneration continued, fertility declined to miserable levels, and in places spectacular gulley erosion spread through the trampled and denuded grassland. By 1950 the worst region in the main Ngoni Reserve had become known as "the Ngoni devastated area." The situation was regarded as "immensely critical," and in 1951 a plan of rehabilitation was drawn up. This included control of watersheds and stream heads, construction of conservation dams, organised early burning, establishment of wind-breaks, and anti-erosion methods of cultivation. But all of these excellent measures are no real answer to problems of acute land shortage. In their report on conditions as they found them in 1954, Priestley and Greening make this comment: "Although many of the suggested measures had been introduced it was apparent that they were palliatives rather than a solution of the problem" (132). They conclude that "Whatever is done to improve agriculture in the reserve there will still not be enough land to provide more than a half of the existing population with a decent living." The picture they draw is one of a typical rural slum, a "nursery and old folks home," whose inhabitants had come to depend largely on wages of labour, remittances from migrant workers, and petty trade, to eke out totally inadequate crop yields from the degraded soil. Without the work outlet "results would have been catastrophic." By 1959 the situation had not changed: other schemes and proposals had been put forward, but the problem remained unsolved and seemingly insoluble.

In the other reserves, where it had been possible to bring about substantial relief of population pressure by resettlement, conditions were certainly no worse than they had been seventeen years earlier, and in some ways they were substantially better. The land continued to feed its populations. The appallingly destructive cultivation of precipitous slopes had long since ceased and the formerly denuded hills carried a good regrowth of protective cover. Anti-erosion practices first introduced in the resettlement areas—contour ridging at 2 feet 6 inches vertical interval and substitution of ridge for mound cultivation—had been spread to the reserves and were commonly practised both there and in the "new" areas. It seemed that the period of respite might last for another decade or more. My impression was that Critical Population Densities had not been over-estimated: but they might have been under-estimated.

The population-land balance had also been preserved in the central area of the Mkushi Lala and the Swaka. The scenes of woodland devastation and the bitter complaints of land shortage were things of the distant past, almost forgotten. The Lala seemed to be growing more sorghum and they had certainly developed a much better sense of soil selection for this crop. The Swaka continued to practise their traditional system, but the Lala had adopted a curious change in their methods of *citemene*. The small circle had almost disappeared, at least near main roads and in the neighbourhood of administrative and Native Authority centres. In place of the traditional circular stacks, brushwood was piled in very long narrow lines, some 4 to 8 yards wide, forming an irregular pattern throughout the clearing. The lines of timber were burned at the customary time and the long ash strips broadcast with finger millet as in normal practice. This peculiar change may have come about as a reaction to a Native Authority Order, which I myself had suggested, limiting the number of small circles a family might make in any one year but placing no restriction on size. The intention was to encourage the use of larger circles and eventual adoption of the single circle which could be fenced and cropped for several years. The order, it seemed, had been evaded by altering the garden form—a small but striking illustration of the fact that the best-intentioned measures may have the most unexpected results. At least, this was the only explanation I was given or could think of: there was no apparent advantage in the long strips and the traditional pattern had not altered in the remoter areas and among the other small-circle *citemene* peoples, the Serenje Lala and the Bisa.

The resettlement area south of the Copperbelt in Ndola district remained greatly underpopulated, as it had been in the beginning. Nearly every block was occupied, but village populations were small. The area had been intended for an initial population of over 10,000 from three overcrowded areas of reserve bordering the Copperbelt, and it was settled on the basis of population figures provided by the Administration which purported to show this number. Perhaps the Native Authorities had boosted the figures somewhat in order to lessen their own difficulties. Although the need for more land was keenly felt, nearly every village wanted to stay close to the attractions of the Copperbelt and felt that they had the best claim to do so: it was not easy to find volunteers or to induce a sufficient number of villages to move, especially to the more distant blocks. Whatever the reason, it was found when 106 villages had been established in the new areas that the total population was only about half the expected number: a count made in 1945 showed the population of these villages to be 5,737. Some effort was made to rectify this situation by the transfer of more villages but a further count in 1949 showed that population had fallen to 4,966 and indicated a return drift to the Copperbelt. The resettlement scheme in this region was then branded as a failure and all interest was lost for a number of years. It would seem, however, that at some time during this period of apparent stagnation the drift was reversed, for counts made in 1957 showed the following much more satisfactory position.[1]

Worsening conditions in the reserves, the greater attractiveness of the fully established villages in the new area once the pioneer work had been completed, and, perhaps, freedom from supervision and interference, may have accounted for the reversal of the population drift and the growth of the resettlement villages.

An Agricultural Officer who investigated the situation in the

[1] District Administration Tour Report, 1957.

POPULATIONS IN RESERVES AND RESETTLEMENT AREAS, 1957

	RESERVES	RESETTLEMENT AREA
Mushiri	5,487	4,437
Nkambo	—[1]	1,109
Chiwala	5,152	3,142
	10,639	8,688

Resettlement Area in 1956 gave this answer to the question he had been posed—has the scheme been a failure? "It has not gone as well as might have been hoped but it did relieve a very dangerous situation that existed twelve years ago. Development has been negligible but the possibilities are there just as they were before. It can never be a failure: it can yet succeed" (191).

He recommended, in addition to further settlement, the stimulation of vegetable production and the organisation of marketing, the establishment of a stock farm to supply cattle, and the encouragement of poultry husbandry, all of which had featured in the original resettlement programme.

In 1959 the resettlement area did not present as depressing a picture as I had expected. Interest had revived and the roads were open and in good condition. Beacons and traces demarcating village areas had been well maintained, for here too the villagers had developed a proprietary interest in their land and were jealous of their boundaries. Vegetable growing for the Copperbelt market had expanded, though not to the extent that had been hoped. The original bulk-buying scheme had ended when the mines stopped issuing vegetable rations to their workers, but produce continued to be bought by small traders. At Chileshi, near the centre of the area, the boarding school established by the Education Department was flourishing with 230 pupils and the headmaster told us that the number was increasing rapidly, although three other centres of education, a Government day-school, and two Mission schools had opened in the area. There were indications of some degree of prosperity; quite a number of small African-owned stores and tea shops had opened up, and bicycles were numerous.

On the other hand, villages were generally small and, with a

---

[1] The entire population of this little chiefdom was transferred.

few exceptions, still far below the numbers for which the blocks had been designed. Some blocks remained unoccupied, usually because the water supply had failed: but the water supply pro- gramme as a whole had been successful and the great majority of wells were yielding adequate supplies. There were some indica- tions that village populations might be growing by an influx of new members. I had time to make a count in only one village block: here I found a resident population of 74 where only 48 had been recorded three years previously—but the block had been designed to support over 200 people. It was evident, however, that not all of the newcomers were emigrants from the old reserves, for there were occasional indications of Lala methods of clearing in new gardens. Enquiry confirmed that a number of immigrant Lala from Serenje and Mkushi had settled, and in some cases married, in the Lamba villages.

The outcome, as I saw it after fifteen years, was disappointing considering the initial effort that had been put into the area—a combined effort of the Administration and the Agricultural, Water Development, Game and Tsetse, and Education Departments de- signed to make the area attractive and lay the foundations of economic advance—but the picture was not one of unrelieved failure. Although the planned redistribution of population was only partly effected, relief of pressure in the more congested parts of the old reserve had been sufficient to stave off disaster. Their condition showed only slight improvement, but there had been no recurrence of famine comparable with that of 1940 and it seemed that the resettlement area could continue to act as a safety valve for a good many years.

In this area also, conditions are not unfavourable for the de- velopment of farming. This had been foreseen as an eventual line of development at the time the resettlement programme was being planned and some twenty pioneer farms were then laid out. It was hoped that these would be taken up after the War by return- ing Lamba soldiers or volunteers, but as it happened there were no Lamba soldiers and no suitable volunteers. A group of sixteen immigrant Shona from Southern Rhodesia was therefore settled on the farms, each with his own holding containing 16 acres of arable and a market-garden site. By 1959 only five remained. Six had been ejected for thoroughly bad land-use, five had left voluntarily because they had failed to make farming pay, and another was about to leave for the same reason. The four who had succeeded, out of the original group of sixteen, seemed to be content with their achievement and likely to remain permanently. They had a reasonable cash income from their well-run market gardens, in addition to a full food supply and a saleable grain surplus from the arable. The best of them was making a regular gross income of £5 a week from an acre of vegetables, and a net annual cash income—he employed a good deal of labour—probably in the neighbourhood of £150, and he was talking of buying a power pump to extend his irrigated acreage.

This group, it will be noted, consisted not of ordinary villagers but of experienced men free from the incubus of kinship obligations, and anxious to farm. It seems doubtful if a higher proportion of genuine successes, or even a comparable proportion, is to be expected of any scheme for the development of advanced farming or intensive horticulture under present circumstances.

4. The Problem of the Serenje Lala

In the plateau region of Serenje, where in 1945 Peters had estimated a considerable degree of overpopulation for the small-circle *citemene* system, there had been no resettlement of populations, for no land had been taken and none could be added. Nevertheless, by 1959 the area showed only slight further deterioration, much less than might have been expected on the basis of Peters's forecasts. It may be that he had somewhat underestimated the human carrying capacity of the land and system, but other explanations also suggested themselves. Judging by the available demographic data for the district, resident populations had not increased and might even have declined significantly in the intervening period of fourteen years. Such a decline could be attributed partly if not wholly to migration. We have already noted a movement of Lala from the most congested area of Serenje northward into sparsely occupied Bisa country, and I also saw some evidence of a less conspicuous southerly and westerly drift into Mkushi and even as far as the Ndola resettlement area, which may in the aggregate have been no less significant. In addition, the number of men absent at work had increased, from rather more than 40 per cent at the time of Peters's survey to over 60 per cent, and it is probable that more of these migrants had taken their families with them. Agricultural practice also showed some change. There was a noticeable increase in the use of mound gardens for cassava, sorghum, and maize, particularly where the cycle of tree regeneration had been much reduced, and a corresponding reduction of *citemene* which may have been assisted by the loss of man-power for tree cutting. It seemed that the Serenje Lala had reacted to the situation of land degeneration, as I have suggested they reacted in the past (p. 113), by reducing their *fiteme* and increasing the size of their hoed gardens, and by sending out a plethora of population. The sparsely inhabited country to the north and the resettlement areas to the south and west had, it seemed, provided an unintended safety valve. Of course, this is little more than conjecture; much more data, including vital statistics and accurate estimates of population movements, would be required to make a reliable assessment of the situation.

What is certain is that the Serenje Lala decisively rejected another alternative open to them—the adoption of the large-circle form of *citemene*. A serious effort was made to induce the Lala to adopt the advanced northern system by introducing Bemba cultivators with their families and carrying out demonstrations. The results demonstrated the superiority of the method very conclusively: higher yields of finger millet were obtained from the Bemba large circles in the opening year, in spite of interplanting with sorghum and cassava, and they sustained cultivation for four years under a sequence of finger millet followed by a crop of sorghum and two crops of legumes. But there was no reaction from the Lala and the Native Authorities were asked to consider compulsion. Their reply to this suggestion is contained in the minutes of a meeting of the Lala Council held on 20 March 1951. "Council agreed that the Large Circle has distinct advantages over the present method but were unwilling to pass an order until demonstration had been extended. A suggestion by Chief Muchinda was then adopted: that all chiefs should have a large circle this year."

I doubt if the chiefs carried out their resolution, but if so their lead was no more effective than the demonstrations and in 1953 the project was abandoned as hopeless.

Yet the migrants to Swaka and Lamba country seemed to have adopted readily enough the agricultural practices of the people among whom they had settled.

CHAPTER XXIV

NEW HORIZONS

ECONOMIC TRANSITION

The African political scene has changed with bewildering rapidity in the last decade, but the land and its problems have not changed. Inter-tropical Africa remains a region of great poverty. Here there are thirty-three countries with a total population which cannot now be far short of 182 million. Mortality rates continue to fall with the increase of medical services and the success of mass campaigns such as the World Health Organisation's attack on yellow fever, the control of yaws and leprosy, and the reduction of malaria. Birth rates do not decrease. It is commonly conceded that population growth over most of West Africa and the highlands of East Africa is of the order of 2·5 per cent per annum, and it is not very much lower elsewhere, except perhaps in the equatorial region. Growth rates such as Kuczynski rejected are now regarded as commonplace and the imminence of a population explosion is freely predicted.[1]

Yet the value of the whole production of the vast region and this growing multitude of people is only some £4,500 million, which is about a quarter of that of the United Kingdom alone. The average income equivalent, including the value of subsistence crops and animal products, is therefore rather less than £25 per head of population, and this includes also the high incomes of foreign individuals and enterprises, and such favoured African groups as the larger cocoa planters of southern Ghana and the coffee growers of East Africa. Millions of subsistence and semi-subsistence cultivators contrive somehow to exist on a *per capita* income of £10 a year or even less.

Over the region as a whole, nearly 90 per cent of the people

[1] For an account of the present situation with particular reference to problems of rural development, see *FAO Africa Study: Report on the Possibilities of African Rural Development in Relation to Economic and Social Growth*, C61/15, Food and Agriculture Organisation of the United Nations, 1963.

are still employed in the rural sectors of the economies, mostly at near-subsistence levels of production. In underdeveloped countries, generally, some 80 per cent of the labour force is engaged in producing the nation's food supply and other soil products, largely for consumption within a subsistence economy, while in advanced countries 12–30 per cent suffices and this small proportion of the labour force produces much more and better soil products. Indeed, it may be stated as a general rule that national living standards are inversely proportional to the ratio between the numbers employed in agriculture and in other sectors of the economy,[1] as the following figures indicate.

PROPORTION OF POPULATION SUPPORTED BY (a) AGRICULTURE (b) OTHER SECTORS		NATIONAL INCOME PER HEAD
(a)	(b)	U.S. $
United States 1	7	2,100
Britain 1	5	950
Western Europe 1	4	750
U.S.S.R. 1	2	550
Underdeveloped countries (generally) 4	1	100
Inter-tropical Africa 7	1	74

Even in the United States the proportion of population employed in agriculture is probably still above the economic optimum. The spectacular rise in farm productivity achieved by that country in recent decades was not the result of improved technologies alone, but of a combination of improved technologies, heavy capital investment, and larger production units. It has been argued[2] that the continuing demand for price supports for United States agriculture is due to the existence of too many small producers "who cannot hope to prosper as farmers because they do not have and cannot get enough capital," and that the only real remedy is "more city jobs." In Britain, the high proportion of small farmers whose net returns are less than the wage of an agri-

[1] A few countries, such as Denmark and New Zealand, may be quoted as apparent exceptions but these can readily be explained as economic parts of advanced industrial communities.

[2] Edward Higbee, *Farms and Farmers in an Urban Age.*

cultural labourer has been cited as the main cause of agricultural inefficiency, while the chief weakness of the Soviet economy lies in a high (but decreasing) degree of rural over-population. Japan's "economic miracle" of the last decade was accompanied by a great reduction of employment in agriculture and an increase of production from a level at which the country could not feed herself to one which threatens an outbreak of that fashionable disease of the affluent nations, an unmanageable farm surplus.

The process of development in underveloped countries consists, essentially, in reversing the proportion of employment in agriculture and in other sectors. This, of course, implies industrialisation. A great increase in the number of jobs is needed not only to relieve population pressure on the land and create markets for agriculture but also to prevent the rapid growth of social unrest. The outflow to the centres of economic opportunity continues, on a scale much in excess of the opportunities. In most of the African countries the larger towns have become greatly swollen within the last decade and the pool of urban unemployed grows steadily. This movement to the towns has been described as "a manifestation of the individual's desire to break from the fetters of rural society." Yet, though the individual may thus escape his obligations to his society, as a rule he retains his rights, his place in the society, and his claim to land. This is his ultimate safeguard and his one form of social security. Although the migration is large enough to create a grave problem at the receiving end, it is small in relation to the rural population as a whole and does little to relieve pressure on the land. Furthermore, the loss by migration is more than counter-balanced by natural increase rates and the growing numbers of people for whom the land must provide a living.

In inter-tropical Africa industrial development is in its early beginnings. Apart from the processing of export produce, manufacturing activity has as yet gone little beyond the setting up of flour mills, cement plants, soft drinks factories, breweries, an occasional cigarette factory and textile mill, and some development in other comparatively simple fields. Many factors inhibit the growth of industrialisation, including lack of entrepreneurship and skills, and of ability to acquire advanced skills in a community where, taken overall, barely one in ten can read and write: but economists generally point to the static nature of the rural sector as a factor of crucial importance. The market for manufactured goods among a population consisting largely of subsistence and semi-subsistence cultivators and petty commodity producers is far too small to encourage industrial development. There can be no significant increase in purchasing power without a very large increase of agricultural output. Yet any general and substantial increase in agricultural productivity and prosperity depends on the development of the non-agricultural sectors, the creation of jobs for the rural surplus, and the consequent generation of expanding markets for farm products.

Without this, the agricultural economies must remain tied to the few export crops for which bulk markets are available in the highly industrialised countries. The most valuable of these crops are restricted by soil and climate to limited environments. They yield incomes to relatively few producers, and these incomes have only a small diffusion effect. Cocoa, a product of a very small part of the zone of sub-equatorial climate, accounts for nearly 23 per cent of the value of all crop exports from the inter-tropical region. Coffee, which is confined mainly to the best soils of the Guinea and East African double-rainfall zones, accounts for about 19 per cent. Cotton and groundnuts are much more widely distributed products of the savannah regions but they account for only 16 and 14 per cent respectively of the value of all crop exports. Tobacco, rubber, and sisal, which are largely products of the European-owned and -operated farms and estates of Rhodesia, Liberia, and Tanganyika, together account for a further 14 per cent.

During the 1950s there was a marked increase in the output of coffee, rubber, groundnuts, tobacco, and cocoa. Coffee production in particular increased at a phenomenal rate, approximating to 11 per cent per annum. This was due largely to the sudden popularity of "instant" coffee and the world demand for the cheaper robusta type used in making this product. Exports of groundnuts and tobacco doubled, the increase of the former coming mainly from Nigeria and Senegal and the latter from the European farms of Rhodesia. Output of cocoa from the West African production zone went up by about 40 per cent. But there was little increase of cotton production in spite of attractive and fairly constant prices. Probably, it was already near its zenith under current methods of production.

These increases were a reaction to high export prices and the growing demands of the affluent nations. They produced an illusion of continuing economic growth. By the end of the 1950s the terms of trade were changing as supplies of the commodities from Africa and other parts of the world caught up with and outpaced the demand. Prices declined, disposal became more difficult, and the growth of national incomes in the producing countries, which had been expanding at rates of 4 to 7 per cent per annum, began to slow down. The present outlook is not encouraging—except, perhaps, for cocoa, consumption of which may increase further if incomes continue to rise in the importing countries. Stocks of robusta coffee are accumulating, the market for African vegetable oils is threatened by competition from other sources and the increasing use of synthetic detergents, while cotton is faced with similar competition from other areas and, especially, from synthetic fibres.

While the growth rate of national incomes tends to decline—a decline which in some countries has been hastened by the repatriation of European private capital and enterprise—there are increasing pressures on the fledgling governments for new and enlarged expenditures. These include not only demands for expanded social services and development investments but also altogether new commitments on national consolidation and the costly trappings of nationhood. Added to this there has been, in many cases, the cost of compensation to officials of the former regimes and recurrent costs of development projects started by suzerain Governments in the post-war decade.

It is in these circumstances that the leaders of the new nations have to effect a dramatic economic transition. They are committed to accelerated economic development within an African social framework because, as Prime Minister Jomo Kenyatta of Kenya has so often reminded his countrymen, "freedom must be buttressed by sound economics, sound business practices and sound development planning to ensure that the people's standard of living keeps on improving."

The transition will not be easy. Indeed, it has been said with some truth that rapid economic development is the most traumatic experience a nation can undergo.

The first essential is the formation of capital. This is the only way to develop the economy of a country, whatever its political structure. The means differ with political concepts and ideologies but the process is the same. There are three main sources of capital: public international investment or foreign aid, private foreign investment, and internal investment.

The development plans of many of the emergent African countries are based on expectations of foreign and international aid to an extent that seems far from certain of fulfilment. It is true that an impressive volume of aid has already been given and this has helped to redress the balance of loss: but the amount of aid, though impressive in itself, is very small in relation to the need. By the end of 1961 the annual total of all official contributions to the countries of the region amounted to less than 2 per cent of gross national expenditures. Furthermore, the effectiveness of this aid has been reduced by the multiplicity of independent sources from which it derives. Most of it is provided under bilateral national programmes which are often operated by more than one national agency. The United States, for example, has her Agency for International Development (AID), the Food for Peace Programme, the Peace Corps, and the Export-Import Bank. Britain provides assistance principally to Commonwealth countries, including Kenya, Tanganyika, Uganda, Nyasaland, Nigeria, and Northern Rhodesia. This takes the form of development loans and grants and various forms of technical assistance operated through the Department of Technical Co-operation and the Overseas Service Aid Scheme. France devotes almost all of her efforts to the former French colonies. Belgium also gives assistance to her former colonies and mandates of the Congo, Ruanda, and Urundi. The U.S.S.R. provides aid for Ghana, Guinea, Somalia, Mali, and the Sudan. The Federal Republic of Germany operates aid programmes in the Congo (Leopoldville), Togo, and Guinea, while Canada has programmes in Nigeria and Ghana. Other countries also have bilateral aid programmes, including Austria, Sweden, Switzerland, Israel, the United Arab Republic, Czechoslovakia, Hungary, Poland, Australia, New Zealand, and India. The last three, however, give assistance under the Colombo plan which does not affect Africa.

Expenditures in the form of capital and goods amount to nearly 93 per cent of all economic aid costs. Expenditures on service in the form of technical assistance, which account for the major part of the United Nations effort, amount to only about 7 per cent of the global aid pattern.

Efforts to improve the co-ordination of aid given by its member countries are now being made by the recently formed Development Assistance Committee of the Organisation for Economic Co-operation and Development (OECD). The members include Britain and the major European donor nations together with the United States, Canada, Japan, and the Commission of the European Economic Community.

The effectiveness of this complex of international aid has been reduced not only by the diversity of sources but also by lack of co-ordination between financial and development programmes and by the inevitable inefficiency of the emergent countries' young and inexperienced bureaucracies.

Most national leaders appear to be aware of the need to attract private foreign investment, but the way in which this is to be fitted into an African social framework is not always clear.

Kenya's Minister of Commerce and Industry, Dr Kiano, said recently: "We anticipate rapid development of our economic and industrial sector based partly on local resources and partly on overseas investors. We plan for the wide development of orthodox businesses and firms and a similar development of Government-aided firms; but we intend to do this within an African social framework—in other words, through organisations which, as far as possible, will ensure an equitable distribution of wealth and equal economic opportunities for all."[1]

Private investment may be discouraged by limiting conditions based on admirable but unpractical concepts of social justice, in disregard of the Keynesian precept that "the engine which drives enterprise is not thrift but profit." The tendency in the developing countries is to want the best of both worlds—high wages, costly welfare programmes, national prestige, and rapid industrial and general economic development all at the same time. The unpalatable truth is that this cannot be done. Wages are a direct result of the investment of capital and they will not rise, nor will the number of jobs increase and national revenues expand, unless secure, substantial, and continuing profits are made by those who supply capital and enterprise. Social justice is one of the fruits of economic development and it is a characteristic of fruits that they cannot be reaped until the tree is mature. Patience is essential, but it is not a characteristic of the present temper of African nationalism.

[1] "Kenya's Economic Outlook," *Commonwealth Journal*, VI, No. 6, Dec. 1963.

Public international investment is not likely to increase very greatly, since one cannot expect the peoples of the donor nations to tolerate a reduction of their own standards of living. Private foreign capital is likely to be wary. Considering the magnitude of the task, the entire sum which may be donated or lent by the advanced nations and international agencies and subscribed by private foreign investors will almost inevitably fall far short of the need. In the final analysis, the new African nations must generate from their own resources the greater part of the investment capital they need, as every developed country in the world has done. Japan achieved her economic miracle by creating a mass stock market and diverting more than a quarter of her national income into new investments each year.

The immediately exploitable resources of inter-tropical Africa are land, minerals, hydropower, and labour. Mineral potential is very considerable, and increased exports are badly needed to supply foreign exchange. At the present time export prospects for minerals appear to be better than for crops, partly because large-scale mining is in the hands of foreign firms which in some cases have safe or guaranteed markets abroad. But the capital of these firms is almost entirely foreign and consequently much of the profit accrues abroad. For these reasons the expansion of mining is apt to be suspect as a form of "neo-colonial exploitation."

One of the larger assets of the region lies in its potential abundance of hydro-electric power. This potential is enormous. It has been estimated at 40 per cent of the world total, and some of the most important sites have been found to be capable of development at low cost.

Labour also is abundant; the problem is to find jobs for men, not men for jobs. This is recognised in some national plans which include "direct labour investment" or "direct personal taxation" as a considerable part of the domestic contribution. The former expression refers to the value of voluntary labour given to development works while the latter appears to be a euphemism for a labour contribution which may not be entirely voluntary.

2. THE ROLE OF AGRICULTURE

When we consider the part that the land must play in the process of economic development we come back to the old dilemma. The economists point to the need for a crucial effort in the rural sector, but at the same time they agree, or most of them agree, that the development of this sector will be conditioned by progress in others, that economic growth must be sustained by industrialisation, and that a major increase of non-agricultural employment is essential.[1]

The conclusion is inescapable that *pari passu* with agricultural development must go industrial development, that the two must be balanced and integrated, and that neither can proceed faster than the other. Infrastructural development, the provision of roads, railways, ports, and all the other basic things that do not themselves develop a country but make development possible, must also be geared to the programme.

During the first post-war decade the suzerain Powers in Africa initiated and largely financed development programmes on a considerable scale. A high proportion of the resources which became available at that time were absorbed in infrastructural development, partly because the need was obvious and partly because this form of investment presents no special problems and is relatively easy to organise: but the provision of basic facilities still calls for heavy expenditures and this must inevitably slow down the rate of directly productive investment.

From the viewpoint of the agriculturist, the effects of industrialisation and general economic expansion are to take redundant men off the land, to create expanding markets for farm products, and eventually to leave the land to those who have the means and ability to farm it efficiently. Without this take-off, and if population pressure on the land continues to grow, the process of agricultural development will not only be retarded and limited, it will be reversed. Developed systems of agriculture have their own "carrying capacities" and "critical population densities"; their structure is based on a fixed number of farm families and any continuing increase in that number must result in degeneration of the agrarian structure and relapse towards subsistence levels of production.

The role of agriculture in the early stages of economic development is fourfold:

---

[1] For a stimulating general discussion of this topic from the economist's point of view see John W. Mellor, "The Process of Agricultural Development in Low Income Countries," *Journal of Farm Economics* (American Farm Economic Association), XLIV, No. 8, Aug. 1962.

(a) to generate capital for the economic transition, including foreign exchange gained by the export of soil products,

(b) to provide the labour force required for expansion of the non-agricultural sectors of the economy,

(c) to meet the growth in demand for agricultural products created by industrial consumption, an increasing non-rural population, and rising *per capita* incomes,

(d) to support a surplus population until such time as this can be absorbed by the general expansion of the economy.

The tasks of generating capital, providing the raw materials of industry, and producing the food needs of a developing nation cannot be left to petty commodity producers and sellers of uncertain and violently fluctuating subsistence surpluses. The development of systems of modern commercial farming is an essential concomitance of the economic revolution.

Agricultural development in this sense, the creation of viable commercial farms, is possible only under certain conditions. The production unit, the farm-holding, must take the form of a single enclosed area of adequate size and of suitable shape for working with modern cultivating equipment. The soils must be capable of responding to good management and of sustaining cultivation at high yield levels. The farmer must have security of tenure, to an extent that will encourage him to invest in long-term development —and he must have the means of investment. This, in turn, implies capital formation. Unless a substantial surplus is saved and re-invested in the land each year there can be no sustained development. Agriculture, therefore, has the heavy task of generating capital both for investment in other sectors and for its own transformation. Capital accretion, in turn, requires the existence of adequate markets and reasonably remunerative and stable prices for farm products. These are basic essentials; there are others, including farming skills and the means of acquiring them.

A developing agriculture also must have its own "infrastructure." This consists of institutions and services which are essential to agricultural development but which farmers cannot provide for themselves. Most of them must be provided by Government, or they require Government decision in allocating resources to provide them. These institutions and services may be grouped under four heads, (a) research, experiment, and investigation, (b) production facilities for new inputs, (c) institutions to service agricultural production, (d) education.

Inadequate provision for research is a frequent weakness of development programmes. This may arise partly from preoccupation with investment which will yield immediate rather than future benefits and partly from the failure of research in the past to provide all the results expected of it. The failure was due in part to the nature of the research, which was directed largely to export commodity production, and in part to inability to carry the results to the point of final application at farm level—since there were usually no farms, in a technical and economic sense, to which they could be applied.

The great variation of physical, economic, and cultural factors characteristic of agriculture as a whole but particularly marked in the African environment makes it necessary to devote very considerable resources to regionally decentralised practical research. Decentralisation is essential, since innovations, unless they are of a purely mechanical nature, are not usually directly transferable from one environment to another. Programmes should be directed to the evolution of farming systems and the continuous generation of production techniques suited to specific environments.

The main material input requirements of a developing agriculture fall into two categories. The first comprises machinery, fertilisers, pesticides, herbicides, fencing materials, and other products which it is the function of industry to produce. The second is the biological input of new and improved crops and livestock. The former calls for new industrial plant or the use of foreign exchange, and the latter for trained workers and local facilities for the production, propagation, and distribution of planting material and breeding stock under an effective system of control. Fulfilment of these needs is likely to be difficult in most of the African countries, since trained and experienced agricultural workers are among the scarcest of scarce resources, while industrial plant and foreign exchange are forms of capital subject to competing demands from other sectors of the expanding economies.

Once the new inputs have been produced, and research has demonstrated how they can be most profitably applied, a complex of institutions is required to ensure their effective use. This complex includes facilities for the distribution of the inputs, an ample supply of credit for their purchase, and effective machinery for its operation, and institutions for processing, marketing, transporting, and distributing the new and increased outputs. Each country must decide on the institutional forms best suited to service agriculture, in the light of national circumstances and philosophical and political goals.

We may, however, take it as axiomatic that the rate of progress will be determined by the rate at which trained personnel can be provided for all of the institutions and services required for the development of agriculture. Education, in the broadest sense and range, is a key condition for economic development in intertropical Africa.

Practically all of the new nations are committed by their philosophical and political aims to greatly enlarged programmes of education. If agriculture is to progress, it is necessary that technical education and training should form part of these expanding programmes. The field is a very wide one, ranging from the training of professional agriculturists at university level to elementary rural education. Between these two extremes comes the training of technical service personnel and the functional training of farmers and farm workers. Provision for the functional training of farmers is essential, whether the trained individuals are to operate as private farmers or as leaders of some form of co-operative enterprise. This need for practical training of individual farmers is often overlooked on account of preoccupation with group methods of extension work and community development which, however necessary they may be in present circumstances, are usually productive only of limited ameliorative effects. As in the case of adaptive research and for the same reasons, farmer-training programmes must be "tailored" as flexibly as possible to relatively small geographical areas.

It is noteworthy that the drift to the towns and the consequent growth of urban unemployment is most marked in those countries where primary education in rural areas has made most progress. Education is regarded as a means of escape from the rural environment. This attitude must change if there is to be any progress in agriculture. It will change only if the rural areas offer adequate opportunities for able educated men, either as private farmers or as leaders of co-operative production units.

The history of co-operative farming in Africa is one of almost unrelieved failure: but it does not follow that this failure will be repeated under African initiation and leadership. The past failures were due, in part at least, to political opposition and suspicion of the motives of the suzerain Powers, and to the lack of trained and able African leadership. The fact remains, however, that the adequately equipped and skilfully managed individual farm has so far proved in general experience to be the most efficient unit of agricultural production.

Some of the new countries pin their faith in co-operative farming or are prepared to try it out on a relatively large scale. Western Nigeria has allocated funds for co-operative farm settlements which are planned to cover 7,000 hectares by 1970–1. As one would expect, the countries of strong socialist influence show a more complete acceptance of the co-operative ideal. Mali plans a new socialist framework for her economy, with community work and voluntary labour as the basis of agricultural improvement. Guinea's agricultural plans hinge on the creation of a co-operative structure which is designed to end in the collective exploitation of all village lands and livestock.

Most national plans for the agricultural sector are more limited in scope and the methods proposed are similar for large groups of countries and do not differ greatly from those of the past. They aim at increasing agricultural production within the existing institutional framework by such means as the extension of cultivation and the increase of yields. Many have a strong bias towards increased output of the traditional export crops, but some show a concern for the improvement of nutrition by means such as the partial replacement of cassava by sorghum and millets, extended cultivation of pulses, and an increased supply of animal proteins from poultry and pond fisheries.

Most plans devote a high proportion of expenditure, sometimes as much as half the total investment, to infrastructural development, particularly transport and communications designed to bring the remoter areas within the market economy. This includes such costly items as port and railway construction and improvement. Social infrastructural development—education, health, and other social services—also absorbs large amounts. The importance accorded to agriculture in the national plans varies greatly: but few countries have devoted as much as one-third of their planned public expenditure to investment in this sector and most intend to devote less than one-fifth. In general, the plans appear to be too limited in scope, and the resources too exiguous, to allow of a major breakthrough on the agricultural front.

In any event, the areas in which such a breakthrough is possible are as yet very limited and it is evident that a large proportion of the people of the region must continue for many years to live within subsistence and semi-subsistence economies which cannot differ greatly from the systems of the past. Here the remoulding of the old systems of land-holding and land-use may still play a major part in the process of amelioration and development, where they remain sufficiently viable.

The devastated areas, where the traditional systems have altogether broken down under overwhelming pressure of human and livestock populations, present one of the most urgent problems of all. They call for immediate emergency measures, including the provision of adequate employment, if they are to be saved at the last moment before complete destruction.

There can be little doubt that solution of the complex problems with which they are beset lies within the capacities of the African peoples, but it will require inspired leadership to release and direct these capacities. Without such leadership, reinforced by technical assistance and financial aid on a larger scale than has hitherto been available, Africa may remain, as it has been described in the past, "A riddle without an answer."

BIBLIOGRAPHY

1. *African Land Development in Kenya.* Nairobi (Min. of Agric., Animal Resources and Husbandry) 1956.
2. *Agriculture Congolaises.* Brussels (Ministère des Colonies) 1954.
3. *Agricultural Productivity Committee Report.* Entebbe (Government Printer) 1954.
4. AHN, P. M. *The Principal Areas of Remaining Original Forest in Western Ghana and their Agricultural Potential,* Accra (Ghana Div. of Agric., Soil and Land-Use, Survey Branch) 1959.
5. AKENHEAD, M. "Dagomba Agriculture," in *Monthly News Letter Supplement,* Accra (Dept. of Agric.) 1957.
6. ALDER, J. Unpublished Report. Dept. of Agric, N. Rhodesia, 1957.
7. —— Unpublished Report. Dept. of Agric., N. Rhodesia, 1958.
8. —— Personal Communication. 1960.
9. ALLAN, W. *Studies in African Land Usage in Northern Rhodesia,* Rhodes-Livingstone Papers, No. 15, 1949.
10. ——, M. GLUCKMAN,, and others. *Land-Holding and Land Usage Among the Plateau Tonga,* Rhodes-Livingstone Papers, No. 14, 1948.
11. *Annual Report of the Dept. of Agriculture, Northern Rhodesia.* Lusaka (Government Printer) 1932.
12. *Annual Report of the Dept. of Agriculture, Northern Rhodesia.* Lusaka (Government Printer) 1938.
13. *Annual Report of the Dept. of Agriculture, Northern Rhodesia.* Lusaka (Government Printer) 1940.
14. *Annual Report of the Dept. of Agriculture, Northern Rhodesia.* Lusaka (Government Printer) 1941.
15. *Annual Report of the Dept. of Agriculture, Northern Rhodesia.* Lusaka (Government Printer) 1943.
16. *Annual Report of the Dept. of Agriculture, Northern Rhodesia.* Lusaka (Government Printer) 1958.
17. *Annual Report of the Dept. of Agriculture, Northern Rhodesia* (Eastern Province). Unpublished [1958].
18. *Annual Report of the Dept. of Agriculture, Tanganyika.* Dar-es-Salaam (Government Printer) 1960.
19. *Annual Report of the Dept. of Agriculture, Uganda,* Appendices IIIa, IIIb, and VII. Entebbe (Government Printer) 1958.
20. *Annual Report of the Dept. of Agriculture, Uganda,* Appendices IVa and VII. Entebbe (Government Printer) 1959.
21. *Aperçu sur l'économie agricole de la province de Kasai.* Brussels (Direction de L'Agriculture) 1955.
22. *Aperçu sur l'économie agricole de la province Orientale.* Brussels (Direction de L'Agriculture) 1955.

23. *Atlas of the Gold Coast.* Accra (Gold Coast Survey Dept.) 1949.
24. BAKER, O. E. U.S. Dept. of Agric. Misc. Pub., No. 321.
25. BALLANTYNE, A. O. *Preliminary Agricultural-Soils Map of Northern Rhodesia.* Lusaka (Dept. of Agriculture) 1958.
26. BECKETT, W. H. *Akokasa—A Survey of a Gold Coast Village.* Monograph on Social Anthropology, No. 10, London (London School of Economics and Political Science) 1944.
27. BENNET, H. H. in *Agriculture, Journal of Ministry of Agriculture,* Nov. 1953
28. BIRCH, H. F. "Humus Decomposition and Soil Nitrogen," in *Annual Report* (East African Agricultural and Forestry Research Organisation, Record of Research), Nairobi 1957.
29. BLEWITT, W. V. "Agricultural Development in Tropical Africa," in *Journal of Royal Society of Arts,* Aug. 1950.
30. BRIXHE, A. *Les Lotissements agricoles du Nord-Sankuru.* Elisabethville (Edition du Centre D'Etude des Problèmes Sociaux Indigènes).
31. BROWN, E. L. "Development and Farm Planning in the African Areas of Kenya," in *East African Agricultural Journal,* Oct. 1957.
32. BROWN, J. A. "Land Tenure in Somaliland," in *Chartered Surveyor,* Oct. 1957.
33. BURNETT, J. R. "Crop Production," in *Agriculture in the Sudan* (ed. J. D. Tothill), Oxford (O.U.P.) 1948.
34. CAROL, SIR OLAF. *Soviet Empire.* London (Macmillan) 1953.
35. CARR-SAUNDERS, A. M. *World Population.* Oxford (O.U.P.) 1936.
36. CHAMBERS, P. C. "Planned Group Farming in the Nyanza Province of Kenya," in *Tropical Agriculture,* No. 27, 1950.
37. —— "Progress with Mixed Farming in the Northern Region, Nigeria," in *Report of Conference of Directors of Agriculture,* London (Colonial Office Misc. No. 531) 1958.
38. COCKING, W. P., and R. P. LORD, "Review of the Farming Settlement Scheme Operated by the Tanganyika Agricultural Corporation at Nachingwea," in *Tropical Agriculture,* Apr. 1958.
39. COLSON, E. "Native Cultural and Social Patterns in Contemporary Africa," in *Africa Today* (ed. C. Grove Haines), Baltimore (Johns Hopkins Press) 1951.
40. —— "The Social Organization of the Gwembe Tonga," in *Human Problems of Kariba,* VOL. 1, Manchester (Manchester U.P. for the Rhodes-Livingstone Institute) 1960.
41 (*sic*)——"The Tonga and the Shortage of Implements," in *Rhodes-Livingstone Journal,* No. 14, 1954.
42 (*sic*). COSTER, R. N. *Peasant Farming in the Petauke and Katete Areas of the Eastern Province of Northern Rhodesia.* Bull. No. 15, Lusaka (Dept. of Agric.) 1955.
43. COURCY-IRELAND, M. G. DE. "Agricultural Survey, Teso District: Wera Gombolola: Amuria Saza," in *A Report on Nineteen*

Surveys done in Small Agricultural Areas in Uganda, Entebbe (Government Printer) 1938.

44. CUNNISON, I. G. "The Humr and their Land," in *Sudan Notes and Records*, XXXV, 1954.

45. —— *The Luapula People of Northern Rhodesia*. Manchester (Manchester U.P.) 1959.

46. —— "The Social Role of Cattle," in *Sudan Journal of Veterinary Sciences and Animal Husbandry*, I, No. 1, Mar. 1960.

47. DARLING, M. L. *The Punjab Peasant in Prosperity and Debt* (4th edn.). Oxford (O.U.P.) 1947.

48. DAVIDSON, B. *Old Africa Rediscovered*. London (Gollancz) 1959.

49. DEBENHAM, F. "The Bushman's Way of Life," in *The Times British Colonies Review*, Spring 1954.

50. DEPT. OF NATIVE AFFAIRS, TRANSVAAL. *Report 1954–57*. Pretoria (Government Printer) 1959.

51. DOKE, C. M. *The Lambas of Northern Rhodesia*. London (Harrap) 1931.

52. DUMONT, R. *Types of Rural Economy*. London (Methuen) 1957.

53. ELLISON, W. D. In *Empire Journal of Experimental Agriculture*, Apr. 1952.

54. EPSTEIN, A. L. *Politics in an Urban African Community*. Manchester (Manchester U.P. for the Rhodes-Livingstone Institute) 1958.

55. FARNELL, H. M. McD. "Dearth of Children Among the Azande," in *Sudan Notes and Records*, 1954.

56. FARSON, NEGLEY. *Behind God's Back*. London (Gollancz) 1943.

57. —— *Last Chance in Africa*. London (Gollancz) 1949.

58. FLOYD, BARRY N. "The Land Husbandry Act," in *Rhodes-Livingstone Journal*, No. 25, 1959.

59. FORTES, M. "The Ashante Social Survey: A Preliminary Report," in *Rhodes-Livingstone Journal*, No. 6, 1948.

60. GALLETTI, R., K. D. S. BALDWIN, and I. O. DINA. *An Economic Survey of Yoruba Cocoa Farming*. Oxford (O.U.P.) 1956.

61. GILLILAND, H. B. "The Vegetation of Eastern British Somaliland," in *Journal of Ecology*, 1952.

62. GILLMAN, C. "Population Problems of Tanganyika Territory," in *East Africa Agricultural Journal*, XI, 2 Oct. 1945.

63. —— "A Vegetation-Types Map of Tanganyika Territory," in *Geographical Review*, XXXIX, Jan. 1949.

64. GILLMAN, H. "Bush Fallowing on the Makonde Plain," in *Tanganyika Notes and Records*, No. 19, June 1945.

65. GLUCKMAN, M. *The Economy of the Central Barotse Plain*. Rhodes-Livingstone Papers, No. 7, 1941.

66. —— *Essays on Lozi Land and Royal Property*. Rhodes-Livingstone Papers, No. 10, 1943.

67. —— "The Technical Vocabulary of Barotse Jurisprudence," in *American Anthropologist*, LXI, 1959.

68. GOLDTHORPE, J. E. "African Population of East Africa," Appendix

VII, *East African Royal Commission Report 1953–1955*, London (H.M.S.O.) 1956.

69. GOUROU, PIERRE. *Les Pays Tropicaux*. Paris (Presses Universitaires de France 1953).
70. GULLIVER, P. H. *The Family Herds*. London (Routledge) 1955.
71. GUPPY, N. *Wai Wai: Through the Forests North of the Amazon*. London (John Murray) 1957.
72. GUTMANN, BRUNO VON. *Das Recht von der Dschagga*. Munich 1926.
73. HALL, SIR DANIEL. *The Improvement of Native Agriculture in Relation to Population and Public Health*. Oxford (O.U.P.) 1936.
74. HALLOWELL, A. I. "The Size of Algonkian Hunting Territories," in *American Anthropologist*, LI, No. 1, 1949.
75. HARRISON, M. N. Report on a Grazing Survey of the Sudan. Unpublished [1955]. Quoted by Cunnison (46).
76. HARTNELL, A. V., and N. R. FUGGLES-COUCHMAN. "The Mashokora Cultivation of the Coast," in *Tanganyika Notes and Records*, No. 8, Apr. 1939.
77. HAWDON, JOSEPH. Unpublished Journal. Quoted by ERNESTINE HILL, *Water into Gold*, Melbourne (Robertson and Mullins) 1951.
78. HENDERSON, G. R., and G. N. WILLIAMSON. *The Field Unit System for Importing Flexibility to Farm Layouts and Plans for Smallholdings*. Nairobi (Dept. of Agric.) 1959.
79. HENRY, J. "Les bases théorique des essais de paysannat indigène," in *Bulletin agriculture du Congo Belge*, XLIII, 1952.
80. HEWISON, J. W. "Northern Province Agriculture," in *Agriculture in the Sudan* (ed. J. D. Tothill). Oxford (O.U.P.) 1948.
81. HILL, POLLY. *The Gold Coast Cocoa Farmer*. Oxford (O.U.P.) 1956.
82. HOLLIS, SIR A. C. *The Masai*. Oxford (Clarendon Press) 1905.
83. HORNBY, H. E. "Overstocking in Tanganyika Territory," in *East African Agricultural Journal*, V, Mar. 1936.
84. HOWARTH, DAVID. *The Shadow of the Dam*. London (Collins) 1961.
85. HUMPHREY, N. *The Kikuyu Lands*. Nairobi (Government Printer) 1945.
86. —— *The Relationship of Population to Land in South Nyeri*. Nairobi (Government Printer) 1946.
87. HUNT, J. A. *A General Survey of British Somaliland*. London (Crown Agents) 1951.
88. HUNTINGFORD, C. W. B., and C. R. V. BELL. East African Background, London (Longmans, Green) 1950.
89. HUNTON, W. ALPHONSO. *Decision in Africa*. London (Calder) 1957.
90. HUXLEY, ELSPETH. *Four Guineas*. London (Chatto) 1954.
91. —— *A New Earth*. London (Chatto) 1960.
92. JACKS, J. V. In *Endeavour*, Jan. 1942.
93. JACKSON, J. K., and M. K. SHAWKI. "Shifting Cultivation in the Sudan," in *Sudan Notes*, XXXI, 1950.
94. JOHNSON, C. E. *African Farming Improvement in the Plateau Tonga*

Maize Area of Northern Rhodesia. Bull. No. 11, Lusaka (Dept. of Agric.) 1956.

95. JOHNSON, SIR HARRY. *The Colonization of Africa.* Cambridge (C.U.P.) 1899.

96. JONES, D. K., L. F. H. MERTON, M. E. D. POORE, and D. R. HARRIS. *Report on Pasture Research, Survey and Development in Cyprus.* Nicosia (Govt. of Cyprus) 1958.

97. KETTLEWELL, R. W. "The Master Farmer Scheme and the Village Lands Improvement Scheme in Nyasaland," in *Report on Conference of Directors of Agriculture.* London (Colonial Office Misc. No. 531) 1958.

98. KOLBE, L. H., and S. J. FONCHE. *Land Consolidation and Farm Planning in the Central Province.* Nairobi (Government Printer) 1959.

99. KUCZYNSKI, R. R. *A Demographic Survey of the British Colonial Empire.* Oxford (O.U.P.) 1949.

100. *Land Control (Native Lands) Bill.* Nairobi (Government Printer) 1959.

101. LEACOCK, ELEANOR. "The Montagnais Hunting Territory and the Fur Trade," in *American Anthropologist*, LVI, No. 5, 1954.

102. LEAKEY, L. S. B. *Kenya Contrasts and Problems.* London (Methuen) 1936.

103. LORIMER, F. *Culture and Human Fertility.* Paris (UNESCO) 1954.

104. LUGARD, LORD. *The Dual Mandate in British Tropical Africa.* Edinburgh (Blackwood) 1926.

105. LUNAN, M., and D. BREWIN. "The Agriculture of Ukara Island," in *Empire Cotton Growing Review*, XXXIII, No. 4, Oct. 1956.

106. LYNN, C. W. *Agriculture in North Mamprusi.* Bull. No. 34. Accra (Dept. of Agric.) 1937.

107. McMASTER, D. N. "Change of Regional Balance in the Bukoba District of Tanganyika," in *Geographical Review*, L, No. 1, 1960.

108. MACMILLAN, W. M. *Africa Emergent.* Harmondsworth (Pelican Books) 1949.

109. MARSHALL, R. *Arctic Village.* London (Jarrolds) 1934.

110. MASTERS, D. *Structure of the Economy of Sunson and Sambu in Eastern Dagomba.* Accra (Dept. of Agric. Records) 1955.

111. MERKER, M. *Die Masai*, Berlin 1910.

112. METTAM, R. W. M. "A Short History of Rinderpest with Special Reference to Agriculture," in *Uganda Journal*, V, 1937.

113. MILNE, G. "Essays in Applied Pedology, III: Bukoba—High and Low Fertility in a Laterised Soil," in *East African Agricultural Journal.*

114. —— and others. *A Provisional Soil Map of East Africa.* Amani (East African Agricultural Research Station) 1936.

115. MITCHELL, J. C. "Preliminary Notes on Land Tenure and Agriculture among the Machinga Yao," in *Journal of the Rhodes-Livingstone Institute.*

116. MITCHELL, J. C. *The Kalela Dance.* Rhodes-Livingstone Papers, No. 27, 1956.
117. MITCHELL, SIR PHILIP. Dispatch No. 193, 16 Nov. 1951, in *Land and Population in East Africa,* London (H.M.S.O. Colonial Office Pub. No. 290) 1952.
118. —— *African Afterthoughts,* London (Hutchinson 1954).
119. MOFFAT, U. J. *Native Agriculture in the Abercorn District.* Lusaka (Dept. of Agric.) 1932.
120. MOOREHEAD, A. *No Room in the Ark,* London (Collins) 1959.
121. MURRAY, A. K. "The Fula of Northern Sierra Leone," in *Tropical Agriculture,* Apr. 1958.
122. *Native Land Husbandry Act, Southern Rhodesia.* No. 52, Salisbury (Government Printer) 1951.
123. *Native Lands Registration Bill, Kenya.* Nairobi (Kenya Gazette Supplement No. 14) 1959.
124. *Overseas Food Corporation: Report and Accounts for 1954–5.* London (H.M.S.O.) 1956.
125. PARSONS, D. ST JOHN. *Legends of Northern Ghana.* London (Longmans, Green) 1958.
126. PAWSON, E. *Maize Fertilizer Experiments in Northern Rhodesia, 1950–53.* Bull. No. 7, Lusaka (Dept. of Agric.) 1955.
127. *Paysannat et colonat dans le district du Tanganyika.* Brussels (Direction de L'Agriculture) 1957.
128. PEREIRA, H. C., and V. R. S. BECKLEY. "Grass Establishment on Eroded Soils in a Semi-Arid African Reserve," in *Empire Journal of Experimental Agriculture,* XXXI, Jan. 1953.
129. PETERS, D. U. *Land Usage in Serenje Districts.* Rhodes-Livingstone Papers, No. 19, 1950.
130. —— *Land Usage in Barotseland* (ed. N. W. Smyth, with a Preface by W. Allan and M. Gluckman). Rhodes-Livingstone Communication, No. 19, 1960.
131. PIKE, A. H. "Soil Conservation Among the Matengo Tribe," in *Tanganyika Notes and Records,* No. 6, 1938.
132. PRIESTLEY, M. J. S. W., and R. GREENING. *Ngoni Land-Utilization Survey, 1954–5.* Lusaka (Government Printer) 1956.
133. PURSEGLOVE, J. W. "Land Use in the Overpopulated Areas of Kabale, Kigezi District, Uganda," in *East African Agricultural Journal,* July 1946.
134. RASMUSSEN, K. *Greenland by the Polar Seas.* London (Heinemann) 1921.
135. —— *Across Arctic America,* London (Putnam) 1927.
136. REES, MORGAN A. M. *An Economic Survey of Plateau Tonga Improved Farmers,* Bull. No. 14, Lusaka (Dept. of Agric.) 1958.
137. —— and R. H. HOWARD. *An Economic Survey of Commercial African Farming among the Sala of the Mumbwa District in Northern Rhodesia,* Bull. No. 10, Lusaka (Dept. of Agric.) 1955.
138. *Report of the East African Royal Commission, 1953–55,* London (H.M.S.O.) 1956.

139. RICHARDS, AUDREY I. *Land, Labour and Diet in Northern Rhodesia.* Oxford (O.U.P. for the International Institute of African Languages and Culture) 1939.

140. RICHARDS, P. W. *The Tropical Rain Forest.* Cambridge (C.U.P.) 1952.

141. ROBERTS, D. F. "What of the Future?" in *Transactions of the South African Institute of Civil Engineers,* Apr. 1954.

142. ROBINSON, D. A. "Land Use Planning in Native Reserves in Southern Rhodesia," in *Rhodesian Agricultural Journal,* L, No. 4, 1953.

143. ROSS, R. "Ecological Stuᴅies in the Rain Forest of Southern Nigeria," in *Journal of Ecology,* XLIII, 1954.

144. ROUNCE, N. V. *The Agriculture of the Cultivation Steppe of the Lake, Central, and Western Provinces.* Salisbury (Longmans, Green for Dept. of Agric., Tanganyika) 1946.

145. SAMPSON, H. C., and E. M. CROWTHER. *Technical Reports of the West African Commission of the Leverhulme Trust, 1938–39.* London 1943.

146. SCHLIPPE, P. DE. *Shifting Cultivation in Africa: The Zande System of Agriculture.* London (Routledge) 1956.

147. SHAUL, J. R. H. "Population Analysis of Central Africa," in *The Times British Colonies Review,* Spring 1958.

148. SHEDDICK, V. *Land Tenure in Basutoland.* Colonial Research Studies, No. 13, London (H.M.S.O.) 1954.

149. SMITH, ELLIOTT G. *Human History.* London (Cape) 1934.

150. SMITH, J. *Distribution of Tree Species in the Sudan in Relation to Rainfall and Land Texture.* Bull. No. 4, Khartoum (Min. of Agric.) 1950.

151. SMITH, R. *A Report on Kusasi Agriculture.* Accra (Records, Dept. of Agric.) 1957.

152. SMYTH, N. W. Unpublished Report. Dept. of Agric., N. Rhodesia, 1958.

153. SPENCER, SIR BALDWIN, and F. J. GILLEN. *The Arunta.* London (Macmillan) 1927.

154. *Statistiques. Principales cultures indigènes.* Unpublished [Leopold-ville 1958].

155. STEBBING, E. P. *The Creeping Desert in the Sudan and Elsewhere in Africa.* Khartoum (Min. of Agric.) 1953.

156. STENHOUSE, A. S. "Agriculture in the Matengo Highlands," in *East African Agricultural Journal,* Jul. 1944.

157. STENNING, D. J. *Household Viability Among the Pastoral Fulani.* Cambridge Papers in Social Anthropology, No. 1, 1958.

158. —— *Savannah Nomads.* Oxford (O.U.P. for the International African Institute) 1959.

159. STENT, H. B. "Observations on the Fertilizing Effects of Wood Burning in the Citemene Systems," in *Annual Bulletin,* Dept. of Agric., N. Rhodesia, 1933.

160. STEWARD, J. H. "Economic and Social Basis of Primitive Bands,"

in *Essays in Anthropology in Honour of Alfred Louis Kroeber.* Berkeley (University of California Press) 1936. Quoted by Hallowell (74).

161. SWYNNERTON, R. J. M. "Planned African Farming in Kenya," in *Report of Conference of Directors of Agriculture,* London (Colonial Office Misc. No. 531) 1958.

162. TAYLOR, C. J. *The Vegetation Zones of the Gold Coast.* Bull. No. 4, Accra (Forestry Dept.) 1942.

163. TEMPANY, SIR HAROLD. *The Practice of Soil Conservation in the British Colonial Empire.* Commonwealth Bureau of Soil Science, Tech. Comm. No. 45, 1949.

164. THOMAS, ELIZABETH MARSHALL. *The Harmless People.* London (Secker & Warburg) 1959.

165. THORNTON, D. and N. V. ROUNCE. *Ukara Island and the Agricultural Practices of the Wakara.* Monthly Letter, Dept. of Agric., Tanganyika, Oct. 1933. Revised edn., Nairobi (Kenya Pamphlet) 1945.

166. TINDALE, N. B. "Aborigines: The White Contact," in *Australian Encyclopaedia,* Sydney (Butterworth) 1958.

167. TOBIAS, P. "On the Survival of the Bushmen," *Africa,* XXVI, No. 2, Apr. 1956.

168. TOPHAM, D. C. *The Atamore Survey: A Report on the Problems of Fra Fra.* Accra (Dept. of Agric. Records) 1957.

169. TOTHILL, J. D. *A Report on Nineteen Surveys Done in Small Agricultural Areas in Uganda.* Entebbe (Government Printer) 1938.

170. —— (ed.). *Agriculture in the Sudan.* Oxford (O.U.P.) 1948.

171. TRAPNELL, G. G. *The Soils, Vegetation and Agricultural Systems of North Eastern Rhodesia.* Lusaka (Government Printer) 1943. Reprinted 1959.

172. —— *Vegetation-Soil Map of Northern Rhodesia: Explanatory Memorandum.* Lusaka (Government Printer) 1947.

173. —— Memorandum for the East African Royal Commission. Unpublished [1955].

174. —— In *Journal of Ecology,* Jan.–Mar. 1959.

175. —— and CLOTHIER, J. N. *The Soils Vegetation and Agricultural Systems of North-Western Rhodesia.* Lusaka (Government Printer) 1937. Reprinted 1959.

176. ——, J. D. MARTIN, and W. ALLAN. *Vegetation-Soil Map of Northern Rhodesia.* Lusaka (Government Printer) 1947.

177. TROUP, L. G. *Report on the General Economy of Farming in the Kenya Highlands.* Nairobi (Government Printer) 1953.

178. TURNER, V. W. *Schism and Continuity in An African Society: A Study of Ndembu Village Life.* Manchester (Manchester U.P.) 1957.

179. VOGT, W. *Road to Survival.* London (Gollancz) 1949.

180. WATSON, J. M. "Some Aspects of Teso Agriculture," in *East African Agricultural Journal,* VI, No. 207, 1941.

181. WATSON, W. *Tribal Cohesion in a Money Economy.* Manchester (Manchester U.P.) 1958.
182. *What the Native Land Husbandry Act Means to the Rural Africans and to Southern Rhodesia.* Salisbury (Government Printer) 1955.
183. WHITE, C. M. N. *A Preliminary Survey of Luvale Rural Economy.* Rhodes-Livingstone Papers, No. 29, 1959.
184. WHITE, STANHOPE. "Agricultural Economy of the Hill Pagans of Dikwa Emirate, Cameroons," in *Empire Journal of Experimental Agriculture,* IX, No. 3, 1941.
185. WILLIMOTT, S. G. "Cultivable Land and Land-Use in Equatoria Province, Sudan," in *Malay Journal of Tropical Geography,* Aug. 1940.
186. —— and K. R. M. ANTHONY. "Agricultural Research and Development in the Southern Sudan," in *Tropical Agriculture,* Jan. 1958.
187. WILSON, MONICA. *Good Company.* Oxford (O.U.P.) 1951.
188. WILSON, P. N. "An Agricultural Survey of Moruita Erony, Teso," in *Uganda Journal,* XXII, No. 1, Mar. 1958.
189. —— and WATSON, J. M. "Two Surveys of Kasilang Erony, Teso, 1937 and 1953," in *Uganda Journal,* XX, No. 2, Sep. 1956.
190. WISSLER, C. *The American Indian.* New York (O.U.P.) 1922.
191. WOOD, R. M. *A Report on a Survey of the Ndola Settlement Area.* Dept. of Agric., Northern Rhodesia. Unpublished [Jul. 1956].

INDEX